TOURO COLLEGE LIBRARY
Midwood Campus

550
P 71 i

WITHDRAWN

Illustrations of the
Huttonian Theory of the Earth

by

JOHN PLAYFAIR

a Facsimile Reprint, with an Introduction by
GEORGE W. WHITE
Chairman, Department of Geology
University of Illinois

ST. PETER'S COLLEGE
LIBRARY
BALTIMORE, MD.

WITHDRAWN

TOURO COLLEGE LIBRARY
Midwood Campus

Dover Publications, Inc., New York

Copyright © 1956 by the Board of Trustees of the University of Illinois

All rights reserved under Pan American and International Copyright Conventions.

Published in the United Kingdom by Constable and Company, Limited, 10 Orange Street, London W.C.2.

This Dover edition, first published in 1964, is an unabridged and unaltered republication of the facsimile reprint of Playfair's *Illustrations of the Huttonian Theory of the Earth* (1802) published by the University of Illinois, together with an Introduction by George W. White, in 1956. This edition is published by special arrangement with the Board of Trustees of the University of Illinois.

Library of Congress Catalog Card Number 64-18366

Manufactured in the United States of America

Dover Publications, Inc.
180 Varick Street
New York 14, N.Y.

INTRODUCTION AND
BIOGRAPHICAL NOTES
By George W. White

INTRODUCTION

At the meetings of March 7 and April 4, 1785, of the Royal Society of Edinburgh was read Dr. James Hutton's paper *Concerning the Systems of the Earth, its Duration, and Stability.* The paper was published in 1788 in the first volume of the Transactions of the Society as *Theory of the Earth; or an Investigation of the Laws observable in the Composition, Dissolution, and Restoration of Land upon the Globe.* This paper, almost unchanged, formed the first chapter of the two-volume *Theory of the Earth, with Proofs and Illustrations,* published in 1795, two years before Dr. Hutton died, in an edition of only 400 or 500 copies.[1]

Hutton's publications attracted only modest attention and much of that in the form of strong criticism from vigorous proponents of the antithetical theories of Abraham Gottlob Werner, the German mineralogist. Hutton's friends encouraged his friend and former associate, John Playfair, professor of mathematics (later of natural philosophy) in the University of Edinburgh, to publish a summary of and commentary on Hutton's *Theory,* which appeared in 1802 as *Illustrations of the Huttonian Theory of the Earth,* here reprinted. It is through these *Illustrations* and not through Hutton's original publications that Hutton's system has affected geological thinking for 150 years. The effect was direct in the earlier years of the nineteenth century and later indirect through the writings of Lyell and many others who based all geology on the uniformitarian doctrine promulgated by Hutton, but which they knew almost entirely from Playfair.

Neither Hutton's *Theory* nor Playfair's *Illustrations* have been reprinted since their first appearance. It is to be hoped that the *Theory* — now available in only a few libraries — may someday appear in another edition. However, only a few persistent persons would read through the two long volumes, including the many pages of quotations of original descriptions from foreign sources, mainly French and Swiss. The famous flashes of brilliant statement that (as Playfair himself puts it so kindly) "burst thru the clouds that so often veil from us the clearest ideas of his understanding" unfortunately are too often found only between repetitious and long passages which are most discouraging.

The *Illustrations,* on the other hand, is readable and persuasive to the intelligent and delightfully convincing to those acquainted with "natural philosophy." The "Advertisement" tells the reader that here is to be set forth a concise summary of a system of geology which merits attention. The following two pages of introduction contain some of the finest geological writing of any time or language. The first part of the book in three sections of 140 pages contains the summary of Hutton's *Theory.* The remainder of the 528 pages is made up of notes in which Playfair amplifies, explains, and expands the *Theory.* It is in these notes that many of the famous passages occur: on unconformities in note 12; on rivers and valleys and their origin in note 16 ("Playfair's Law" of concordant stream junction, however is in the body of text on p. 102); and on glacial transport of erratics in note 18. The pages on "unstratified granite" and "stratified granite," beginning on page 334 of note 15 contain a prescient discussion of data and uncertainties of interpretation reminiscent of present-day writings on granitization and its extent. The great summary of the theory of the geological cycle is in the body of the text as paragraph 126, beginning on page 127.

The conclusion of Playfair (paragraph 134) is a masterful recognition that the bold strokes of Hutton left many blanks to be filled in by future work, but that these future discoveries would indeed fit into their proper place in explaining an earth of which, as Hutton said in 1785, "we find no vestige of a beginning, — no prospect of an end."

Playfair's exposition of Hutton's work did not lead to general and immediate acceptance; what is now regarded as the most important part of the theory, the concept of uniformitarianism, including the formation of sedimentary rocks from sediment eroded from former lands, was often lost sight of or at least minimized in earlier days, even by those not unfriendly to Hutton's theory. Bakewell, in his textbook of 1813,[2] accepted the igneous origin of basalt and granite, derided Werner's theories repeatedly, but did not grasp the principle of uniformitarianism. Phillips[3] presented catastrophic views in 1816 and Conybeare[4] in 1822 specifically disclaimed the uniformitarianism of Hutton and Playfair.

In America, acceptance of uniformitarianism came slowly.[5] William Maclure[6] in 1817 did not mention Hutton and used a Wernerian classification of rocks; I can find no evidence that his very extensive library included copies of Hutton's or Playfair's works. Amos Eaton was an avowed Wernerian and did not even mention Hutton or Playfair in 1818 and 1820,[7] although by 1830 he realized that part of the theory required acceptance.[8] Parker Cleaveland,[9] who knew of Hutton's work through Playfair's *Illustrations,* was decidedly Wernerian and a catastrophist. Jeremiah van Rennselaer, writing in 1825,[10] appears to have had a reasonable concept of Hutton's theory, apparently derived from Playfair's *Illustrations,* but was not very favorable to uniformitarianism. In the first American edition of Bakewell's text, edited by Benjamin Silliman in 1829,[11] uniformitarianism was not accepted. In the appendix by Silliman the tone is catastrophic, Wernerian, and even favorable to the aqueous origin of granite. But by 1833 in America, W. W. Mather[12] had carefully compared various theories and regarded Hutton's as pre-eminent. He may have been influenced by Lyell or may have reached his conclusion through his own analysis.

It remained for Lyell in 1830 to recognize the correctness of the essential parts of the Huttonian theory[13] and to relegate "its greatest defect, the undue influence attributed to subterranean heat, which was supposed necessary for the consolidation of all submarine deposits" to a position of unimportance in the grand and fundamental concept. Lyell analyzed at some length the effect of the revolutionary events of the time on the religious temper which led to often intemperate opposition to Hutton and Playfair. "At any other time the force and elegance of Playfair's style must have insured popularity to the Huttonian doctrines," but Neptunianism — and hence Wernerianism — was associated with orthodoxy and Huttonianism with its "no beginning and no end" with atheism. Lyell's *Principles* set forth the uniformitarianism of Hutton based on the summary and notes of Playfair persuasively and compellingly; the intellectual climate was more propitious than it had been thirty years earlier; and soon all joined in the acclaim of Hutton, in the appreciation of his commentator Playfair, and in the approbation of his proponent Lyell.

Those reading Playfair for the first time will probably be well advised to omit section 2, pp. 15-40, on "Consolidation of the Strata." Although Playfair takes only twenty-five pages to summarize what Hutton used hundreds for, the fact remains that the Huttonian views, followed by Playfair, on consolidation by heat are the most unhappy ones of the whole system. Hutton believed that consolidation took place while sediments were still beneath the sea and before uplift took place. It is to be noted that the strident critic of Hutton, the Irish chemist Richard Kirwan,[14] seized upon this weakest part of the *Theory* for his most savage attack, about the only case in which Kirwan was in the right in his disputes with Hutton.

The terminology of Hutton and Playfair will cause the modern reader only occasional minor difficulty. The term "schistus" is used with various meaning: usually "schist" will convey the meaning, although "gneiss" is sometimes meant. Occasionally it is used in the way we now use "basement complex." The meaning will usually be clear from the context. "Vein" is used in the modern sense of "dike" as well as of actual "vein." The discussion of igneous origin of "veins" will be clearer if the reader remembers that "dike" is really meant in many places. The term "fossil" is often used in the older sense of "something dug up"; therefore minerals are sometimes referred to as "fossils." (The old use lingers on in the present-day occasional use of "fossil fuel" for coal.)

This reprinting is a facsimile of the original 1802 edition. It is printed from the exceptionally fine copy in the Spindletop Engineering Library of the Lamar State College of Technology of Beaumont, Texas. We are indebted to Dr. H. E. Eveland, head of the Department of Geology and to Miss Flora Richardson, Librarian of the College, for making this copy available.

1956

BIOGRAPHICAL SKETCH OF JAMES HUTTON

James Hutton,[15] son of William Hutton, a merchant of Edinburgh, was born June 3, 1726. He was educated at the High School and at Edinburgh University, first in classical subjects and later in medicine. He continued his medical studies in Paris and Leyden, where he was made Doctor of Medicine in 1749.

Hutton never practiced medicine; he observed farming practices in Norfolk and Flanders and from 1754 to 1768 operated his family farm in Berwickshire. In his travels in England and on the continent, in an excursion to Caithness and the north of Scotland in 1764, and to Wales in 1774, he observed "the surface of the earth, and was looking with anxious curiosity into every pit, or ditch or bed of a river that fell in his way." He was likewise attentive to mineralogical and petrological observation.

For several years before 1768 Hutton had been engaged as a partner in a firm manufacturing sal ammoniac, and after moving to Edinburgh he employed part of his time in chemical experiments of some importance.

After moving to Edinburgh in 1768, he was a member of the group of scholars in the city and in the University who met to discuss scientific matters. He found their company agreeable and stimulating and he in turn was highly regarded in the circle. When the Royal Society of Edinburgh was established in 1783, he took an important part in it. This stimulus to Hutton's geological work is most feelingly recorded by Playfair.[16]

The institution of the Royal Society of Edinburgh had the good effect of calling forth from Dr Hutton the first sketch of a theory of the earth, the formation of which had been the great object of his life. From the date formerly mentioned, when he was yet a very young man, and making excursions on foot through the different counties of England, till that which we are now arrived at, a period of about thirty years, he had never ceased to study the natural history of the globe, with a view of ascertaining the changes that have taken place on its surface, and of discovering the causes by which they have been produced.

He had become a skilful mineralogist, and had examined the great facts of geology with his own eyes, and with the most careful and scrupulous observation. In the course of these studies he had brought together a considerable collection of minerals peculiarly calculated to illustrate the changes which fossil bodies have undergone. He had also carefully perused almost every book of travels from which any thing was to be learned concerning the natural history of the earth; and, in consequence both of reading and observation, was eminently skilled in physical geography.

If to all this it be added, that Dr Hutton was a good chemist, and possessed abilities excellently adapted to philosophical research, it will be acknowledged, that few men have entered with better preparation on the arduous task of investigating the true theory of the earth. . . .

It might have been expected, when a work of so much originality as this Theory of the Earth, was given to the world, a theory which professed to be the result of such an ample and accurate induction, and which opened up so many views, interesting not to mineralogy alone, but to philosophy in general, that it would have produced a sudden and visible effect, and that men of science would have been every where eager to decide concerning its real value. Yet the truth is, that it drew their attention very slowly, so that several years elapsed before any one shewed himself publicly concerned about it, either as an enemy or a friend.

Several causes probably contributed to produce this indifference. The world was tired out with unsuccessful attempts to form geological theories, by men often but ill informed of the phenomena which they proposed to explain, and who proceeded also on the supposition that they could give an account of the origin of things, or the first establishment of that system which is now the order of nature. . . .

Truth, however, forces me to add, that other reasons certainly contributed not a little to prevent Dr. Hutton's theory from making a due impression on the world. It was proposed too briefly, and with too little detail of facts, for a system which involved so much that was new, and opposite to the opinions generally received. The descriptions which it contains of the phenomena of geology, suppose in the reader too great a knowledge of the things described. The reasoning is sometimes embarrassed by the care taken to render it strictly logical; and the transitions, from the author's peculiar notions of arrangement, are often unexpected and abrupt. These defects run more or less through all Dr Hutton's writings, and produce a degree of obscurity astonishing to those who knew him, and who heard him every day converse with no less clearness and precision, than animation and force. From whatever causes the want of perspicuity in his writings proceeded, perplexity of thought was not among the number; and the confusion of his ideas can neither be urged as an apology for himself, nor as a consolation to his readers.

In 1785 Hutton observed in Glen Tilt the intrusive contact between the granite and country rock. The observation itself is important, and it is noteworthy that Hutton had deduced the presence of such a contact from his theory. Playfair records the event in lively fashion.

One of the places where he knew that a junction of the kind he wished to examine must be found, was the line where the great body of granite which runs from Aberdeen westward, forming the central chain of the Grampians, comes in contact with the schistus which composes the inferior ridges of the same mountains toward the south. The nearest and most accessible point of this line seemed likely to be situated not far to the eastward of Blair in Athol, and could hardly fail to be visible in the beds of some of the most northern streams which run into the Tay. Dr Hutton having mentioned these circumstances to the Duke of Athol, was invited by that nobleman to accompany him in the shooting season into Glentilt, which he did accordingly, together with his friend Mr Clerk of Elden, in summer 1785.

The Tilt is, according to the seasons, a small river, or an impetuous torrent, which runs through a glen of the same name, nearly south-west, and deeply intersects the southern ridges of the Grampian Mountains. The rock through which its bed is cut is in general a hard micaceous schistus; and the glen presents a scene of great boldness and asperity, often embellished, however, with the accompaniments of a softer landscape.

When they had reached the Forest Lodge, about seven miles up the valley, Dr Hutton already found himself in the midst of the objects which he wished to examine. In the bed of the river, many veins of red granite, (no less, indeed, than six large veins in the course of a mile), were seen traversing the black micaceous schistus, and producing, by the contrast of colour, an effect that might be striking even to an unskilful observer. The sight of objects which verified at once so many important conclusions in his system, filled him with delight; and as his feelings, on such occasions, were always strongly expressed, the guides who accompanied him were convinced that it must be nothing less than the discovery of a vein of silver or gold, that could call forth such strong marks of joy and exultation. . . . In the year following, Dr Hutton and Mr Clerk also visited Galloway, in search of granitic veins, which they found at two different places, where the granite and schistus come in contact. .... In summer 1787, Dr Hutton visited the island of Arran in the mouth of the Clyde, one of those spots in which nature has collected, within a very small compass, all the phenomena most interesting to a geologist. A range of granite mountains, placed in the northern part of the island, have their sides covered with primitive schistus of various kinds, to which, on the seashore, succeed secondary strata of grit, limestone, and even coal. Here, therefore, Dr Hutton had another opportunity of examining the junction of the granite and schistus, and found abundance of the veins of the former penetrating into the latter. In three different places he met with this phenomenon; in the torrents that descend from the south side of Goatfield; in Glenrosa, on the west, and in the little river Sannax, on the northeast, of that mountain. From the first of these he brought a specimen of some hundred weight, consisting of a block of schistus, which includes a large vein of granite.

At the northern extremity of the island he had likewise a view of the secondary strata lying upon the primary, with their planes at right angles to one another. In the great quantity, also, of puddingstone, containing rounded quartzy gravel, united by an arenaceous cement; in the multitude of whinstone dikes, which abound in this island; and in the veins of pitchstone, a fossil which he had not before met with in its native place; he found other interesting subjects of observation; so that he returned from this tour highly gratified, and used often to say that he had no where found his expectations so much exceeded, as in the grand and instructive appearances with which nature has adorned this little island.

That Hutton understood the importance of unconformities and their method of formation is well shown in his writings. Playfair's description of the examination of one of these indicates that he was as skilled as Hutton in interpreting geologic phenomena.

The ridge of the Lammer-muir Hills, in the south of Scotland, consists of primary micaceous schistus, and extends from St Abb's-head westward, till it joins the metalliferous mountains about the sources of the Clyde. The sea-coast affords a transverse section of this alpine tract at its eastern extremity, and exhibits the change from the primary to the secondary strata, both on the south and on the north. Dr Hutton wished particularly to examine the latter of these, and on this occasion Sir James Hall and I had the pleasure to accompany him. We sailed in a boat from Dunglass, on a day when the fineness of the weather permitted us to keep close to the foot of the course southwards, in search of the termination of the secondary strata. We made for a high rocky point or head-land, the Siccar, near which, from our observations on shore, we knew that the object we were in search of was likely to be discovered. On landing at this point, we found that we actually trode on the primeval rock, which forms alternately the base and the summit of the present land. It is here a micaceous schistus, in beds nearly vertical, highly indurated, and stretching from S. E. to N. W. The surface of this rock runs with a moderate ascent from the level of low-water, at which we landed, nearly to that of high-water, where the schistus has a thin covering of red horizontal sandstone laid over it; and this sandstone, at the distance of a few yards farther back, rises into a very high perpendicular cliff. Here, therefore, the immediate contact of the two rocks is not only visible, but is curiously dissected and laid open by the action of the waves. The rugged tops of the schistus are seen penetrating into the horizontal beds of sandstone, and the lowest of these last form a breccia containing fragments of schistus, some round and others angular, united by an arenaceous cement.

Dr Hutton was highly pleased with appearances that set in so clear a light the different formations of the parts which compose the exterior crust of the earth, and where all the circumstances were combined that could render the observation satisfactory and precise. On us who saw these phenomena for the first time, the impression made will not easily be forgotten. The palpable evidence presented to us, of one of the most extraordinary and important facts in the natural history of the earth, gave a reality and substance to those theoretical speculations, which, however probable, had never till now been directly authenticated by the testimony of the senses. We often said to ourselves, What clearer evidence could we have had of the different formation of these rocks, and of the long interval which separated their formation, had we actually seen them emerging from the bosom of the deep? We felt ourselves necessarily carried back to the time when the schistus on which we stood was yet at the bottom of the sea, and when the sandstone before us was only beginning to be deposited, in the shape of sand or mud, from the waters of a superincumbent ocean. An epocha still more remote presented itself, when even the most ancient of these rocks, instead of standing upright in vertical beds, lay in horizontal planes at the bottom of the sea, and was not yet disturbed by that immeasurable force which has burst asunder the solid pavement of the globe. Revolutions still more remote appeared in the distance of this extraordinary perspective. The mind seemed to grow giddy by looking so far into the abyss of time; and while we listened with earnestness and admiration to the philosopher who was now unfolding to us the order and series of these wonderful events, we became sensible how much farther reason may sometimes go than imagination can venture to follow. As for the rest, we were truly fortunate in the course we had pursued in this excursion; a great number of other curious and important facts presented themselves, and we returned, having collected, in one day, more ample materials for future speculation, than have sometimes resulted from years of diligent and laborious research.

For some years after presenting his *Theory* in 1785, Hutton occupied himself in travel and observation and in writing a voluminous work on metaphysics and principles of knowledge. He was also accumulating notes and observations for an expanded theory of the earth. He postponed its publication, partly because of ill health, however, until the strident criticism of Richard Kirwan, the Irish chemist, aroused him.

The very day, however, after Mr Kirwan's paper was put into his hands, he began the revisal of his manuscript, and resolved immediately to send it to the press. The reason he gave was, that Mr Kirwan had in so many instances completely mistaken, both the facts, and the reasonings in his *Theory,* that he saw the necessity of laying before the world a more ample explanation of them. The work was accordingly published, in two volumes octavo, in 1795; and contained, besides what was formerly given in the *Edinburgh Transactions,* the proofs and reasonings much more in detail, and a much fuller application of the principles to the explanation of appearances. The two volumes, however, then published, do not complete the theory: a third, necessary for that purpose, remained behind, and is still in manuscript.

Dr. Hutton's health continued to be uncertain and he died on March 26, 1797. His grave in Grayfriars Churchyard in Edinburgh was marked on the 150th anniversary of his death and is a scene of pilgrimage by geological visitors to Edinburgh.

BIOGRAPHICAL SKETCH OF JOHN PLAYFAIR

John Playfair[17] was born on March 10, 1748, at Benvie in Forfarshire, where his father was minister. He was educated for the ministry at the University of St. Andrews, but so distinguished himself in mathematical studies that at the age of eighteen he was considered for a professorship in that subject at Aberdeen. In 1773 he was appointed minister at Benvie and Liff in succession to his father. He continued in this position until 1782, when he removed to Edinburgh and in 1785 became professor of mathematics at the University of Edinburgh. In 1805 he was appointed professor of natural philosophy.

At Edinburgh Playfair was immediately accepted into the scientific society of the city. His acquaintance with James Hutton early ripened into friendship and close association extending to joint trips to observe geological features. After Hutton's death in 1797 Playfair began to write a memoir of his life. As he attempted to summarize Hutton's *Theory of the Earth,* the abstract gradually began to take the shape we now see in the *Illustrations.* Because of the attacks, especially those by Kirwan, on the *Theory* after its appearance in 1795, Playfair, from his own inclination, and no doubt also at the urging of friends, prepared the summary and accompanying notes, taking particular pains to answer Hutton's critics. These were published in 1802 as *Illustrations of the Huttonian Theory.* According to the biographer of Playfair, "the fame and credit which have been attached to Hutton's theory . . . but for its commentary, seemed likely to be known only through the erroneous statements of its opponents."

Playfair's research and writing in Edinburgh was in mathematics, astronomy, physics, meteorology, geophysics and geology. It is unfortunate that he was never able to complete a second edition of the *Illustrations* that would have been so modified and expanded as to have been an independent and almost entirely original work.

This edition, of much greater magnitude than the former, was likewise completely different in the arrangement of its contents. It was intended to commence with a description of all the well authenticated facts in geology collected during his extensive reading and personal observation, without any mixture of hypothesis whatever. To this followed the general inferences which may be deduced from the facts. An examination of the various geological systems hitherto offered to the world, and the exclusion of those which involved any contradiction of the principles previously ascertained; while the conclusion would have presented the development of the system adopted by the author, and the application of it to explain the phenomena of geology. It must be viewed by everyone as a great loss to science this design was never completed. . . .

Playfair spent a part of each year in travel to many parts of Great Britain and Ireland. In 1815 he made a journey of more than a year on the continent, especially in France, Switzerland, and Italy. His biographer has included in his memoir a summary of Playfair's geological notes on this long trip.

Upon his return he completed some of his mathematical and physical writing so he could proceed to a series of papers on the geology observed on his travels and to his enlarged edition of the *Illustrations*. But his health failed and he died July 19, 1819.

In the present instance we are concerned with Playfair's work in geology and as a clarifier, commentator, and protagonist of Hutton and his theory. It must be remembered that Playfair was first a mathematician and physicist; his friends "regretted that so much of his time and so large a proportion of his publications, should have been devoted to the subjects of the Indian Astronomy; and the Huttonian Theory of the Earth."

NOTES

[1] A third volume existed in manuscript which was partly preserved and published as volume 3 in 1899.

V. A. Eyles has recently discovered that a 32-page printed abstract was available in 1785 and possibly at the meetings. Only a very few copies of this abstract are now known. For complete bibliographical details of this and later forms of publication of the *Theory* see Eyles, V. A., "Note on the Original Publication of Hutton's 'Theory of the Earth,' and on the subsequent Forms in which it was Issued," *Roy. Soc. Edinburgh Proc.*, Vol. 63, pt. 4, pp. 377-386, 1950; "A bibliographical note on the earliest printed version of James Hutton's Theory of the Earth; its form and date of publication," *Jour. Soc. Bibliog. Nat. Hist.*, vol. 3, pt. 2, pp.

105-108, 1955. The only copy of the abstract known to be in North America is in the University of Illinois Library.

[2] Bakewell, Robert. An Introduction to Geology, London, J. Harding, 1813, pp. 113-322.

[3] Phillips, William. Outlines of Mineralogy and Geology, London, William Phillips, 1816.

[4] Conybeare, W. D., and Phillips, William. Outlines of the Geology of England and Wales, London, William Phillips, 1822.

[5] The early knowledge in America of Werner's system, its enthusiastic acceptance and long persistence, contrasted to the little knowledge of Hutton and Playfair and that little apparently derived from secondary sources, is a chapter in the history of science in America that requires investigation. The fortuitous experiences of Thomas Latham Mitchill and Benjamin Silliman under the persuasive Jameson at Edinburgh may turn out to be an important factor.

[6] Maclure, William. Observations on the Geology of the United States, Philadelphia, Abraham Small, 1817.

[7] Eaton, Amos. An Index to the Geology of the Northern States, Leicester, Hori Brown, 1818; second edition Troy, Wm. S. Parker, 1820, p. vi.

[8] Eaton, Amos. Geological Textbook, Albany, Webster and Skinners, 1830, p. 13.

[9] Cleaveland, Parker. An Elementary Treatise on Mineralogy and Geology, Boston, Cummings and Hilliard, 1822 (First edition 1816).

[10] Van Rensselaer, Jeremiah. Lectures on Geology, New York, 1825.

[11] An Introduction to Geology by Robert Bakewell, edited by Benjamin Silliman, with an Appendix Containing an Outline of his Course of Lectures in Geology; New Haven, 1829.

[12] Mather, W. W. Elements of Geology, Norwich, Wm. Lester, Jr., 1833.

[13] Lyell, Charles. Principles of Geology, being an Attempt to Explain the Former Changes of the Earth's Surface, by Reference to Causes now in Operation. London, John Murray, 1830.

[14] Kirwan, Richard. Geological Essays, London, D. Bremner. 1799, pp. 433-499.

[15] The most extensive biography of Hutton is a memorial by John Playfair, "Biographical Account of the late Dr. James Hutton, F.R.S. Edin.," *Roy. Soc. Edin. Trans.*, Vol. 5, pt. 3, pp. 39-99, 1805; reprinted in *Collected Works of John Playfair Esq.*, vol. 4, pp. 33-118, 1822. Further and additional details, illustrations and analytical essays will be found in a series of papers in "James Hutton, 1726-1797 — Commemoration of the 150th Anniversary of his Death," *Roy. Soc. Edin. Proc.*, vol. 63, sect. B, pt. 4, 1950.

[16] The quotations given in this sketch are from Playfair's account

in volume 4 of the *Collected Works*. The lucid and charming style of Playfair is well displayed in the quotations.

[17] This sketch is derived from the biography by his nephew, William Henry Playfair, "Biographical Account of the late Professor Playfair," in volume 1, pp. xi-lxxvi, of *Collected works of John Playfair, Esq. with a Memoir of the Author,* Edinburgh, Arnold Constable and Co., 1822, 4 vols. The quotation is from the "Biographical Account."

It may be noted that Playfair had at least a very tenuous connection with the United States — his younger brother, William Playfair, resident in Paris, was a principal in the Paris operations of the Scioto Purchase from the Ohio Company in 1787 which led to the founding of Gallipolis on the Ohio River. (Dawes, E. C. The Scioto Purchase in 1787, *Mag. Am. History,* vol. 22, pp. 470-482, 1889.) There is no known indication that John Playfair took any part in this activity, but it would be interesting to know how much he may have known about it.

ILLUSTRATIONS

OF THE

HUTTONIAN THEORY

OF THE EARTH.

By JOHN PLAYFAIR,

F. R. S. EDIN. AND PROFESSOR OF MATHEMATICS
IN THE UNIVERSITY OF EDINBURGH.

*Nunc naturalem caufam quærimus et affiduam, non raram et
fortuitam.*

SENECA.

EDINBURGH:

PRINTED FOR CADELL AND DAVIES, LONDON, AND
WILLIAM CREECH, EDINBURGH.

1802.

ADVERTISEMENT.

THE Treatife here offered to the Public, was drawn up with a view of explaining Dr Hutton's Theory of the Earth in a manner more popular and perfpicuous than is done in his own writings. The obfcurity of thefe has been often complained of; and thence, no doubt, it has arifen, that fo little attention has been paid to the ingenious and original fpeculations which they contain.

THE fimpleft way of accomplifhing the object propofed, feemed to be, to prefent a General Outline of the Syftem, in one continued Difcourfe; and to introduce afterwards, in the form of Notes, what farther Elucidation any particular fubject was thought to demand. Through the whole, I have aimed at little more than a clear expofition of facts, and a plain deduction of the conclufions grounded on them; nor fhall I claim any merit to myfelf, if, in the order which I have found it neceffary to adopt, fome arguments may have taken a

new

new form, and fome additions may have been made to a fyftem naturally rich in the number and variety of its illuftrations.

OF the qualifications which this undertaking requires, there is one that I may fafely fuppofe myfelf to poffefs. Having been inftructed by Dr Hutton himfelf in his theory of the earth; having lived in intimate friendfhip with that excellent man for feveral years, and almoft in the daily habit of difcuffing the queftions here treated of; I have had the beft opportunity of underftanding his views, and becoming acquainted with his peculiarities, whether of expreffion or of thought. In the other qualifications neceffary for the illuftration of a fyftem fo extenfive and various, I am abundantly fenfible of my deficiency, and fhall therefore, with great deference, and confiderable anxiety, wait that decifion from which there is no appeal.

EDINBURGH COLLEGE,
1ft March 1802.

TABLE

OF

CONTENTS.

———————

2. Whinstone. Page 66

3. Granite. p. 82

SECTION

SECTION III.

PHENOMENA COMMON TO STRATIFIED AND UN-
STRATIFIED BODIES.   Page 97

Chemical agents which produce the decomposition of mineral substances at the surface, § 92, 93. Mechanical
agents, § 95, 96. Proofs of wearing from the sea shore,
§ 97, 98. Rivers, § 99, 100. Defiles among mountains,
§ 102. Supply of the soil from the decomposition of
rocks, § 103. Gravel in the soil, § 104, 105. Gold
found in the soil, § 106. Tin, § 107. Proofs of waste
from mountainous countries, § 108, 109. Structure
of valleys, § 111. Transportation of stones, § 112.
Nearest measure of the waste, § 113. General remarks, § 114, 115. No production of minerals on
the surface, § 116. Reproduction at the bottom of
the sea, § 117. Continued system of decay and renovation, § 118. Defence against the charge of impiety, 119. Antiquity and order of the revolutions of
the globe, § 120, 121, 122, 123, 124. Consistency
with the Sacred Writings, § 125. Scope of this theory
of the earth distinguishes it from others; beauty and
extent of its views, § 126. New facts, § 127.
Comparison of this theory with that of Buffon, § 129.
of Lazzaro Moro, § 130. *Plutonic* system, § 131. Distinguished by the principle of compression, § 132.
Explains the oblate figure of the earth, *ib.* Prejudices against this system, § 133. What may be expected from the progress of science, § 134.

                                        NOTES

NOTES AND ADDITIONS.

by

Note xiv.—On Whinftone.   Page 26σ

2. Granite

                                              IL-

ERRATA.

Page 44. *line* 4. *from the bottom, for* that re*æd* as
——— 189. —— 6. ————————— *for* appearanes. *read* appearances.
——— 464. —— 4. ————————— *for* D'AUBENTON *read* DAUBENTON
——— 482. —— 12. ———————— *or* adverfaries *read* adverfary

ILLUSTRATIONS, &c.

A VERY little attention to the phenomena of the mineral kingdom, is sufficient to convince us, that the condition of the earth's surface has not been the same at all times that it is at the present moment. When we observe the impressions of plants in the heart of the hardest rocks; when we discover trees converted into flint, and entire beds of limestone or of marble composed of shells and corals; we see the same individual in two states, the most widely different from one another; and, in the latter instance, have a clear proof, that the present land was once deep immersed under the waters of the ocean. If to this we add, that many masses of rock, the most solid and compact, consist of no other materials but sand and gravel; that, on the other hand, loose gravel, such as is formed only in beds of rivers, or on the sea-shore, now abounds in places remote from both: if we reflect, at the same time, on the irregular

A   and

and broken figure of our continents, and the identity of the mineral ſtrata on oppoſite ſides of the ſame valley, or the ſame inlet of the ſea ; we ſhall ſee abundant reaſon to conclude, that the earth has been the theatre of many great revolutions, and that nothing on its ſurface has been exempted from their effects.

To trace the ſeries of theſe revolutions, to explain their cauſes, and thus to connect together all the indications of change that are found in the mineral kingdom, is the proper object of a Theory of the Earth.

But, though the attention of men may be turned to the theory of the earth by a very ſuperficial acquaintance with the phenomena of geology, the formation of ſuch a theory requires an accurate and extenſive examination of thoſe phenomena, and is inconſiſtent with any but a very advanced ſtate of the phyſical ſciences. There is, perhaps, in thoſe ſciences, no reſearch more arduous than this ; none certainly where the ſubject is ſo complex ; where the appearances are ſo extremely diverſified, or ſo widely ſcattered, and where the cauſes that have operated are ſo remote from the ſphere of ordinary obſervation. Hence the attempts to form a theory of the earth are of very modern origin, and as, from the ſimplicity of its ſubject, aſtronomy is the eldeſt, ſo, on account of the com-

plexneſs

plexnefs of its fubject, geology is the youngeft of the fciences.

It is foreign from the prefent purpofe, to enter on any hiftory of the fyftems that, fince the rife of this branch of fcience, have been invented to explain the phenomena of the mineral kingdom. It is fufficient to remark, that thefe fyftems are ufually reduced to two claffes, according as they refer the origin of terreftrial bodies to FIRE or to WATER; and that, conformably to this divifion, their followers have of late been diftinguifhed by the fanciful names of *Vulcanifts* and *Neptunifts*. To the former of thefe Dr HUTTON belongs much more than to the latter; though, as he employs the agency both of fire and of water in his fyftem, he cannot, in ftrict propriety, be arranged with either.

In the fuccinct account which I am now about to give of this fyftem, I fhall confider the mineral kingdom as divided into two parts, namely, ftratified and unftratified fubftances. I fhall treat, firft, of the phenomena peculiar to the ftratified; next, of thofe peculiar to the unftratified; and, laftly, of the phenomena common to both. Beginning, then, with the firft, the fubject naturally divides itfelf into three branches; viz. the *materials*, the *confolidation*, and the *pofition* of the ftrata.

SECTION I.

OF THE PHENOMENA PECULIAR TO STRATIFIED BODIES.

1. *Materials of the Strata.*

1. IT is well known that, on removing the loofe earth which forms the immediate furface of the land, we come to the folid rock, of which a great proportion is found to be regularly difpofed in ftrata, or beds of determinate thicknefs, inclined at different angles to the horizon, but feparated from one another by equidiftant fuperficies, that often maintain their parallelifm to a great extent. Thefe ftrata bear fuch evident marks of being depofited by water, that they are univerfally acknowledged to have had their origin at the bottom of the fea; and it is alfo admitted, that the materials which they confift of, were then either foft, or in fuch a ftate of comminution and feparation, as rendered them capable of arrangement by the action of the water in which they were immerfed. Thus far moft of the theories of the earth agree; but

but from this point they begin to diverge, and each to assume a character and direction peculiar to itself. Dr Hutton's does so, by laying down this fundamental proposition, That in all the strata we discover proofs of the materials having existed as elements of bodies, which must have been destroyed before the formation of those of which these materials now actually make a part *.

2. The calcareous strata are the portion of the mineral kingdom that gives the clearest testimony to the truth of this assertion. They often contain shells, corals, and other exuviæ of marine animals in so great abundance, that they appear to be composed of no other materials. Though these remains of organized bodies are now converted into stone or into spar, their shape and interior structure are often so well preserved, that the species of animal or plant of which they once made a part, can still be distinguished and pointed out among the living inhabitants of the ocean.

Others of the calcareous strata appear to be composed of fragments of some ancient rocks, which, after having been broken, have been again united into a compact stone. In these we find pieces clearly marked as having been once continuous, but now placed at a distance from

A 3   one

* Hutton's Theory, vol. i. p. 20. &c.

one another, and exhibiting exactly the same appearances as if they floated in a fluid of the same specific gravity with themselves.

From these, therefore, and a variety of similar appearances, Dr Hutton concludes, that the materials of all the calcareous strata have been furnished, either from the dissolution of former strata, or from the remains of organized bodies. But, though this conclusion is meant to be extended to all the calcareous strata, it is not asserted that every cubic inch of marble or of limestone contains in it the characters of its former condition, and of the changes through which it has passed. It may, however, be safely affirmed, that there is scarce any entire stratum where such characters are not to be found. These must be held as decisive with respect to the whole system of strata to which they belong; they prove the existence of calcareous rocks before the formation of the present; and, as the destruction of those is evidently adequate to the supply of the materials of these that we now see, to look for any other supply were superfluous, and could only embarrass our reasonings by the introduction of unnecessary hypotheses *.

3. The same conclusions result from an examination of the siliceous strata; under which we may comprehend the common sand-stone,

and

* Note i.

and alſo thoſe pudding-ſtones or breccias where the gravel conſiſts of quartz. In all theſe inſtances, it is plain, that the ſand or gravel exiſted in a ſtate quite looſe and unconnected, at the bottom of the ſea, previous to its conſolidation into ſtone. But ſuch bodies of gravel or ſand could only be formed from the attrition of large maſſes of quartz, or from the diſſolution of ſuch ſand-ſtone ſtrata as exiſt at preſent; for it will hardly be alleged, that ſand is a cryſtallization of quartz, formed from that ſubſtance, when it paſſes from a fluid to a ſolid ſtate.

Thoſe pudding-ſtones in which the gravel is round and poliſhed, carry the concluſion ſtill farther, as ſuch gravel can only be formed in the beds of rivers or on the ſhores of the ſea; for, in the depths of the ocean, though currents are known to exiſt, yet there can be no motion of the water ſufficiently rapid to produce the attrition required to give a round figure and ſmooth ſurface to hard and irregular pieces of ſtone. There muſt have exiſted, therefore, not only a ſea, but continents, previouſly to the formation of the preſent ſtrata.

The ſame thing is clearly ſhewn by thoſe petrifactions of wood, where, though the vegetable ſtructure is perfectly preſerved, the whole maſs is ſiliceous, and has, perhaps, been found

A 4   in

in the heart of fome mountain, deep imbedded in the folid rock.

4. Characters of the fame import are alfo found among the argillaceous ftrata, though perhaps more rarely than among the calcareous or filiceous. Such are the impreffions of the leaves and ftems of vegetables ; alfo the bodies of fifh and amphibious animals, found very often in the different kinds of argillaceous fchiftus, and in moft inftances having the figure accurately preferved, but the fubftance of the animal replaced by clay or pyrites. Thefe are all remains of ancient feas or continents ; the latter of which have long fince difappeared from the furface of the earth, but have ftill their memory preferved in thofe archives, where nature has recorded the revolutions of the globe.

5. Among bituminous bodies, pit-coal is the only one which conftitutes regular and extenfive ftrata ; and no foffil has its origin from the wafte of former continents, marked by ftronger and more diftinct characters. Not to mention that the coal ftrata are alternated with thofe that have been already enumerated, and that they often contain fhells and corals, perfectly mineralized, it is fufficient to remark, that there are entire beds of this foffil, which appear to confift wholly of wood, and in which the fibrous ftructure is perfectly preferved. From thefe in-

ftances,

ſtances, the appearances of vegetable ſtructure may be traced through all poſſible gradations, down to an evaneſcent ſtate. This laſt ſtate is undoubtedly the moſt common; and though coal does not then, on bare inſpection, make known its vegetable origin, yet, if we take it in connection with the other terms of the ſeries, as we may call them; if we conſider that the two extremes, viz. coal, with the vegetable ſtructure perfect, and coal without any ſuch ſtructure viſible, are often found in the ſame or in contiguous beds; and, if we remark, that through all theſe gradations coal contains near-ly the ſame chemical elements, and yields, on analyſis, bitumen and charcoal, combined with a greater or leſs proportion of earth : if we take all theſe circumſtances into account, we cannot doubt that this foſſil is every where the ſame, and derives its origin from the trees and plants that grew on the ſurface of the earth before the formation of the preſent land.

6. Dr Hutton has further obſerved, that if thoſe ancient continents were at all ſimilar to the preſent, we can be at no loſs to account for the want of any diſtinct mark of vegetable or-ganization in the greater part of the coal ſtrata. It is plain, that the daily waſte of animal and vegetable ſubſtances on the ſurface of the earth, muſt diſengage a great quantity of oily as well

as

as carbonic matter, which, with whatever element it is at firſt combined, is ultimately delivered into the ocean. Thus, the oily or fuliginous parts of animal and vegetable ſubſtances, let looſe by burning, firſt aſcend into the atmoſphere, but are at length precipitated, and either fall immediately into the ſea, or are, in part at leaſt, waſhed down into it from the land. From other cauſes alſo, much vegetable matter is carried down by the rivers ; and the whole quantity of animal and vegetable ſubſtances thus delivered into the ſea, muſt be very conſiderable, amounting annually to the whole reſiduum of thoſe ſubſtances, not employed in the maintenance or reproduction of animal and vegetable bodies. Whether chemically united to the waters of the ocean, or ſimply ſuſpended in them, this matter is at laſt precipitated, and, mingling with earthy ſubſtances, is formed into ſtrata, the place of which will be determined by the currents, the poſition of the preſent continents, and many other circumſtances not eaſily enumerated.

If, then, an order of things ſimilar to what we now ſee, exiſted before the formation of the preſent ſtrata, it would neceſſarily happen, that the animal and vegetable ſubſtances, diffuſed through the ocean, being ſeparated from the water, would be depoſited at the bottom of the
ſea,

fea, and, in the courfe of ages, would form beds, lefs or more pure, according to the quantity of earth and other fubftances depofited at the fame time. Thefe beds being confolidated and mineralized by operations that are afterwards to be confidered, have been converted into pit-coal, the parts of which are impalpable, and retain nothing of their primitive ftructure *.

If, then, the formation of coal from animal and vegetable bodies be admitted, the general pofition which derives the origin of the ftrata from the wafte of former land, as it is applicable to all the kinds already enumerated, and of courfe to all thofe with which they are alternated, comprehends a very large portion of the earth's furface. It comprehends, indeed, all the ftrata ufually diftinguifhed by the name of *Secondary ;* but there is another great divifion of the mineral kingdom, viz. the rocks, called *Primitive*, which, as they are never alternated with the fecondary, but are always inferior to them, muft be further examined, before we can decide whether the fame conclufion extends to them or not.

7. Here it muft be carefully obferved, that, among the primary rocks, the granite is not meant to be included, except where that ftone is ftratified, and either coincides with veined

granite

* Note ii.

granite or with gneiſs. The primitive ſtrata, in Dr Hutton's theory, comprehend, beſides gneiſs, the micaceous, chlorite, hornblend, and ſiliceous ſchiſtus, together with ſlate, and ſome other kinds of argillite ; to which we muſt add, ſerpentine, micaceous limeſtone, and the greater part of marbles. Theſe are moſtly diſtinguiſhed by their laminated ſtructure, by having their planes much elevated with reſpect to the horizon, and by belonging more to the mountainous than the level parts of the earth's ſurface. They rarely contain veſtiges of organized bodies ; ſo rarely, indeed, that they were called primitive by the geologiſts who firſt diſtinguiſhed them from other rocks, on the ſuppoſition of their being part of the primeval nucleus of the globe, which had never undergone any change whatſoever ; but this, I believe, has now almoſt ceaſed to be the opinion of any geologiſt *. The Neptuniſts hold the rocks, here enumerated, and alſo granite, to be produced by aqueous depoſition ; but maintain them to be in the ſtricteſt ſenſe primeval, and of a formation antecedent to all organized bodies.

8. In oppoſition to this, Dr Hutton maintained, that the primary ſchiſtus, like all the other ſtrata, was formed of materials depoſited at the

bottom

* Note III.

ST. PETER'S COLLEGE LIBRARY BALTIMORE. M

bottom of the fea, and collected from the wafte of rocks ftill more ancient. When, therefore, he conformed to the received language of mineralogifts, by calling thefe ftrata primitive, he only meant to defcribe them as more ancient than any other ftrata now exifting, but not as more ancient than any that ever had exifted. They are diftinguifhed, in his fyftem, by the name of *Primary*, rather than of *Primitive* ftrata.

That the account now given of their origin is well founded, may be proved by unqueftionable facts. For, firft, though, agreeably to the obfervation juft made, the ancient ftrata do but rarely contain any remains of organized bodies, they are not entirely deftitute of them. Different places in this ifland have been pointed out by Dr Hutton, where marine objects have been difcovered in primary limeftone, either by himfelf or others, and it would not be difficult to add more inftances of the fame kind *. In Dauphiny, coal, which is certainly a derivative fubftance, has been found among mountains which have a title to the character of primitive, fuch as no one will difpute. Thefe facts put the compofition of fuch rocks from loofe materials, beyond all doubt, and also prove their formation to be pofterior to the exiftence of

* Note iv.

of an animal and vegetable fyftem. They do indeed prove this in the ftricteft fenfe, only of the particular beds in which they are found; but as thefe beds are in all other refpects as much to be accounted primary as any part of the mineral kingdom, it is evident that the negative inftances are here of no force, and that nothing can be gained to the adverfaries of this opinion by denying it in general, if they are obliged to admit it in a fingle cafe.

9. Again, it is certain, as Dr Hutton remarks, that there are few confiderable bodies of fchiftus, even the moft decidedly primitive, where fand and gravel may not in fome parts be obferved. Indeed, it is not only true that they are to be found in fome parts of them; but, in fact, among many of the primitive mountains, we find large tracts, compofed entirely of a fchiftofe and much indurated fand-ftone, in beds highly inclined, fometimes alone, fometimes alternated with other fchifti. In many of them, the fand of which they confift appears to be entirely of granite, from the detritus of which rock it fhould feem that they were chiefly formed.

10. Thus we conclude, that the ftrata both primary and fecondary, both thofe of ancient and thofe of more recent origin, have had their materials furnifhed from the ruins of former continents, from the diffolution of rocks, or the

deftruction

destruction of animal or vegetable bodies, similar, at least in some respects, to those that now
occupy the surface of the earth. This conclusion is not indeed proved of every individual
portion of rock, but it is demonstrated of many
and large parts, and those scattered indifferently
through all the varieties of the strata; and
therefore, from the rules of the strictest reasoning, we must infer, that the whole is derived
from the same origin *.

Thus far concerning the materials of the strata; and, as these were originally loose and unconnected, we must next consider by what means
they were consolidated into stone.

2. *Consolidation of the Strata.*

11. Though Dr Hutton has no where defined the meaning of the term consolidation, he
has been scrupulously exact in using it constant-
ly in the same sense. He understands by it, not
merely that quality in a hard body by which its
parts cohere together, but also that by which it
fills up the space comprehended within its surface, being to sense without porosity, and impervious to air and moisture.

Now,

* NOTE v.

Now, a porous mafs of unconnected materials, such as the ftrata appear originally to have been, can acquire hardnefs and folidity only in two ways, that is, either when it is firft reduced by heat into a ftate of fufion, or at leaft of foftnefs, and afterwards permitted to cool; or when matter that is diffolved in fome fluid menftruum, is introduced along with that menftruum into the porous mafs, and, being depofited, forms a cement by which the whole is rendered firm and compact. Fire and water, therefore, are the only two phyfical agents to which we can afcribe the confolidation of the ftrata ; and, in order to determine to which of them that effect is to be attributed, we muft inquire whether there are any certain characters that diftinguifh the action of the one from that of the other, and which may be compared with the phenomena actually obferved among mineral fubftances.

12. Firft, then, it is evident, that the confolidation produced by the action of water, or of any other fluid menftruum, in the manner juft referred to, muft necefarily be imperfect, and can never entirely banifh the porofity of the mafs. For the bulk of the folvent, and of the matter it contained in folution, being greater than the bulk of either taken fingly, when the latter was depofited, the former would have fufficient room left, and would continue to oc-

cupy

cupy a certain fpace in the interior of the ftrata. A liquid folvent therefore could never
fhut up the pores of a body to the entire exclufion of itfelf; and, had mineral fubftances been
confolidated, as here fuppofed, the folvent ought
either to remain within them in a liquid ftate,
or, if evaporated, fhould have left the pores
empty, and the body pervious to water. Neither of thefe, however, is the fact ; many ftratified bodies are perfectly impervious to water,
and few mineral fubftances contain water in
a liquid ftate. That they fometimes contain
it, chemically united to them, is no proof of
their folidity having been brought about by
that fluid ; for fuch chemical union is as confiftent with the fuppofition of igneous as of
aqueous confolidation, fince the region in which
the fire was applied, on every hypothefis, muft
have abounded with humidity.

13. Again, if water was the folvent by which
the confolidating matter was introduced into the
interftices of the ftrata, that matter could confift
only of fuch fubftances as are foluble in water,
whereas it confifts of a vaft variety of fubftances,
altogether infoluble either in it, or in any fingle
menftruum whatfoever. The ftrata are confolidated, for example, by quartz, by fluor, by
feltfpar, and by all the metals, in their endlefs

B   combinations

combinations with fulphureous bodies. To affirm that water was ever capable of diffolving
thefe fubftances, is to afcribe to it powers which
it confeffedly has not at prefent ; and, therefore,
it is to introduce an hypothefis, not merely gratuitous, but one which, phyfically fpeaking, is
abfurd and impoffible.

This is not all, however ; for, even if this
difficulty were to be paffed over, it would ftill
be required to explain, how the water, which,
together with the matter which it held in folution, had infinuated itfelf into the pores of the
ftrata, became fuddenly difpofed to depofite that
matter, and to allow it, by cryftallization or
concretion, to affume a folid form *. The Neptunifts muft either affign a fufficient reafon for
this great and univerfal change, or muft expect
to fee their fyftem treated as an inartificial accumulation of hypothefes which affigns oppofite
virtues to the fame fubject, and is alike at va-
riance with nature and with itfelf ; in a word,
a fyftem that might pafs for the invention of
an age, when as yet found philofophy had not
alighted on the earth, nor taught man that
he is but the minifter and interpreter of nature,
and can neither extend his power nor his knowledge

* NOTE VI.

ledge a hair's-breadth beyond his experience and obfervation of the prefent order of things *.

14. Such are the more obvious, but I think unanfwerable objections, that may be urged againft the aqueous confolidation of the ftrata. It is true, that ftony concretions, fome of them much indurated, are formed in the humid way under our eyes. Very particular conditions, however, are required for that purpofe, and conditions fuch as can hardly have exifted at the bottom of the fea. Firft, The water muft diffolve the fubftance of which the concretion is to be formed, as it actually does in the cafe of calcareous, and in certain circumftances, in that of filiceous, earth. Secondly, It muft be feparated from that fubftance, as by evaporation, or by a combination of the matter diffolved with fome third fubftance, to which it has a greater affinity than to water, fo as to form with it an infoluble compound. Laftly, The water that is deprived of its folution muft be carried off, and more of that which contains the folution muft be fupplied, as fometimes happens

B 2   where

---

* Homo naturæ minifter, et interpres tantum facit et intelligit, quantùm de naturæ ordine re, vel mente, obfervaverit; nec amplius fcit, aut poteft.

Nov. Org. lib. i. aph. i.

where water runs in a ftream, or drops from the roof of a cavern. The two laft conditions are peculiarly inapplicable to the bottom of the fea, where the ftate of the furrounding fluid would neither permit the water that was deprived of its folution from being drawn off, nor that which contained the folution from fucceeding it.

It is further to be obferved, that the confolidation of ftalactitical concretions, that is, the filling up of their pores, is always imperfect, and is brought about by the repeated action of the fluid running through the porous mafs, and continuing to depofite there fome of the matter it holds in folution. This, which is properly infiltration, is incompatible with the nature of a fluid, either nearly, or altogether quiefcent.

15. In order to judge whether objections of equal weight can be oppofed to the hypothefis of igneous confolidation, we muft attend to a very important remark, firft made by Dr Hutton, and applied with wonderful fuccefs to explain the moft myfterious phenomena of the mineral kingdom.

It is certain, that the effects of fire on bodies vary with the circumftances under which it is applied to them, and therefore a confiderable allowance muft be made, if we would compare

pare the operation of that element when it confolidated the ftrata, with the refults of our daily
experience. The materials of the ftrata were
difpofed, as we have already feen, loofe and
unconnected, at the bottom of the fea ; that
is, even on the moft moderate ftimation, at the
depth of feveral miles under its furface. At
this depth, and under the preffure of a column
of water of fo great a height, the action of heat
would differ much from that which we obferve
here upon the furface; and, though our experience does not enable us to compute with accuracy the amount of this difference, it neverthelefs points out the direction in which it muft
lie, and even marks certain limits to which it
would probably extend.

The tendency of an increafed preffure on
the bodies to which heat is applied, is to reftrain the volatility of thofe parts which o-
therwife would make their efcape, and to
force them to endure a more intenfe action of
heat. At a certain depth under the furface
of the fea, the power even of a very intenfe heat might therefore be unable to drive
off the oily or bituminous parts from the inflammable matter there depofited, fo that, when the
heat was withdrawn, thefe principles might be
found ftill united to the earthy and carbonic
parts, forming a fubftance very unlike the re-

B 3   fiduum

fiduum obtained after combuſtion under a preſ-
fure no greater than the weight of the atmofphere. It is in like manner reaſonable to believe, that, on the application of heat to calcareous bodies under great compreſſion, the carbonic gas would be forced to remain ; the generation of quicklime would be prevented, and
the whole might be ſoftened, or even completely melted ; which laſt effect, though not directly deducible from any experiment yet made,
is rendered very probable, from the analogy of
certain chemical phenomena.

16. An analogy of this kind, derived from a
property of the barytic earth, was ſuggeſted by
that excellent chemiſt and philoſopher, the late
Dr BLACK. The barytic earth, as is well known,
has a ſtronger attraction for fixed air than common calcareous earth has, ſo that the carbonate
of barytes is able to endure a great degree of
heat before its fixed air is expelled. Accordingly, when expoſed to an increaſing heat, at a
certain temperature, it is brought into fuſion,
the fixed air ſtill remaining united to it : if the
heat be further increaſed, the air is driven off,
the earth loſes its fluidity, and appears in a
cauſtic ſtate. Here, it is plain, that the barytic
earth, which is infuſible, or very refractory, *per
ſe*, as well as the calcareous, owes its fuſibility
to the preſence of the fixed air ; and it is therefore

fore probable, that the fame thing would happen to the calcareous earth, if by any means the fixed air were prevented from efcaping when great heat is applied to it. This efcape of the fixed air is exactly what the compreffion in the fubterraneous regions is calculated to prevent, and therefore we are not to wonder if, among the calcareous ftrata, we find marks of actual fufion having taken place *.

17. Thefe effects of preffure to refift the decompofition, and augment the fufibility of bodies, being once fuppofed, we fhall find little difficulty in conceiving the confolidation of the ftrata by heat, fince the intervals between the loofe materials of which they originally confifted may have been clofed, either by the foftening of thofe materials, or by the introduction of foreign matter among them, in the ftate of a fluid, or of an elaftic vapour. No objection to this hypothefis can arife from the confiderations ftated in the preceding cafe ; the folvent here employed would want no pores to lodge in after its work was completed, nor would it find any difficulty in making its retreat through the denfeft and moft folid fubftances in the mineral kingdom. Neither can its incapacity to diffolve the bodies fubmitted to its action be alleged. Heat is the moft powerful and moft general of all folvents ; and, though

B 4

fome

* NOTE VII.

fome bodies, fuch as the calcareous, are able
to refift its force on the furface of the earth,
yet, as has juft been fhewn, it is perfectly a-
greeable to analogy to fuppofe, that, under
great preffure, the carbonic ftate of the lime
being preferved, the pureft limeftone or marble might be foftened or even melted. With
refpect to other fubftances, lefs doubt of their
fufibility is entertained ; and though, in our
experiments, the refractory nature of filiceous earth has not been completely fubdued, a
degree of foftnefs and an incipient fufion have
neverthelefs been induced.

Thus it appears, in general, that the fame difficulties do not prefs againft the two theories
of aqueous and of igneous confolidation ; and,
that the latter employs an agent incomparably
more powerful than the former, of more general activity, and, what is of infinite importance
in a philofophical theory, vaftly more definite
in the laws of its operation.

18. A more particular examination of the
different kinds of foffils will confirm this conclufion, and will fhow, that, wherever they bear
marks of having been fluid, thefe marks are fuch
as characterize the fluidity of fufion, and diftinguifh it from that which is produced by folution in a menftruum. Dr Hutton has enumerated many of thefe difcovered in the courfe of
that

that careful and accurate examination of foffils, in which he probably never was excelled by any mineralogift. It will be fufficient here to point out a few of the moft remarkable examples.

19. Foffil-wood, penetrated by filiceous matter, is a fubftance well known to mineralogifts; it is found in great abundance in various fituations, and frequently in the heart of great bodies of rock. On examination, the filiceous matter is often obferved to have penetrated the wood very unequally, fo that the vegetable ftructure remains in fome places entire; and in other places is loft in a homogeneous mafs of agate or jafper. Where this happens, it may be remarked, that the line which feparates thefe two parts is quite fharp and diftinct, altogether different from what muft have taken place, had the flinty matter been introduced into the body of the wood, by any fluid in which it was diffolved, as it would then have pervaded the whole, if not uniformly, yet with a regular gradation. In thofe fpecimens of foffil-wood that are partly penetrated by agate, and partly not penetrated at all, the fame fharpnefs of termination may be remarked, and is an appearance highly characteriftic of the fluidity produced by fufion.

20. The round nodules of flint that are found in chalk, quite infulated and feparate

from

from one another, afford an argument of the same kind; since the flinty matter, if it had been carried into the chalk by any folvent, muft have been depofited with a certain degree of uniformity, and would not now appear collected into feparate maffes, without any trace of its exiftence in the intermediate parts. On the other hand, if we conceive the melted flint to have been forcibly injected among the chalk, and to have penetrated it, fomewhat as mercury may, by preffure, be made to penetrate through the pores of wood, it might, on cooling, exhibit the fame appearances that the chalk-beds of England do actually prefent us with.

The filiceous pudding-ftone is an inftance clofely connected with the two laft; in it we find both the pebbles, and the cement which unites them, confifting of flint equally hard and confolidated; and this circumftance, for which it is impoffible to account by infiltration, or the infinuation of an aqueous folvent, is perfectly confiftent with the fuppofition, that a ftream of melted flint has been forcibly injected among a mafs of loofe gravel.

21. The common grit, or fandftone, though it certainly gives no indication of having poffeffed fluidity, is ftrongly expreffive of the effects of heat. It is fo, efpecially in thofe inftances where the particles of quartzy fand, of
which

which it is compofed, are firmly and clofely united, without the help of any cementing fubftance whatfoever. This appearance, which is very common, feems to be quite inconfiftent with every idea of confolidation, except an incipient fufion, which, with the affiftance of a fuitable compreffion, has enabled the particles of quartz to unite into ftone.

It has indeed been afferted, that the mere appofition of ftony particles, fo as to permit their corpufcular attraction to take place, was fufficient to form them into ftone. To this Dr Hutton has very well replied, that, admitting the poffibility of a hard and firm body being produced in this way, of which, however, we have no proof, the clofe and compact texture, the perfect confolidation of the ftones we are now fpeaking of, would ftill remain to be explained, and of this it is evident that the mere appofition of particles, and the force of their mutual attraction, can afford no folution.

22. Thefe proofs that the ftrata muft have endured the action of intenfe heat, though immediately deduced from thofe of the filiceous genus only, extend in reality to all the ftrata, of every kind, with which they are found alternated. It is impoffible that heat, of the intenfity here fuppofed, can have acted on a particu-

lar

lar ſtratum, and not on thoſe that are contiguous to it ; and, as there are no ſtrata of any kind
with which the quartzy and ſiliceous are not
intermixed, ſo there are none of which the igneous conſolidation is not thus rendered probable.   We need reſt nothing, however, on this
argument, as the foſſils of every genus may be
ſhewn to ſpeak diſtinctly for themſelves.

23. Thoſe of the calcareous genus do ſo
perhaps more ſparingly than the reſt ; yet
even among them there are many facts, that,
though taken unconnected with all others, are
ſufficient to eſtabliſh the action of ſubterraneous
fire.   Such, for example, are the calcareous
breccias, compoſed of fragments of marble or
limeſtone, and not only adapted to each other's
ſhape, but indented into one another, in a manner not a little reſembling the *futures* of the human *cranium*.   From ſuch inſtances, it is impoſſible not to infer the ſoftneſs of the calcareous
fragments when they were conſolidated into
one maſs.   Now, this ſoftneſs could be induced
only by heat ; for it muſt be acknowledged,
that the action of any other ſolvent is quite inadequate to the ſoftening of large fragments of
ſtone, without diſſolving them altogether.

24. In many other inſtances it appears certain, that the ſtones of the calcareous genus
have been reduced by heat into a ſtate of fluidity

dity much more perfect. Thus, the saline or finer kinds of marble, and many others that have a structure highly crystallized, must have been softened to a degree little short of fusion, before this crystallization could take place. Even the petrifactions which abound so much in limestones, tend to establish the same fact ; for they possess a sparry structure, and must have acquired that structure in their transition from a fluid to a solid state *.

25. In accounting, by the operation of heat, for these appearances of fluidity, Dr Hutton has proceeded on the principle already laid down, as conformable to analogy, that calcareous earth, under great compression, may have its fixed air retained in it, notwithstanding the action of intense heat, and may, by that means, be reduced into fusion, or into a state approaching to it. In all this, I do not think that he has departed from the strictest rules of philosophical investigation. The facts just stated prove, that limestone was once soft, its fragments retaining at the same time their peculiar form, an effect to which we know of none similar but those of fire ; and therefore, though we could not conjecture how heat might be applied to limestone so as to melt it, instead of reducing it to a calx, we should, nevertheless, have been forced to

suppose

* NOTE VIII.

ſuppoſe, that this had actually taken place in the bowels of the earth; and was a fact which, though we were not able to explain it, we were not entitled to deny. The principle juſt mentioned relieves us therefore from a difficulty, that would have embarraſſed, but could not have overturned, this theory of the earth.

26. From the arguments which the argillaceous ſtrata afford for the igneous conſolidation of foſſils, I ſhall ſelect one on which Dr Hutton uſed to lay conſiderable ſtreſs, and which ſome of the adverſaries of his ſyſtem have endeavoured to refute. This argument is founded on the ſtructure of certain iron-ſtones called *ſeptaria*, often met with among the argillaceous ſchiſtus, particularly in the vicinity of coal. Theſe ſtones are uſually of a lenticular or ſpheroidal form, and are divided in their interior into diſtinct *ſepta*, by veins of calcareous ſpar, of which one ſet are circular and concentric, the other rectilineal; diverging from the centre of the former, and diminiſhing in ſize as they recede from it. Now, what is chiefly to be remarked is, that theſe veins terminate before they reach the ſurface of the ſtone; ſo that the matter with which they are filled cannot have been introduced from without by infiltration, or in any other way whatſoever. The only other ſuppoſition, therefore, that is left for explaining the ſingular ſtructure

of

of this foffil, is, that the whole mafs was originally fluid, and that, in cooling, the calcareous
part feparated from the reft, and afterwards
cryftallized.

27. It has been urged againft this theory of
the feptaria, that thefe ftones are fometimes
found with the calcareous veins extending all
the way to the circumference, and of courfe
communicating with the outfide. But it muft
be obferved, that this fact does not affect the
argument drawn from fpecimens in which no
fuch communication takes place. It is at beft
only an ambiguous inftance, that may be explained by two oppofite theories, and may be
reconciled either to the notion of igneous or of
aqueous confolidation : but if there is a fingle
clofe feptarium in nature, it can, of courfe, be
explained only by one of thefe theories, and the
other muft, of neceffity, be rejected. Befides,
it is plain, that a clofe feptarium can never have
been open, though an open feptarium may very
well have been clofe ; and indeed, as this ftone
is, in certain circumftances, fubject to perpetual
exfoliation, it would be wonderful if no one was
ever found with the calcareous veins reaching
to the furface. With regard to the light, therefore, that they give into their own hiftory, thefe
two kinds of feptaria are by no means on an
equal footing ; and this may ferve to fhew, how

neceffary

neceffary it is, in all inductive reafoning, and particularly in a fubject fo complex as geology, to feparate with care fuch phenomena as admit of two folutions, from fuch as admit only of one.

28. The bituminous ftrata come next to be confidered ; and they are of great confequence in the prefent argument, becaufe their diffimilarity in fo many particulars to all other mineral fubftances, renders them what Lord BACON calls an *inftantia fingularis*, having the firft rank among facts fubfervient to inductive inveftigation. But though unlike in fubftance to other foffils, and compofed, as has been fhewn, of materials that belonged not originally to the mineral kingdom, they agree in many material circumftances with the ftrata already enumerated. Their beds are difpofed in the fame manner, and are alternated indifcriminately with thofe of all the fecondary rocks, and, being formed in the fame region, muft have been fubject to the fame accidents, and have endured the operation of the fame caufes. They are traverfed too like the other ftrata, by veins of all the metals, of fpar, of bafaltes, and of other fubftances ; and, whatever argument may hereafter be derived from this to prove the action of fire on the ftrata fo traverfed, is as much applicable to coal as to any other mineral. The coal ftra-

ta

ta alfo contain pyrites in great abundance, a fubftance that is perhaps, more than any other, the decided progeny of fire. This compound of metal and fulphur, which is found in mineral bodies of every kind, I believe, without any exception, is deftroyed by the contact of moifture, and refolved into a vitriolic falt. At the fame time it is found in the ftrata, not traverfing them in veins, which may be fuppofed of more recent formation than the ftrata themfelves; but exifting in the heart of the moft folid rocks, often nicely cryftallized, and completely inclofed, on all fides, without the moft minute vacuity. The pyrites muft have been prefent, therefore, when the ftrata were confolidated, and it is inconceivable, if their confolidation was brought about in the wet way, that a fubftance fhould be fo generally found in them, the very exiftence of which is incompatible with humidity. This argument for the igneous origin of the ftrata is applicable to them all, but efpecially to thofe of coal, as abounding with pyrites more than any other.

29. The difficulty that here naturally prefents itfelf, viz. how vegetable matter, fuch as coal is fuppofed to have been, could be expofed to the action of intenfe heat, without being deprived of its inflammable part, is obviated by the principle formerly explained concerning the effects

C   of

of compreffion. The weight incumbent on the strata of coal, when they were exposed to the intense heat of the mineral regions, may have been such as to retain the oily and bituminous, as well as sulphureous parts, though the whole was reduced almost to fusion; and thus, on cooling, the sulphur uniting with iron might crystallize, and assume the form of pyrites.

30. The compreffion, however, has not in every instance preserved the bituminous, in union with the carbonic part of coal; and hence a mark of the operation of fire quite peculiar to this fossil, and found in those infusible kinds of it which contain no bitumen, and burn without flame. These resemble, some of them very precisely, and all of them in a great degree, the products obtained by the distillation of the common bituminous coal; that is, they consist of charcoal, united to an earthy basis in different proportions. It is natural therefore to conclude, that this substance was prepared in the mineral regions by the action of heat, which, in some instances, has driven off the inflammable part of the coal. That the heat should, in some cases, have done so, is not inconsistent with the general effect attributed to compreffion. The conditions necessary for retaining the more volatile parts, may not have been present every where in the same degree,

gree, ſo that the latter, though they could not eſcape, may have been forced from one part of a ſtratum, or body of ſtrata, to another.

31. In confirmation of this it muſt be obſerved, that, as the fixed part of coal is thus found in the bowels of the earth, ſeparate from the volatile or bituminous, ſo, in the neighbourhood of coal ſtrata, the latter is ſometimes found without any mixture of the former. The fountains of naphtha and petroleum are well known ; and Dr Hutton has deſcribed a ſtratum of limeſtone, lying in the centre of a coal country, which is pervaded and tinged by bituminous matter, through its whole maſs, and has, at the ſame time, many cloſe cavities in the heart of it, lined with calcareous ſpar, and containing foſſil pitch, ſometimes in large pieces, ſometimes in hemi-ſpherical drops, ſcattered over the ſurface of the cavities. This combination could only be ef-fected by a part of the inflammable matter of the beds of coal underneath, being driven off by heat, and made to penetrate the limeſtone, while it was yet ſoft and pervious to heated va-pours *.

32. Hitherto we have enumerated thoſe foſ-ſils that are either not at all, or very ſparingly ſoluble in water. There are, however, ſaline

C 2

bodies

* Note ix.

bodies among the mineral ftrata, fuch for inftance as rock-falt, which are readily diffolved
in water; and it yet remains to examine by
what caufe their confolidation has been effected.

Here the theorifts who confider water as the
fole agent in the mineralization of foffils, are indeed delivered from one difficulty, but it is only that they may be harder preffed on by another. It cannot now be faid, that the menftruum which they employ is incapable of diffolving the fubftances expofed to its action, as
in the cafe of metallic or ftony bodies; but it
may very well be afked, how the water came
to depofite the falts which it held in folution,
and to depofite them fo copioufly as it has done
in many places, without any veftige of fimilar depofition in the places immediately contiguous. If they refufe to call to their affiftance
any other than their favourite element, they
will not find it eafy to anfwer this queftion,
and muft feel the embarraffment of a fyftem,
fubject to two difficulties, fo nicely, but fo
unhappily adjufted, that one of them is always prepared to act whenever the other is removed. If, on the other hand, they will admit the operation of fubterraneous heat, it appears poffible, that the local application of fuch
heat

heat may have driven the water, in vapour, from one place to another, and by such action often repeated in the same spot, may have produced those great accumulations of saline matter, that are actually found in the bowels of the earth.

33. But granting that, either in the way just pointed out, or in some other that is unknown, the salt and the water have been separated, some further action of heat seems requisite, before a compact, and highly indurated body, like rock-salt, could be produced. The mere precipitation of the salt, would, as Dr Hutton has observed, form only an assemblage of loose crystals at the bottom of the sea, without solidity or cohesion: and to convert such a mass into a firm and solid rock, would require the application of such heat as was able to reduce it into fusion. The consolidation of rock-salt, therefore, however its separation from the water is accounted for, cannot be explained but on the hypothesis of subterraneous heat.

34. Some other phenomena that have been observed in salt mines, come in support of the same conclusion. The salt rock of Cheshire, which lies in thick beds, interposed between strata of an argillaceous or marly stone, and is itself mixed with a considerable portion of the same earth, exhibits a very great peculiarity in its structure. Though it forms a mass extreme-

C 3   ly

ly compact, the falt is found to be arranged in round maffes of five or fix feet in diameter, not truly fpherical, but each compreffed by thofe that furround it, fo as to have the fhape of an irregular polyhedron. Thefe are formed of concentric coats, diftinguifhable from one another by their colour, that is, probably by the greater or lefs quantity of earth which they contain, fo that the roof of the mine, as it exhibits a horizontal fection of them, is divided into polygonal figures, each with a multitude of polygons within it, having altogether no inconfiderable refemblance to a *mofaic* pavement. In the triangular fpaces without the polygons, the falt is in coats parallel to the fides of the polygons.

The circumftances which gave rife to this fingular ftructure we fhould in vain endeavour to define; yet fome general conclufions concerning them feem to be within our reach. It is clear that the whole mafs of falt was fluid at once, and that the forces, whatever they were, which gave folidity to it, and produced the new arrangement of its particles, were all in action at the fame time. The uniformity of the coated ftructure is a proof of this, and, above all, the compreffion of the polyhedra, which is always mutual, the flat fide of one being turned to the flat fide of another, and never an angle to an angle, nor an angle to a fide. The coats formed as it

were

were round so many different centres of attraction, is also an appearance quite inconsistent with the notion of deposition; both these, however, are compatible with the notion of solidity acquired by the refrigeration of a fluid, where the whole mass is acted on at the same time, and where no solvent remains to be disposed of after the induration of the rest.

35. Another species of fossil-salt exhibits appearances equally favourable to the theory of igneous consolidation. This is the trona of Africa, which is no other than soda, or mineral alkali, in a particular state. The specimen of this fossil in Dr Black's, now Dr Hope's, collection, is of a sparry and radiated structure, and is evidently part of the contents of a vein, having a stony crust adhering to it, on one side, with its own sparry structure complete, on the opposite. It contains but about one-sixth of the water of crystallization essential to this salt when obtained in the humid way; and, what is particularly to be remarked, it does not lose this water, nor become covered with a powder, like the common alkali, by simple exposure to the air. It is evident, therefore, that this fossil does not originate from mere precipitation; and when we add, that in its sparry structure it contains evident marks of having once been fluid, we have

C 4

little

little reafon to entertain much doubt concerning the principle of its confolidation.

Thus, then, the teftimony given to the operation of fire, or heat, as the confolidating power of the mineral kingdom, is not confined to a few foffils, but is general over all the ftrata. How far the unftratified foffils agree in fupporting the fame conclufion, will be afterwards examined.

3. *Pofition of the Strata* *.

36. We have feen of what materials the ftrata are compofed, and by what power they have been confolidated ; we are next to inquire, from what caufe it proceeds, that they are now fo far removed from the region which they originally occupied, and wherefore, from being all covered by the ocean, they are at prefent raifed in many places fifteen thoufand feet above its furface. Whether this great change of relative place can be beft accounted for by the depreffion of the fea, or the elevation of the ftrata themfelves, remains to be confidered.

Of

---

* Theory of the Earth, vol. i. p. 120.

Of these two suppositions, the former, at first fight, seems undoubtedly the most probable, and we feel less reluctance to suppose, that a fluid, so unstable as the ocean, has undergone the great revolution here referred to, than that the solid foundations of the land have moved a single fathom from their place. This, however is a mere illusion.   Such a depression of the level of the sea as is here supposed, could not happen without a change proportionally great in the solid part of the globe ; and, though admitted as true, will be found very inadequate to explain the present condition of the strata.

37. Suppofing the appearances which clearly indicate submersion under water to reach no higher than ten thousand feet above the present level of the sea, and of course the surface of the sea to have been formerly higher by that quantity than it is now ; it necessarily follows, that a bulk of water has disappeared, equal to more than a seven-hundredth part of the whole magnitude of the globe *.   The existence of empty caverns, of extent sufficient to contain this vast body of water, and of such a convulsion as to lay them open, and give room to the retreat of the sea, are suppositions which a philosopher could only be justified in admitting, if they promised to furnish a very complete explanation of appearances.

* Note x.

appearances. But this juftification is entirely
wanting in the prefent cafe ; for the retreat of
the ocean to a lower level, furnifhes a very partial and imperfect explanation of the phenomena of geology. It will not explain the num-
berlefs remains of ancient continents that are
involved, as we have feen, in the prefent, unlefs
it be fuppofed that the ancient ocean, though it
rofe to fo great a height, had neverthelefs its
fhores, and was the boundary of land ftill higher than itfelf. And, as to that which is now more
immediately the object of inquiry, the pofition
of the ftrata, though the above hypothefis would
account in fome fort for the change of their
place, relatively to the level of the fea ; yet, if it
fhall be proved, that the ftrata have changed
their place relatively to each other, and relatively to the plane of the horizon, fo as to have
had an angular motion impreffed on them, it is
evident that, for thefe facts, the retreat of the
fea does not afford even the fhadow of a theory.

38. Now, it is certain, that many of the ftrata have been moved angularly, becaufe that,
in their original pofition they muft have been all
nearly horizontal. Loofe materials, fuch as fand
and gravel fubfiding at the bottom of the fea,
and having their interftices filled with water,
poffefs a kind of fluidity : they are difpofed to
yield

yield on the fide oppofite to that where the preffure is greateft, and are therefore, in fome degree, fubject to the laws of hydroftatics. On this account they will arrange themfelves in horizontal layers; and the vibrations of the incumbent fluid, by impreffing a flight motion backward, and forward, on the materials of thefe layers, will very much affift the accuracy of their level.

It is not, however, meant to deny, that the form of the bottom might influence, in a certain degree, the ftratification of the fubftances depofited on it. The figure of the lower beds depofited on an uneven furface, would neceffarily be affected by two caufes; the inclination of that furface, on the one hand, and the tendency to horizontality, on the other; but, as the former caufe would grow lefs powerful as the diftance from the bottom increafed, the latter caufe would finally prevail, fo that the upper beds would approach to horizontality, and the lower would neither be exactly parallel to them, nor to one another. Whenever, therefore, we meet with rocks, difpofed in layers quite parallel to one another, we may reft affured, that the inequalities of the bottom have had no effect, and that no caufe has interrupted the ftatical tendency above explained.

Now,

Now, rocks having their layers exactly parallel, are very common, and prove their original horizontality to have been more precise than we could venture to conclude from analogy alone. In beds of fand-ftone, for inftance, nothing is more frequent than to fee the thin layers of fand, feparated from one another by layers ftill finer of coaly, or micaceous matter, that are almoft exactly parallel, and continue fo to a great extent without any fenfible deviation. Thefe planes can have acquired their parallelifm only in confequence of the property of water juft ftated, by which it renders the furfaces of the layers, which it depofites, parallel to its own furface, and therefore parallel to one another. Though fuch ftrata, therefore, may not now be horizontal, they muft have been fo originally ; otherwife it is impoffible to difcover any caufe for their parallelifm, or any rule by which it can have been produced.

39. This argument for the original horizontality of the ftrata, is applicable to thofe that are now fartheft removed from that pofition. Among fuch, for inftance, that are highly inclined, or even quite vertical, and among thofe that are bent and incurvated in the moft fantaftical manner, as happens more efpecially in the

the primary fchifti, we obferve, through all
their finuofities and inflections, an equality of
thicknefs and of diftance among their component laminæ. This equality could only be
produced by thofe laminæ having been originally fpread out on a flat and level furface,
from which fituation, therefore, they muft afterwards have been lifted up by the action of
fome powerful caufe, and muft have fuffered
this difturbance while they were yet in a certain degree flexible and ductile. Though the
primary direction of the force which thus elevated them muft have been from below upwards, yet it has been fo combined with the
gravity and refiftance of the mafs to which it
was applied, as to create a lateral and oblique
thruft, and to produce thofe contortions of the
ftrata, which, when on the great fcale, are
among the moft ftriking and inftructive phenomena of geology.

40. Great additional force is given to this argument, in many cafes, by the nature of the materials of which the ftratified rocks are compofed. The beds of breccia and pudding-ftone,
for inftance, are often in planes almoft vertical,
and at the fame time contain gravel-ftones, and
other fragments of rock, of fuch a fize and
weight, that they could not remain in their prefent

fent pofition an inftant, if the cement which
unites them were to become foft; and therefore they certainly had not that pofition at the
time when this cement was actually foft. This
remark has been made by mineralogifts who
were not led to it by any fyftem. The judicious
and indefatigable obferver of the Alps, defcribing the pudding-ftone of Valorfine, near the
fources of the Arve, tells us, that he was
aftonifhed to find it in beds almoft vertical,
a fituation in which it could not poffibly
have been formed. " That particles," he adds,
" of extreme tenuity, fufpended in a fluid,
might become agglutinated, and form vertical beds, is a thing that may be conceived;
but that pieces of ftone, of feveral pounds weight,
fhould have refted on the fide of a perpendicular wall, till they were enveloped in a ftony
cement, and united into one mafs, is a fuppofition impoffible and abfurd. It fhould be confidered, therefore, as a thing demonftrated, that
this pudding-ftone was formed in a horizontal
pofition, or one nearly fuch, and elevated after
its induration. We know not," he continues,
" the force by which this elevation has been
effected; but it is an important ftep among the
prodigious number of vertical beds that are to
be met with in the Alps, to have found fome
                                    that

that muſt certainly have been formed in a horizontal ſituation*."

41. Nothing can be more ſound and concluſive than this reaſoning ; and, had the ingenious author purſued it more ſyſtematically, it muſt have led him to a theory of mountains very little different from that which we are now endeavouring to explain. If ſome of the vertical ſtrata are proved to have been formed horizontally, there can be no reaſon for not extending the ſame concluſion to them all, even if we had not the ſupport of the argument from the parallelifm of the layers, which has been already ſtated.

42. The highly inclined poſition, and the manifold inflexions of the ſtrata, are not the only proofs of the diſturbance that they have ſuffered, and of the violence with which they have been forced up from their original place. Thoſe interruptions of their continuity which are obſerved, both at the ſurface and under it, are evidences of the ſame fact. It is plain, that if they remained now in the ſituation in which they were at firſt depoſited, they would never appear to be ſuddenly broken off. No ſtratum would terminate abruptly ; but, however its nature

ture

---

* Voyages aux Alpes, tom. ii. § 690.

ture and properties might change, it would conftitute an entire and continued rock, at leaft
where the effects of wafte and *detritus* had not
produced a feparation. This, however, is very
far from being the actual condition of ftratified
bodies. Thofe that are much inclined, or that
make confiderable angles with the horizontal
plane, muft terminate abruptly where they
come up to the furface. Their doing fo is a neceffary confequence of their pofition, and furnifhes no argument, it may be faid, for their having
been difturbed, different from that which has
been already deduced from their inclination.
There are, however, inftances of a breach of continuity in the ftrata, under the furface, that afford
a proof of the violence with which they have been
difplaced, different from any hitherto mentioned. Of this nature are the *flips* or *fhifts*, that
fo often perplex the miner in his fubterraneous
journey, and which change at once all thofe
lines and bearings that had hitherto directed his
courfe. When his mine reaches a certain plane,
which is fometimes perpendicular, fometimes
oblique to the horizon, he finds the beds of
rock broken afunder, thofe on the one fide of
the plane having changed their place, by fliding
in a particular direction along the face of the
others. In this motion they have fometimes
preferved their parallelifm, that is, the ftrata
on

on one fide of the *flip* continue parallel to thofe on the other ; in other cafes, the ftrata on each fide become inclined to one another, though their identity is ftill to be recognifed by their poffeffing the fame thicknefs, and the fame internal characters. Thefe *fhifts* are often of great extent, and muft be meafured by the quantity of the rock moved, taken in conjunction with the diftance to which it has been carried. In fome inftances, a vein is formed at the plane of the fhift or flip, filled with materials of the kinds which will be hereafter mentioned ; in other inftances, the oppofite fides of the rock remain contiguous, or have the interval between them filled with foft and unconfolidated earth. All thefe are the undeniable effects of fome great convulfion, which has fhaken the very foundations of the earth ; but which, far from being a diforder in nature, is part of a regular fyftem, effential to the conftitution and economy of the globe.

The production of the appearances now defcribed, belongs, without doubt, to different periods of time ; and, where flips interfect one another, we can often diftinguifh the lefs from the more ancient. They are all, however, of a date pofterior to that at which the waving and undulated forms of the ftrata were acquired, as they do not carry with them any marks of

D

the

the foftnefs of the rock, but many of its complete induration.

The fame phenomenon which is thus exemplified on a great fcale in the bowels of the
earth, is often moft beautifully exhibited in fingle fpecimens of ftone, and is accompanied with
this remarkable circumftance, that the *inte-
grity* of the ftone is not deftroyed by the fhifts,
whatever wounds had been made in it being
healed, and the parts firmly re-united to one another *.

43. Though fuch marks of violence as have
been now enumerated are common in fome degree to all the ftrata, they abound moft among
the primary, and point out thefe as the part
of our globe which has been expofed to the
greateft viciffitudes. At their junction with the
fecondary, or where they emerge, as it were,
from under the latter, phenomena occur, which
mark fome of thofe viciffitudes with aftonifhing
precifion; phenomena of which the nature was
firft accurately explored, and the confequences
fully deduced, by the geologift whofe fyftem I
am endeavouring to explain. He obferved,
in feveral inftances, that where the primary
fchiftus rifes in beds almoft vertical, it is covered by horizontal layers of fecondary fandftone, which laft are penetrated by the irregular

NOTE XI.

gular tops of the fchiftus, and alfo involve fragments of that rock, fome angular, others round and fmooth, as if worn by attrition. From this he concluded, that the primary ftrata, after being formed at the bottom of the fea, in planes nearly horizontal, were raifed, fo as to become almoft vertical, while they were yet covered by the ocean, and before the fecondary ftrata had begun to be depofited on them. He alfo argued, that, as the fragments of the primary rock, included in the fecondary, are many of them rounded and worn, the depofition of the latter muft have been feparated from the elevation of the former by fuch an interval of time, as gave room for the action of wafte and decay, allowing thofe fragments firft to be detached, and afterwards wrought into a round figure *.

44. Indeed, the interpofition of a breccia between the primary and fecondary ftrata, in which the fragments, whether round or angular, are always of the primary rock, is a fact fo general, and the quantity of this breccia is often fo great, that it leads to a conclufion more paradoxical than any of the preceding, but from which, neverthelefs, it feems very difficult to with-hold affent. Round gravel, when in great abundance, agreeably to a remark already made, muft neceffarily be confidered as a production

D 2

peculiar

* NOTE XII.

peculiar to the beds of rivers, or the fhores of continents, and as hardly ever formed at great depths under the furface of the fea. It fhould feem, then, that the primary fchiftus, after attaining its erect pofition, had been raifed up to the furface, where this gravel was formed; and from thence had been let down again to the depths of the ocean, where the fecondary ftrata were depofited on it. Such alternate elevations and depreffions of the bottom of the fea, however extraordinary they may feem, will appear to make a part of the fyftem of the mineral kingdom, from other phenomena hereafter to be defcribed.

45. On the whole, therefore, by comparing the actual pofition of the ftrata, their erectnefs, their curvature, the interruptions of their continuity, and the tranfverfe ftratification of the fecondary in refpect of the primary, with the regular and level fituation which the fame ftrata muft have originally poffeffed, we have a complete demonftration of their having been difturbed, torn afunder, and moved angularly, by a force that has, in general, been directed from below upwards. In eftablifhing this conclufion, we have reafoned more from the facts which relate to the *angular elevation* of the ftrata, than from thofe which relate to their *abfolute elevation*, or their tranflation to a greater diftance

diſtance from the centre of the earth. This has been done, becauſe the appearances, which reſpect the abſolute lifting up of the ſtrata are more ambiguous than thoſe, which reſpect the change of their angular poſition. The former might be accounted for, could they be ſeparated from the latter, in two ways, viz. either by the retreat of the ſea, or the raiſing up of the land; but the latter can be explained only in one way, and force us of neceſſity to acknowledge the exiſtence of an expanding power, which has acted on the ſtrata with incredible energy, and has been directed from the centre toward the circumference.

46. When we are aſſured of the exiſtence of ſuch a power as this in the mineral regions, we ſhould argue with ſingular inconſiſtency if we did not aſcribe to it all the other appearances of motion in thoſe regions, which it is adequate to produce. If nature in her ſubterraneous abodes is provided with a force that could burſt aſunder the maſſy pavement of the globe, and place the fragments upright upon their edges, could ſhe not, by the ſame effort, raiſe them from the greateſt depths of the ſea, to the higheſt elevation of the land? The cauſe that is adequate to one of theſe effects, is adequate to them both together; for it is a principle well known in mechanical philoſophy, that the force which

produces

produces a parallel motion, may, according to
the way in which it is applied, produce alfo an
angular motion, without any diminution of the
former effect. It would, therefore, be extremely unphilofophical to fuppofe, that any other
caufe has changed the relative level of the ftrata, and the furface of the fea, than that which
has, in fo many cafes, raifed the ftrata from a
horizontal to a highly inclined, or even vertical fituation : it would be to introduce the action of more caufes than the phenomena require, and to forget, that nature, whofe operations we are endeavouring to trace, combines
the poffeffion of infinite refources with the moft
economical application of them.

47. From all, therefore, that relates to the
pofition of the ftrata, I think I am juftified in
affirming, that their difturbance and removal
from the place of their original formation, by a
force directed from below upwards, is a fact in
the natural hiftory of the earth, as perfectly
afcertained as any thing which is not the fubject of immediate obfervation. As to the
power by which this great effect has been
produced, we cannot expect to decide with
equal evidence, but muft be contented to pafs
from what is certain to what is probable. We
may, then, remark, that of the forces in nature
to which our experience does in any degree extend,

tend, none feems fo capable of the effect we would afcribe to it, as the expanfive power of heat; a power to which no limits can be fet, and one, which, on grounds quite independent of the elevation of the ftrata, has been already concluded to act with great energy in the fubterraneous regions. We have, indeed, no other alternative, but either to adopt this explanation, or to afcribe the facts in queftion to fome fecret and unknown caufe, though we are ignorant of its nature, and have no evidence of its exiftence.

We are therefore to fuppofe, that the power of the fame fubterraneous heat, which confolidated and mineralized the ftrata at the bottom of the fea, has fince raifed them up to the height at which they are now placed, and has given them the various inclinations to the horizon which they are found actually to poffefs.

48. The probability of this hypothefis will be greatly increafed, when it is confidered, that, befides thofe now enumerated, there are other indications of movement among the bodies of the mineral kingdom, where effects of heat more characteriftic than fimple expanfion are clearly to be difcovered. Thus, on examining the marks of diforder and movement which are found among the ftrata, it cannot fail to be obferved, that notwithftanding

D 4

withstanding the fracture and dislocation, of which they afford so many examples, there are few empty spaces to be met with among them, as far as our observation extends. The breaches and separations are numerous, and distinct; but they are, for the most part, completely filled up with minerals of a kind quite different from the rock on each side of them, and remarkable for containing no vestiges of stratification. We are thus led to consider the unstratified fossils, the second of the divisions into which the whole mineral kingdom, viewed geologically, ought to be distinguished. These fossils are immediately connected with the disturbance of the strata, and appear, in many instances, to have been the instruments of their elevation.

S E C-

SECTION II.

OF THE PHENOMENA PECULIAR TO UNSTRATI-
FIED BODIES.

1. *Metallic Veins.*

49. THE unftratified minerals exift either in
veins, interfecting the ftratified, or in
maffes furrounded by them. Veins are of various kinds, and may in general be defined, fe-
parations in the continuity of a rock, of a determinate width, but extending indefinitely in
length and depth, and filled with mineral fubftances, different from the rock itfelf. The mineral veins, ftrictly fo called, are thofe filled
with fparry or cryftallized fubftances, and containing the metallic ores.

That thefe veins are of a formation fubfequent to the hardening and confolidation of the
ftrata which they traverfe, is too obvious to require any proof; and it is no lefs clear, from
the cryftallized and fparry ftructure of the fubftances contained in them, that thefe fubftances
muft have concreted from a fluid ftate. Now,
that this fluidity was fimple, like that of fufion
by heat, and not compound, like that of folution in a menftruum, is inferred from many phenomena. It is inferred from the acknowledged
infolubility

infolubility of the fubftances that fill the veins, in any one menftruum whatfoever ; from the total difappearance of the folvent, if there was any ; from the complete filling up of the vein by the fubftances which that folvent had depofited ; from the entire abfence of all the appearances of horizontal or gradual depofition ; and, laftly, from the exiftence of clofe cavities, lined with cryftals, and admitting no egrefs to any thing but heat.

50. To the fame effect may be mentioned thofe groups of cryftals compofed of fubftances the moft different, that are united in the fame fpecimen, all interfecting and mutually impreffing one another. Thefe admit of being explained, on the fuppofition that they were originally in fufion, and became folid by the lofs of heat ; a caufe that acted on them all alike, and alike impelled them to cryftallize : But the appearances of fimultaneous cryftallization feem incompatible with the nature of depofition from a folvent, where, with refpect to different fubftances, the effects muft take place flowly, and in fucceffion.

51. The metals contained in the veins which we are now treating of, appear very commonly in the form of an ore, mineralized by fulphur. Their union with this latter fubftance can be produced, as we know, by heat, but hardly by the way of folution in a menftruum, and certainly

tainly not at all, if that menftruum is nothing elfe than water. The metals, therefore, when mineralized by fulphur, give no countenance to the hypothefis of aqueous folution ; and ftill lefs do they give any when they are found native, as it is called, that is, malleable, pure and uncombined with any other fubftance. The great maffes of native iron found in Siberia and South America are well known ; and nothing certainly can lefs refemblé the products of a chemical precipitation. Gold, however, the moft perfect of the metals, is found native moft frequently ; the others more rarely, in proportion nearly to the facility of their combination with fulphur. Of all fuch fpecimens it may be fafely affirmed, that if they have ever been fluid, or even foft, they muft have been fo by the action of heat ; for, to fuppofe that a metal has been precipitated, pure and uncombined from any menftruum, is to trefpafs againft all analogy, and to maintain a phyfical impoffibility. But it is certain, that many of the native metals have once been in a ftate of foftnefs, becaufe they bear on them impreffions which they could not have received but when they were foft. Thus, gold is often impreffed by quartz and other ftones, which ftill adhere to it, or are involved in it. Specimens of quartz, containing gold and filver fhooting through
them,

them, with the moſt beautiful and varied ramifications, are every where to be met with in the
cabinets of the curious ; and contain, in their
ſtructure, the cleareſt proof, that the metal and
the quartz have been both ſoft, and have cryſtallized together. By the compactneſs, alſo, of
the body which they form, they ſhow, that
when they acquired ſolidity, it was by the concretion of the whole maſs, and not by ſuch partial concretion as takes place when a ſolvent
is ſeparated from ſubſtances which it held in ſolution.

52. Native copper is very abundant ; and
ſome ſpecimens of it have been found cryſtallized. Here the cryſtallization of the metal is
a proof that it has paſſed from a fluid to a ſolid ſtate ; and its purity is a proof that it did
not make that tranſition by being precipitated
from a menſtruum.

53. Again, pieces of native manganeſe have
been found poſſeſſing ſo exactly the characters
peculiar to that metal when reduced in our furnaces, that it is impoſſible to conſider them as
deriving their figure and ſolidity from any cauſe
but fuſion. The ingenious author who deſcribes theſe ſpecimens, La Peyrouſe, was ſo
forcibly ſtruck with this reſemblance, that he
immediately drew the ſame concluſion from it
which is drawn here, attributing the only difference,

ence, which he remarked between the native and the artificial *regulus*, to the different energy with which the fame agent works when employed by nature and by art *.

54. All thefe appearances confpire to prove, that the materials which fill the mineral veins were melted by heat, and forcibly injected, in that ftate, into the clefts and fiffures of the ftrata. Thefe fiffures we muft conceive to have arifen, not merely from the fhrinking of the ftrata while they acquired hardnefs and folidity, but from the violence done to them, when they were heaved up and elevated in the manner which has already been explained †.

55. When thefe fuppofitions are once admitted, the other leading facts in the hiftory of metallic veins will be readily accounted for. Thus, for inftance, it is evident to what we muft afcribe the fragments of the furrounding rock that are often found immerfed in the veins, and encompaffed on all fides by cryftallized fubftances. Thefe fragments being no doubt detached by the concuffion, which at once tore afunder and elevated the ftrata, were fuftained by the melted matter that flowed at the fame time upward

---

* Theory of the Earth, vol. i. p. 68. Journal de Phyf. Janvier 1786.

† Note XIII.

ward through the vein. Large maffes of rock are often found in this manner completely infulated; one of thefe, which M. de Luc has defcribed with great accuracy, is no lefs than a vaft fegment of a mountain *.

56. The immenfe violence which has accompanied the formation of mineral veins, is particularly marked by the flips and fhifts of the ftrata on each fide of them, all tending to fhow what mighty changes have taken place in thofe regions, which our imagination erroneoufly paints as the abode of everlafting filence and reft. This fhifting of the ftrata is beft obferved, where the veins make a tranfverfe fection of beds of rock, confiderably inclined to the horizon. There it is common to fee the beds on one fide of the vein flipped along from the correfponding beds on the other fide, and removed fometimes in a horizontal, fometimes in an oblique direction. In this way, not only the ftrata are fhifted, but veins, which interfect one another, are alfo fhifted themfelves. They are *heaved*, as it is called in the fignificant language of the miners, and forced out of their direction. It is impoffible, in fuch a cafe, but to connect in the mind the formation
of

---

* Lettres Phyfiques, &c. tom. iii. p. 361.

of the vein, and the production of the flips which accompany it, and to regard them as parts of the fame phenomenon.

57. Where thefe flips are horizontal, and exhibit great bodies of ftrata carried from their place, while the parts of the transferred mafs remain undifturbed relatively to one another, they furnifh a clear proof, that this change of place has not arifen from the falling in of the roofs of caverns, as fome geologifts fuppofe. The horizontal direction, and the regularity of the movement, are incompatible with the action of fuch a caufe as this; and indeed it is highly interefting to remark, in the midft of the figns of difturbance which prevail in the bowels of the earth, that there reigns a certain fymmetry and order, which indicate the action of a force of incredible magnitude, but flow and gradual in its effects. The parts of the mafs moved are undifturbed relatively to one another: what has been broken has been cemented: the breaches of continuity have been filled up and healed; and every where we fee the operation of a caufe that could unite as well as feparate. The twofold action of heat to expand and to melt, could fcarce be pointed out more clearly by any fyftem of appearances.

58. As a long period was no doubt required for the elevation of the ftrata, the rents made

in

in them are not all of the fame date, nor the
veins all of the fame formation. This is clear
in the cafe of one vein producing a fhift or
flip in another; for the vein which forces the
other out of its place, and preferves its own direction, is evidently the more recent of the two,
and muft have had its materials in a ftate of activity, when thofe of the other were inert. Sometimes, alfo, at the interfection of two veins, we
may trace the current of the materials of the
one, acrofs thofe of the other; and here, of
confequence, the relative antiquity is determined juft as in the former inftance.

59. The want of any appearance of ftratification in mineral veins has already been taken
notice of. There is, however, to be obferved,
in many inftances, a tendency to a regular arrangement of the fubftances contained in them;
thofe of the fame kind forming coats parallel to
the fides of the vein, and nearly of an equal thicknefs. This phenomenon is confidered as one of
the ftrongeft arguments in favour of the Neptunian fyftem, but has nothing in it, in the leaft incompatible with that theory which afcribes the
formation of veins to the action of fubterraneous
heat. When melted matter from the mineral regions was thrown up into the veins, that which
was neareft to the fides would fooneft lofe its heat.
The fimilar fubftances, alfo, would unite while
this

this procefs was going forward, and would cryftallize, as in other cafes of congelation, from the
fides toward the interior. There is the more reafon for fuppofing this to have been the cafe, that
the fame fort of coating is often obferved on
the infide of clofe cavities, which are, neverthelefs, fo conftructed, as to afford a demonftration
that no chemical folvent was ever included in
them, (§ 74.). Some veins, it muft alfo be confidered, may have been filled by fucceffive in-
jections of melted matter, and this would naturally give rife to a variety of feparate incruftations *.

60. In the view now given of metallic veins,
they have been confidered as traverfing only the
ftratified parts of the globe. They do, however,
occafionally interfect the unftratified parts, particularly the granite, the fame vein often continuing its courfe acrofs rocks of both kinds, without fuffering any material change ; and, if we
have hitherto paid no attention to this circumftance, it is becaufe the order purfued in this
effay required, that the relation of the veins to
ftratified bodies fhould be firft treated of. Befides, the facts in the natural hiftory of veins,
whether contained in ftratified or unftratified

E rocks,

---

* See fome farther remarks on this fubject at Note
XIII.

rocks, are so nearly alike, that in a general view of geology, they do not require to be distinguished. It is material to remark, that, though metallic veins are found indiscriminately in all the different kinds of rock, whether stratified or otherwise, they are most abundant in the class of primary schisti. All the countries most remarkable for their mines, and the mountains distinguished by the name of metalliferous, are primary, and the instance of Derbyshire is perhaps the most considerable exception to this rule, that is known. This preference, which the metals appear to give to the primary strata, is very consistent with Dr Hutton's theory, which represents the rocks of that order as being most changed from their original position, and those on which the disturbing forces of the subterraneous regions have acted most frequently, and with greatest energy. The primary strata are the lowest, also, and have the most direct communication with those regions from which the mineral veins derive all their riches.

2. Of Whinstone.

61. Beside the veins filled with spar, and containing the metallic ores, the strata are intersected by veins of whinstone, porphyry and granite, the

the characters of which are next to be examined.

The term *whin*, or *whinstone*, with Dr Hutton, like the word *trap*, with the German mineralogists, denotes a class of stones, comprehending several distinct species, or at least varieties. The common *basalt*, the *wacken*, *mullen*, and *crag* of Kirwan, the *grünstein* of Werner, and the *amygdaloid*, are comprehended under the name of whin. All these stones have a tendency to a spathose structure, and discover at least the rudiments of crystallization. They are, at the same time, without any mark of stratification in their internal texture, as they are also, for the most part, in their outward configuration; and, as the different species here enumerated compose, not unfrequently, parts of the same continuous rock, the change from one to another being made through a series of insensible gradations, they may safely be regarded by the geologist as belonging to the same *genus*.

62. Whin, though not stratified, exists in two different ways, that is, either in veins, (called in Scotland *dykes*), traversing the strata like the veins already described, or in irregular masses, incumbent on the strata, and sometimes interposed between them. In both these forms, whinstone has nearly the same characters, and

E 2   bears,

bears, in all its varieties, a moſt ſtriking reſemblance to the lavas which have actually flowed
from volcanoes on the ſurface of the earth.
This reſemblance is ſo great, that the two ſubſtances have been often miſtaken for one another ; and many rocks, which have been pronounced to be the remains of extinguiſhed volcanoes, by mineralogiſts of no inconſiderable
name, have been found, on cloſer examination,
to be nothing elſe than maſſes or veins of whinſtone. This latter ſtone is indeed only to be
diſtinguiſhed from the former, by a careful examination of the internal characters of both ;
and chiefly from this circumſtance, that whinſtone often contains calcareous ſpar and zeolite,
whereas neither of theſe ſubſtances is found in
ſuch lavas, as are certainly known to have been
thrown out by volcanic exploſions.

Now, from theſe circumſtances of affinity between lava and whinſtone, on the one hand, and
of diverſity on the other, as the formation of
the one is known, it ſhould ſeem that ſome probable concluſion may be drawn concerning the
formation of the other. The affinity in queſtion is conſtant and eſſential ; the difference
variable and accidental ; and this naturally leads
to ſuſpect, that the two ſtones have the ſame
origin ; and that, as lava is certainly a production of fire, ſo probably is whinſtone.

63. But

63. But, in order to fee whether this hypothefis will explain the diverfity of the two fubftances, without which it will not be entitled
to much attention, we muft remark, that the
prefence of carbonat of lime in a body that has
been fufed, argues, agreeably to the principles
formerly explained, that the fufion was brought
about under a great compreffing force, that is
to fay, deep in the bowels of the earth, or in the
great laboratory of the mineral regions. We
are, therefore, to fuppofe that the fufion of the
whin was performed in thofe regions, where the
compreffion was fufficient to preferve the carbonic gas in union with the calcareous earth,
fo that thefe two fubftances melted together,
and, on cooling, cryftallized into fpar. In
the lavas, again, thrown out by volcanic eruption, the fufion, as we know, wherever it may
begin, continues in the open air, where the preffure is only that of the atmofphere : the calcareous earth, which, therefore, may have been,
in the form of a carbonat, among the materials
of this lava, muft be converted into quicklime,
and become infufible ; hence the want of calcareous fpar in lavas that have flowed at the furface.

Thus, whinftone is to be accounted a fubterraneous, or *un-erupted* lava ; and our theory has
the advantage of explaining both the affinity

E 3   and

and the difference between thefe ftony bodies, without the introduction of any new hypothe-fis. In the Neptunian fyftem, the affinity of whinftone and lava is a paradox which admits of no folution.

64. The columnar ftructure fometimes found in that fpecies of whinftone called bafaltes, is a fact which has given rife to much difcuffion; and it muft be confeffed, that though one of the moft ftriking and peculiar characters of this foffil, it is not that which gives the cleareft and moft direct information concerning its origin. One circumftance, however, very much in fa-vour of the opinion that bafaltic rocks owe their formation to fire, is, that the columnar form is fometimes affumed by the lava actual-ly erupted from volcanoes. Now, it is cer-tainly of no fmall importance, to have the fynthetic argument on our fide, and to know, that bafaltic columns can be produced by fire; though, no doubt, to give abfolute cer-tainty to our conclufion, it would be necef-fary to fhow, that there are in nature no other means but this by which thefe columns can be formed. This fort of evidence is hard-ly to be looked for; but fince the power of fufion, to produce the phenomena in queftion, is perfectly eftablifhed, and fince the production of the fame phenomena in the humid way is a

mere

mere hypothefis, if there be the leaft reafon to fufpect the action of fubterraneous heat as one of the caufes of mineralization, every maxim of found philofophy requires that the bafaltic ftructure, in all cafes, fhould be afcribed to it.

65. The Neptunifts will no doubt allege, with BERGMAN, that, in the drying of ftarch, clay, and a few other fubftances, fomething analogous to bafaltic columns is produced. Here, however, a moft important difference is to be remarked, correfponding very exactly to one of the characters which we have all along obferved to diftinguifh the products of aqueous, from thofe of igneous confolidation. The columns formed by the fubftances juft mentioned, are diftant from one another: they are feparated by fiffures which widen from the bottom to the top, and which arife from the fhrinking and drying of the mafs. In the bafaltic columns, no fuch openings, nor vacuity of any kind is found; the pillars are in contact, and, though perfectly diftinct, are fo clofe, that the fharp edge of a wedge can hardly be introduced between them. This is a great peculiarity in the bafaltic ftructure, and is ftrongly expreffive of this fact, that the mafs was all fluid together, and that its parts took their new arrangement, not in confequence of the feparation of a fluid from a folid part, by which great fhrinking and much empty fpace

E 4   might

might be produced; but in confequence of a caufe which, like refrigeration, acted equally on all the parts of the mafs, and preferved their abfolute contact after their fluidity had ceafed.

66. A mark of fufion, or at leaft of the operation of heat, which whinftone poffeffes in common with many other minerals, is its being penetrated by pyrites, a fubftance, as has been already remarked, that is of all others moft exclufively the production of fire. Another mark of fufion, more diftinctive of whin, is, that both in veins and in maffes it fometimes includes pieces of fandftone, or of the other contiguous ftrata, completely infulated, and having the appearance of fragments of rock, floating in a fluid fufficiently denfe and ponderous to fuftain their weight. Though thefe fragments have been too refractory to be reduced into fufion themfelves, they have not remained entirely unchanged, but are, in general, extremely indurated, in comparifon of the rock from which they appear to have been detached.

67. Similar inftances of extraordinary induration are obferved in the parts of the ftrata in contact with whinftone, whether they form the fides of the veins, or the floors, and roofs of the maffes into which the whinftone is diftributed. The ftrata whether fandy or argillaceous, in fuch fituations, are ufually extremely hard and confolidated;

consolidated; the former in particular lose their
granulated texture, and are sometimes converted into perfect jasper. This interesting remark
was first made by Dr Hutton, and the truth of
it has been verified by a great number of subsequent observations.

68. To the same excellent geologist we are
indebted for the knowledge of an analogous fact,
attendant on the passage of whinstone veins
through coal strata. As the beds of stone where
they are in contact with veins of whin, seem to
acquire additional induration, so those of coal,
in like circumstances, are frequently found to
have lost their fusibility, and to be reduced nearly to the condition of coke, or of charcoal. The
existence of coal of this kind has been already
mentioned, and considered as a proof of the operation of subterraneous heat. In the instances
here referred to, that is, where the charring of
the coal is limited to those parts of the strata
which are in contact with the whin, or in its immediate vicinity, the heat is pointed out as re-
siding in the vein; and this is to be accounted
for only on the supposition of the melted whin,
at a period subsequent to the consolidation of
the coal, having flowed through the openings of
the strata. The heat has been powerful enough,
in many cases, to drive off the bituminous matter
of the coal, and to force it into colder and more

distant

diftant parts.   Few facts, in the hiftory of foffils,
are more remarkable than this, and none more
directly affimilates the operations of the mineral
regions, with thofe that take place at the furface
of the earth.

69. Again, the difturbance of the ftrata,
wherever veins of whinftone abound, if not a
direct proof of the original fluidity of the whinftone, is a clear indication of the violence with
which it was introduced into its place.   This difturbance of the pofition of the ftrata, by fhifting, unufual elevation, and other irregularities,
where they are interfected by whinftone veins,
is a fact fo well known to miners, that when
they meet with any fudden change in the lying
of the *metals*, they are wont to foretel their approach to maffes, or veins of unftratified matter ;
and, in their figurative language, point them
out as the caufes of the confufion with which
they are fo generally accompanied *.   The mineral veins likewife, as well as the ftrata, are
often heaved and fhifted by the veins of whinftone.

70. Whinftone of every fpecies is found frequently interpofed in tabular maffes, between
beds of ftratified rocks ; and it then adds to the
indications

---

* A *Trouble* is the name which the colliers in this
country give to a vein of whinftone.

indications of its igneous origin, already enumerated, some others that are peculiar to it when
in this situation. In such inftances, it is not uncommon to find the ftrata in some places, contiguous to the whin, elevated, and bent with their
concavity upward, fo that they appear clearly to
have been acted on by a force that proceeded
from below, at the fame time that they were
foftened, and rendered in fome degree flexible :
it is needlefs to remark, that thefe effects can
be explained by nothing but the fufion of the
whin ; and that the great force with which it was
impelled againft the ftrata, could be produced
by no caufe but heat, acting in the manner that
is here fuppofed.

71. Again, if it be true that the maffes of
whin, thus interpofed among the ftrata, were
introduced there, after the formation of the latter, we might expect to find, at leaft in many inftances, that the beds on which the whinftone
refts, and thofe by which it is covered, are exactly alike. If thefe beds were once contiguous, and
have been only heaved up and feparated by the
irruption of a fluid mafs of fubterraneous iava,
their identity fhould ftill be recognifed. Now,
this is precifely what is obferved ; it is known
to hold in a vaft number of inftances, and is
ftrikingly exemplified in the rock of *Salifbury
Crag*, near Edinburgh.

This

This fimilarity of the ftrata that cover the maffes of whinftone, to thofe that ferve as the bafe on which they reft, and again the diffimilitude of both to the interpofed mafs, are facts which I think can hardly receive any explanation, on the principles of the Neptunian theory. If thefe rocks, both ftratified and unftratified, are to be regarded as productions of the fea, the circumftances would require to be pointed out, which have determined the whinftone, and the beds that are all round it, to be fo extremely unlike in their ftructure, though formed at the fame time, and in the immediate vicinity of one another; as alfo thofe circumftances, on the other hand, which determined the ftratified depofites above and below the whinftone, to be precifely the fame, though the times of their formation muft have been very different. The homogeneous fubftances, thus, placed at a diftance, and the heterogeneous brought fo clofely together, are phenomena equally unaccountable, in a theory that afcribes their origin to the operation of the fame element, and that neceffarily dates their formation according to the order in which they lie, one above another.

72. If, indeed, in thefe inftances, the gradation were infenfible, as fome have afferted it to be, between the ftrata and the interpofed mafs, fo that it was impoffible to point out the line
where

where the one ended and the other began, whatever difficulties we might perceive in the Neptunian theory, we fhould find it hard to fubftitute a better in its room. But the truth feems to be, that, in the cafes we are now treating of, no fuch gradation exifts ; and that, though where the two kinds of rock come into contact a change is often obferved, by the ftrata having acquired an additional degree of induration, yet the line of feparation is well defined, and can be precifely afcertained. This at leaft is certain, that innumerable fpecimens, exhibiting fuch lines of feparation, are to be met with ; and wherever care has been taken to obtain a frefh fracture of the ftone, and to remove the effects of accidental caufes, even where the two rocks are moft firmly united, and moft clofely affimilated, I am perfuaded that no uncertainty has ever remained as to the line of their feparation. For thefe reafons, it feems probable that the gradual tranfition of bafaltes into the adjoining ftrata, is in all cafes imaginary, and is, in truth, a mere illufion, proceeding from hafty and inaccurate obfervation.

73. Another remarkable fact in the natural hiftory of the whinftone rocks, remains yet to be mentioned, and, with it I fhall conclude the argument, as far as thefe rocks are concerned.

Some

Some of the species of whinstone are the common matrices of agates and chalcedonies, which lie inclosed in them in the form of round nodules. The original fluidity of these nodules is evinced by their figured, and sometimes crystallized structure, and indeed is so generally admitted, that the only question concerning them is, whether this fluidity was the effect of heat or of solution. To answer this question, Dr Hutton observes, that the formation of the concentric coats, of which the agate is usually composed, has evidently proceeded from the circumference toward the centre, the exterior coats always impressing the interior, but never the reverse. The same thing also follows from this other fact, that when there is any vacuity within the agate, it is usually at the centre, and there too are found the regular crystals, when any such have been formed. It therefore appears certain, that the progress of consolidation has been from the circumference inwards, and that the outward coats of the agate were the first to acquire solidity and hardness.

74. Now, it must be considered that these coats are highly consolidated ; that they are of very pure siliceous matter, and are utterly impervious to every substance which we know of, except light and heat. It is plain, therefore, that whatever
ever

ever at any time, during the progrefs of confolidation, was contained within the coats already
formed, muft have remained there as long as the
agate was entire, without the leaft poffibility of
efcape. But nothing is found within the coats
of the agate fave its own fubftance; therefore
no extraneous fubftance, that is to fay no folvent, was ever included within them. The fluidity of the agate was therefore fimple, and un-
affifted by any menftruum.

In this argument, nothing appears to me
wanting, that is neceffary to the perfection of a
phyfical, I had almoft faid of a mathematical,
demonftration. It feems, indeed, to be impoffible that the igneous origin of foffils could be
recorded in plainer language, than by the phenomenon which has juft been defcribed.

75. The examination of particular fpecimens of
agates and chalcedonies, affords many more arguments of the fame kind, which Dr Hutton
ufed to deduce with an acutenefs and vivacity,
which his friends have often liftened to with
great admiration and delight *. Thefe, however,
muft be paffed over at prefent; and I have only further to remark, that a feries of the moft
interefting experiments, inftituted by Sir JAMES
HALL, and publifhed in the Tranfactions of the
Royal Society of Edinburgh †, has removed the

only

---

* NOTE XIV. † Vol. v. p. 43.

only remaining objection that could be urged against the igneous origin of whinstone. This objection is founded on the common observation, that when a piece of whinstone or basaltes is actually melted in a crucible, on cooling, it becomes glass, and loses its original character entirely; and from thence it was concluded, that this character had not been originally produced by fusion. The experiments above mentioned, however, have shewn, in the most satisfactory manner, that melted whin, by *regulated* or by slow cooling, is prevented from assuming the appearance of glass, and becomes a stony substance, hardly to be distinguished from whinstone or lava.

The experiments of another ingenious chemist, Dr KENNEDY, have shewn, that whinstone contains mineral alkali, by which, of course, its fusion must have been assisted *. Dr Hutton used to ascribe its fusibility, in a great measure at least, to the quantity of iron contained in it: both these causes have no doubt united to render it more easily melted than the ordinary materials of the strata.

76. In a word, therefore, to conceive aright the origin of that class of unstratified rocks, distinguished by the name of whinstone, we must suppose,

---

* Transf. R. S. Edin. vol. v. p. 85.

pofe, that long after the confolidation of the
ftrata, and during the time of their elevation,
the materials of the former were melted by the
force of fubterraneous heat, and injected among
the rents and fiffures of the rocks already formed.
In this manner were produced the veins or dikes
of whinftone; and, where circumftances allowed the ftream of melted matter to diffufe itfelf
more widely, tabular maffes were formed, which
were afterwards raifed up, together with the
furrounding ftrata, above the level of the fea,
and have been fince laid open by the operation
of thofe caufes that continually change and
wafte the furface of the land.

Thefe unftratified rocks are not, however, all
the work of the fame period; they differ evidently in the date of their formation, and it is
not unufual, to find tabular maffes of one fpecies of whin, interfected by veins of another
fpecies. Indeed, of all the foffil bodies which
compofe the prefent land, the veins of whin appear to be the moft recently confolidated *.

Porphyry may fo properly be regarded as a
variety of whin, diftinguifhed only by involving cryftallized feltfpar, that, in a geological
fketch like the prefent, it is hardly entitled to
a feparate article. Like the other kinds of

F whin,

* NOTE XIV.

whin, it exifts both in veins and in tabular maffes, having, no doubt, an origin fimilar to that which has juft been defcribed. Porphyry, however, has the peculiarity of being rarely found in any but the primary ftrata; it feems to be the whinftone of the old world, or at leaft that which is of higheft antiquity in the prefent. It no-where, I believe, affumes a columnar, or bafaltic appearance, of any regularity; but this is alfo true of many other varieties of whin, of all, indeed, except the moft compact and homogeneous. Thefe differences are not fo confiderable as to require our entering into any particular detail concerning the natural hiftory of this foffil.

3. *Granite.*

77. The term Granite is ufed by Dr Hutton to fignify an aggregate ftone, in which quartz, feltfpar and mica are found diftinct from one another, and not difpofed in layers. The addition of hornblend, fchorl, or garnet, to the three ingredients juft mentioned, is not underftood to alter the *genus* of the ftone, but only to conftitute a fpecific difference, which it is the bufinefs of lithology to mark by fome appropriate character, annexed to the generic name of granite.

The

The foffil now defined exifts, like whinftone and porphyry, both in maffes and in veins, though moft frequently in the former. It is like them unftratified in its texture, and is regarded here, as being alfo unftratified in its outward ftructure *. One ingredient which is effential to granite, namely, quartz, is not contained in whinftone; and this circumftance ferves to diftinguifh thefe *genera* from one another, though, in other refpects, they feem to be united by a chain of infenfible gradations, from the

F 2   moft

---

* Thofe rocks that confift of the ingredients here enumerated, if they have at the fame time a fchiftofe texture, or a difpofition into layers, are properly diftinguifhed from granite, and called Gneifs, or Granitic Schiftus. But it has been queftioned whether a ftone does not exift compofed of thefe ingredients, and deftitute of a fchiftofe texture, but yet divided into large beds, vifible in its external form. Dr Hutton fuppofes fuch a ftone not to exift, or at leaft not to conftitute any fuch proportion of the mineral kingdom, as to entitle it to particular confideration, in the general fpeculations of geology.

Whether this fuppofition is perfectly correct, may require to be farther confidered: this, however, is certain, that a rock, in all refpects conformable to it, compofes a great proportion of what are ufually called the granite mountains. See NOTE xv.

moſt homogeneous baſaltes, to granite the moſt highly cryſtallized.

78. Granite, it has been juſt ſaid, exiſts moſt commonly in maſſes ; and theſe maſſes are rarely, if ever, incumbent on any other rock : they are the baſis on which others reſt, and ſeem, for the moſt part, to riſe up from under the ancient, or primary ſtrata. The granite, therefore, wherever it is found, is inferior to every other rock ; and as it alſo compoſes many of the greateſt mountains, it has the peculiarity of being elevated the higheſt into the atmoſphere, and ſunk the deepeſt under the ſurface, of all the mineral ſubſtances with which we are acquainted.

Notwithſtanding the circumſtance of not being alternated with ſtratified bodies, which conſtitutes a remarkable difference between granite and whinſtone, the affinity of theſe foſſils is ſuch as to make the ſimilarity of their origin by no means improbable. Accordingly, in Dr Hutton's theory, granite is regarded as a ſtone of more recent formation than the ſtrata incumbent on it ; as a ſubſtance which has been melted by heat, and which, when forced up from the mineral regions, has elevated the ſtrata at the ſame time.

79. That granite has undergone a change from a fluid to a ſolid ſtate, is evinced from the cryſtallized ſtructure in which ſome of its component
                                            nent

nent parts are ufually found. This cryftallization is particularly to be remarked of the feltfpar, and alfo of the fchorl, where there is any
admixture of that fubftance, whether in flender
fpiculæ, or in larger maffes. The quartz itfelf
is in fome cafes cryftallized, and is fo, perhaps,
more frequently than is generally fuppofed.
The fluidity of granite, in fome former period
of its exiftence, is fo evident from this, as to
make it appear fingular that it fhould ever have
been confidered as a foffil that had remained always the fame, and one, into the origin of which
it was needlefs to inquire. If the regular forms
of cryftallization are not to be received as proofs
of the fubftance to which they belong having
paffed from a fluid to a folid ftate, neither are
the figures of fhells and of other fuppofed petrifactions, to be taken as indications of a paffage
from the animal to the mineral kingdom; fo
that there is an end of all geological theories,
and of all reafonings concerning the ancient
condition of the globe. To an argument which
ftrikes equally at the root of all theories, it belongs not to this, in particular, to make any reply.

80. We fhall, therefore, confider it as admitted, that the materials of the granite were originally fluid; and, in addition to this, we think
it can eafily be proved, that this fluidity was

not that of the elements taken feparately, but of the entire mafs. This laft conclufion follows, from the ftructure of thofe fpecimens, where one of the fubftances is impreffed by the forms which are peculiar to another. Thus, in the Portfoy granite *, which Dr Hutton has fo minutely defcribed, the quartz is impreffed by the rhomboidal cryftals of the feltfpar, and the ftone thus formed is compact and highly confolidated. Hence, this granite is not a congeries of parts, which, after being feparately formed, were fomehow brought together and agglutinated ; but it is certain that the quartz, at leaft, was fluid when it was moulded on the feltfpar. In other granites, the impreffions of the fubftances on one another are obferved in a different order, and the quartz gives its form to the feltfpar. This, however, is more unufual ; the quartz is commonly the fubftance which has received the impreffions of all the reft ; and the fpiculæ of fchorl often fhoot both acrofs it and the feltfpar.

The ingredients of granite were therefore fluid when mixed, or at leaft when in contact with one another. Now, this fluidity was not the effect of folution in a menftruum ; for, in that cafe, one kind of cryftal ought not to imprefs another, but each of them fhould have its own peculiar fhape.

81. The

---

* Theory of the Earth, vol. i. p. 104.

81. The perfect confolidation of many granites, furnifhes an argument to the fame effect. For, agreeably to what was already obferved, in treating of the ftrata, a fubftance, when cryftallizing, or paffing from a fluid to a folid ftate, cannot be free from porofity, much lefs fill up completely a fpace of a given form, if, at the fame time, any folvent is feparated from it; becaufe the folvent fo feparated would ftill occupy a certain fpace, and when removed by evaporation or otherwife, would leave that fpace empty. The perfect adjuftment, therefore, of the fhape of one fet of cryftallizing bodies, to the fhape of another fet, as in the Portfoy granite, and their confolidation into one mafs, is as ftrong a proof as could be defired, that they cryftallized from a ftate of fimple fluidity, fuch as, of all known caufes, heat alone is able to produce.

82. This conclufion, however, does not reft on a fingle clafs of facts. It has been obferved in many inftances, that where granite and ftratified rocks, fuch as primary fchiftus, are in contact, the latter are penetrated by veins of the former, which traverfe them in various directions. Thefe veins are of different dimenfions, fome being of the breadth of feveral yards, others of a few inches, or even tenths of an inch; they diminifh as they recede from the main bo-

dy

dy of the granite, to which they are always firmly united, conftituting, indeed, a part of the fame continued rock.

Thefe phenomena, which were firft diftinctly obferved by Dr Hutton, are of great importance in geology, and afford a clear folution of the two chief queftions concerning the relation between granite and fchiftus. As every vein muft be of a date pofterior to the body in which it is contained, it follows, that the fchiftus was not fuper-impofed on the granite, after the formation of this laft. If it be argued, that thefe veins, though pofterior to the fchifti, are alfo pofterior to the granite, and were form-ed by the infiltration of water in which the granite was diffolved or fufpended ; it may be replied, 1*mo*, That the power of water to diffolve granite, is a poftulatum of the fame kind that we have fo often, and for fuch good reafon, refufed to concede ; and, 2*do*, That in many inftances the veins proceed from the main body of the granite *upwards* into the fchiftus ; fo that they are in planes much elevated in refpect of the horizon, and have a direction quite oppofite to that which the hypothefis of infiltration requires. It remains certain, therefore, that the whole mafs of granite, and the veins proceeding from it, are coeval, and both of later formation than the ftrata.

Now,

Now, this being eftablifhed, and the fluidity of the veins, when they penetrated into the fchiftus, being obvious, it neceffarily follows, that the whole granite mafs was alfo fluid at the fame time. But this can have been brought about only by fubterraneous heat, which alfo impelled the melted matter againft the fuper-incumbent ftrata, with fuch force as to raife them from their place, and to give them that highly inclined pofition in which they are ftill fupported by the granite, after its fluidity has ceafed. Thus a conclufion, rendered probable by the cryftallization of granite, is eftablifhed beyond all contradiction by the phenomena of granitic veins *.

83. With the granite, we fhall confider the proof of the igneous origin of all mineral fubftances as completed. Thefe fubftances, therefore, whether ftratified or unftratified, owe their confolidation to the fame caufe, though acting with different degrees of energy. The ftratified have been in general only foftened or penetrated by melted matter, whereas the unftratified have been reduced into perfect fufion.

84. In this general conclufion we may diftinguifh two parts, which, in their degree of certainty, differ perhaps fomewhat from one another. The firft of thefe, and that which ftands higheft in point of evidence, confifts of two propofitions;

* NOTE xv.

propositions; namely, that the fluidity which preceded the confolidation of mineral fubftances was SIMPLE, that is, it did not arife from the combination of thefe fubftances with any folvent; and, next, that after confolidation, thefe bodies have been raifed up by an expanfive force acting from below, and have by that means been brought into their prefent fituation. Thefe two propofitions feem to me to be fupported by all the evidence that is neceffary to conftitute the moft perfect demonftration.

85. The other part of the general conclufion, that fire, or more properly heat, was the caufe of the fluidity of thefe mineral bodies, and alfo of their fubfequent elevation, is not perhaps to be confidered as a truth fo fully demonftrated as the two preceding propofitions; it is, no doubt, a matter of THEORY; or a portion of one of thofe invifible chains by which men feek to connect in the mind the ftate of nature that is prefent, with the ftates of it that are paft; and participates of that uncertainty from which our reafonings concerning fuch caufes as are not direct objects of perception, are hardly ever exempted. That it participates of this uncertainty in a very flight degree, will, however, be admitted, when it is confidered that the caufe affigned has been proved fufficient for the effect; that the fame is not true of any other known caufe; and that

that this theory accounts, with fingular fimplicity and precifion, for a fyftem of facts fo various and complex, as that which is prefented by the natural hiftory of the globe.

86. Neither can it be faid that the exiftence of fubterraneous heat is a principle affumed without any evidence, but that of the geological facts which it is intended to explain: on the contrary, it is proved by phenomena within the circle of ordinary experience, namely, thofe of hot-fprings, volcanoes, and earthquakes. Thefe leave no doubt of the exiftence of heat, and of a moving and expanfive power, in the bowels of the earth; fo that the only queftions are, at what depth is this power lodged? to what extent, and with what intenfity, does it act? That it is lodged at a very confiderable depth, is rendered probable by the permanency of fome of the preceding phenomena: from the earlieft times many fountains have retained their heat to the prefent day; and volcanoes, though they become extinguifhed at length, have a very long period allotted for their duration. The caufe of earthquakes is certainly a force that refides very deep under the furface, otherwife the extent of the concuffion could not be fuch as has been obferved in many inftances.

87. The intenfity of volcanic fire, is another circumftance that favours the opinion of its being

ing feated deep under the furface. That this
intenfity is confiderable, is certain from the experiments made by Sir James Hall on the fufibility of whin-ftone and lava; from which it
appears, that the loweft temperature in which
either of thefe ftones melt, is about 30° of
Wedgewood's pyrometer. Some mineralogifts
have indeed affirmed, that lava is melted, not by
the intenfity of the heat applied to it, but in
confequence of a certain combination formed
between it and bituminous fubftances, in a manner which they do not attempt to explain, and
which has indeed no analogy to any thing that is
known. That a hypothefis, formed in fuch direct oppofition to the moft obvious principles of
inductive reafoning, fhould have been imagined
by a philofopher who had examined the phenomena of Ætna and Vefuvius with much attention, and defcribed them with great accuracy
and truth, is more wonderful than that it fhould
have been adopted by mineralogifts, whofe views
of nature may have been confined within a cabinet or a laboratory. It is, however, a hypothefis, which, having never had any fupport
but from other hypothefes, hardly merited the
direct refutation that it has received from the
experiments juft mentioned.

88. But, if the intenfity of volcanic heat be
fuch as is here ftated, it will be found very
difficult

difficult to account for a fire of such activity, and of such long continuance in the same spot, by any decomposition of mineral substances near the surface. In the place where this combustion is supposed to exist, it must be remembered, that there is no fresh supply of materials to replace those that have been consumed, and that, therefore, the original accumulation of these materials in one spot, must have been very unlike any thing that has ever been observed concerning the disposition of minerals in the bowels of the earth.

89. If, on the other hand we ascribe the phenomena of volcanoes to the central heat, the account that may be given of them is simple, and consistent with itself. According to all the appearances from which the existence of such heat has been inferred above, it is of a nature so far different from ordinary fire, that it may require no circulation of air, and no supply of combustible materials to support it. It is not accompanied with inflammation or combustion, the great pressure preventing any separation of parts in the substances on which it acts, and the absence of that elastic fluid without which heat seems to have no power to decompose bodies, even the most combustible, contributing to the unalterable nature of all the substances in the mineral regions. There, of consequence, the

only

only effects of heat are fufion and expanfion ; and that which forms the nucleus of the globe may therefore be a fluid mafs, melted, but unchanged by the action of heat.

90. If, from the confines of this nucleus, we conceive certain fiffures and openings to traverfe the folid cruft, and to iffue at the furface of the earth, the vapours afcending through thefe may in time heat the fides of the tubes through which they pafs to a vaft diftance from the lower extremities. It is, indeed, difficult to fix the limit to which this diftance may extend, on account of the great difference between the rate at which heat moves when it has a fluid for its vehicle, and when it is left to make its way alone through a folid body. In the prefent cafe, the fupply of heat is rapid, as being made by a vapour afcending through a tube of folid rock ; and the diffipation of it flow, as arifing from its tranfmiffion through the rock. The wafte of heat is therefore fmall, compared with the fupply, and grows fmaller at every given point, the longer the ftream of heated vapour has continued to flow. Such a ftream, therefore, though it may at firft be condenfed within a fmall diftance of its fource, will in time reach higher and higher, and may at laft be able to carry its heat to an immenfe diftance from the place of its original derivation. Thus, it is eafy to conceive,

ceive, that vapours from the mineral regions may convey their heat to refervoirs of water near the furface of the earth, and may in that manner produce hot fprings, and even boiling fountains, like thofe of Rycum and Geyfer.

91. When, inftead of a heated vapour, melted matter is thrown up through the *fhafts* or *tubes*, which thus communicate with the mineral regions, veins of whinftone and bafaltes are formed in the interior of the earth. When the melted matter reaches to the furface, it is thrown out in the form of lava, and all the other phenomena of volcanoes are produced.

Laftly, Where melted matter of this kind, or vapours without being condenfed, have their progrefs obftructed, thofe dreadful concuffions are produced, which feem to threaten the exiftence even of the earth itfelf. Though terrible, therefore, to the prefent inhabitants of the globe, the earthquake has its place in the great fyftem of geological operations, and is part of a feries of events, effential, as will more clearly appear hereafter, to the general order, and to the prefervation of the whole.

Such, according to this theory, are the changes which have befallen mineral fubftances in the bowels of the earth ; and though different for the ftratified and unftratified parts of thofe
fubftances,

fubftances, they are connected together by the fame *principle*, or explained by the fame *caufe*. It remains to confider that part of the hiftory of both which defcribes their changes after their elevation to the furface ; and here we fhall find new caufes introduced, which are more directly the fubjects of obfervation, than thofe hitherto treated of ; caufes, alfo, which act on all foffils alike, and alike prepare them for their ultimate deftination.

S E C-

SECTION III.

OF THE PHENOMENA COMMON TO STRATIFIED AND UNSTRATIFIED BODIES.

92. THE feries of changes which foffil bodies are deftined to undergo, does not ceafe with their elevation above the level of the fea ; it affumes, however, a new direction, and from the moment that they are raifed up to the furface, is conftantly exerted in reducing them again under the dominion of the ocean. The folidity is now deftroyed which was acquired in the bowels of the earth ; and as the bottom of the fea is the great laboratory, where loofe materials are mineralized and formed into ftone, the atmofphere is the region where ftones are decompofed, and again refolved into earth.

This decompofition of all mineral fubftances, expofed to the air, is continual, and is brought about by a multitude of agents, both chemical and mechanical, of which fome are known to us, and many, no doubt, remain to be difcovered. Among the various aëriform fluids which compofe our atmofphere, one is already diftinguifhed as the grand principle of mineral decompofition ; the others are not inactive, and to them we muft

G add

add moisture, heat, and perhaps light; substances which, from their affinities to the elements of mineral bodies, have a power of entering into combination with them, and of thus diminishing the forces by which they are united to one another. By the action of air and moisture, the metallic particles, particularly the iron, which enters in such abundance into the composition of almost all fossils, becomes oxydated in such a degree as to lose its tenacity; so that the texture of the surface is destroyed, and a part of the body resolved into earth.

93. Some earths, again, such as the calcareous, are immediately dissolved by water; and though the quantity so dissolved be extremely small, the operation, by being continually renewed, produces a flow but perpetual corrosion, by which the greatest rocks must in time be subdued. The action of water in destroying hard bodies into which it has obtained entrance, is much assisted by the vicissitudes of heat and cold, especially when the latter extends as far as the point of congelation; for the water, when frozen, occupies a greater space than before, and if the body is compact enough to refuse room for this expansion, its parts are torn asunder by a repulsive force acting in every direction.

94. Besides these causes of mineral decomposition, the action of which we can in some measure

fure trace, there are others known to us only by their effects.

We fee, for inftance, the pureft rock cryftal affected by expofure to the weather, its luftre tarnifhed, and the polifh of its furface impaired, but we know nothing of the power by which thefe operations are performed. Thus alfo, in the precautions which the mineralogift takes to preferve the frefh fracture of his fpecimens, we have a proof how indifcriminately all the pro-ductions of the foffil kingdom are expofed to the attacks of their unknown enemies, and we perceive how difficult it is to delay the begin-nings of a procefs which no power whatever can finally counteract.

95. The mechanical forces employed in the difintegration of mineral fubftances, are more eafily marked than the chemical. Here again water appears as the moft active enemy of hard and folid bodies; and, in every ftate, from tranfparent vapour to folid ice, from the fmalleft rill to the greateft river, it attacks whatever has emerged above the level of the fea, and labours inceffantly to reftore it to the deep. The parts loofened and difengaged by the chemical agents, are carried down by the rains, and, in their de-fcent, rub and grind the fuperficies of other bo-dies. Thus water, though incapable of acting on hard fubftances by direct attrition, is the

G 2   caufe

TOURO COLLEGE LIBRARY

cauſe of their being ſo acted on ; and, when it
deſcends in torrents, carrying with it ſand, gravel, and fragments of rock, it may be truly ſaid
to turn the forces of the mineral kingdom againſt
itſelf. Every ſeparation which it makes is neceſſarily permanent, and the parts once detached can never be united, ſave at the bottom of
the ocean.

96. But it would far exceed the limits of this
ſketch, to purſue the cauſes of mineral decompoſition through all their forms. It is ſufficient
to remark, that the conſequence of ſo many minute, but indefatigable agents, all working together, and having *gravity* in their favour, is a ſyſtem of univerſal decay and degradation, which
may be traced over the whole ſurface of the land,
from the mountain top to the ſea ſhore. That we
may perceive the full evidence of this truth, one
of the moſt important in the natural hiſtory of the
globe, we will begin our ſurvey from the latter
of theſe ſtations, and retire gradually toward the
former.

97. If the coaſt is bold and rocky, it ſpeaks
a language eaſy to be interpreted. Its broken
and abrupt contour, the deep gulphs and ſalient
promontories by which it is indented, and the proportion which theſe irregularities bear to the force
of the waves, combined with the inequality of
hardneſs in the rocks, prove, that the preſent
line

line of the fhore has been determined by the
action of the fea. The naked and precipitous
cliffs which overhang the deep, the rocks hollowed, perforated, as they are farther advanced in
the fea, and at laft infulated, lead to the fame
conclufion, and mark very clearly fo many different ftages of decay. It is true, we do not fee
the fucceffive fteps of this progrefs exemplified
in the ftates of the fame individual rock, but
we fee them clearly in different individuals; and
the conviction thus produced, when the phenomena are fufficiently multiplied and varied, is
as irrefiftible, as if we faw the changes actually
effected in the moment of obfervation.

On fuch fhores, the fragments of rock once
detached, become inftruments of further deftruction, and make a part of the powerful
artillery with which the ocean affails the bul-
warks of the land: they are impelled againft
the rocks, from which they break off other fragments, and the whole are thus ground againft
one another; whatever be their hardnefs, they
are reduced to gravel, the fmooth furface and
round figure of which, are the moft certain
proofs of a *detritus* which nothing can refift.

98. Again, where the fea-coaft is flat, we have
abundant evidence of the degradation of the
land in the beaches of fand and fmall gravel;
the fand banks and fhoals that are continually

changing;

changing ; the alluvial land at the mouths of the rivers ; the bars that feem to oppofe their dif-charge into the fea, and the fhallownefs of the fea itfelf. On fuch coafts, the land ufually feems to gain upon the fea, whereas, on fhores of a bolder afpect, it is the fea that generally appears to gain upon the land. What the land acquires in extent, however, it lofes in eleva-tion ; and, whether its furface increafe or di-minifh, the depredations made on it are in both cafes evinced with equal certainty.

99. If we proceed in our furvey from the fhores, inland, we meet at every ftep with the fulleft evidence of the fame truths, and parti-cularly in the nature and economy of rivers. Every river appears to confift of a main trunk, fed from a variety of branches, each running in a valley proportioned to its fize, and all of them together forming a fyftem of vallies, communi-cating with one another, and having fuch a nice adjuftment of their declivities, that none of them join the principal valley, either on too high or too low a level ; a circumftance which would be infinitely improbable, if each of thefe vallies were not the work of the ftream that flows in it.

If indeed a river confifted of a fingle ftream, without branches, running in a ftraight val-ley, it might be fuppofed that fome great con-cuffion,

cuffion, or fome powerful torrent, had opened at once the channel by which its waters
are conducted to the ocean ; but, when the
ufual form of a river is confidered, the trunk
divided into many branches, which rife at a
great diftance from one another, and thefe again
fubdivided into an infinity of fmaller ramifications, it becomes ftrongly impreffed upon the
mind, that all thefe channels have been cut by
the waters themfelves ; that they have been
flowly dug out by the wafhing and erofion of
the land ; and that it is by the repeated touch-
es of the fame inftrument, that this curious
affemblage of lines has been engraved fo deeply
on the furface of the globe.

100. The changes which have taken place in
the courfes of rivers, are alfo to be traced, in many inftances, by fucceffive platforms of flat alluvial land, rifing one above another, and mark-
ing the different levels on which the river has
run at different periods of time. Of thefe, the
number to be diftinguifhed, in fome inftances,
is not lefs than four, or even five ; and this neceffarily carries us back, like all the operations
we are now treating of, to an antiquity extremely remote : for, if it be confidered, that
each change which the river makes in its bed,
obliterates at leaft a part of the monuments of
former changes, we fhall be convinced, that

G 4   only

only a fmall part of the progreffion can leave
any diftinct memorial behind it, and that there
is no reafon to think, that, in the part which
we fee, the beginning is included *.

101. In the fame manner, when a river under-
mines its banks, it often difcovers depofites of
fand and gravel, that have been made when it
ran on a higher level than it does at prefent.
In other inftances, the fame ftrata are feen on
both the banks, though the bed of the river is
now funk deep between them, and perhaps
holds as winding a courfe through the folid
rock, as if it flowed along the furface ; a proof
that it muft have begun to fink its bed, when it
ran through fuch loofe materials as oppofed but
a very inconfiderable refiftance to its ftream.
A river, of which the courfe is both ferpentine
and deeply excavated in the rock, is among the
phenomena, by which the flow wafte of the
land, and alfo the caufe of that wafte, are moft
directly pointed out.

102. It is, however, where rivers iffue through
narrow defiles among mountains, that the identity of the ftrata on both fides is moft eafily recognifed, and remarked at the fame time with
the greateft wonder. On obferving the Pa-
towmack, where it penetrates the ridge of the
Allegany mountains, or the Irtifh, as it iffues
from the defiles of Altai, there is no man, however

* NOTE XVI.

ever little addicted to geological speculations, who does not immediately acknowledge, that the mountain was once continued quite acrofs the space in which the river now flows; and, if he ventures to reason concerning the cause of so wonderful a change, he ascribes it to some great convulsion of nature, which has torn the mountain afunder, and opened a passage for the waters. It is only the philosopher, who has deeply meditated on the effects which action long continued is able to produce, and on the simplicity of the means which nature employs in all her operations, who sees in this nothing but the gradual working of a stream, that once flowed as high as the top of the ridge which it now so deeply intersects, and has cut its course through the rock, in the same way, and almost with the same instrument, by which the lapi-dary divides a block of marble or granite.

103. It is highly interesting to trace up, in this manner, the action of causes with which we are familiar, to the production of effects, which at first seem to require the introduction of unknown and extraordinary powers; and it is no less interesting to observe, how skilfully nature has balanced the action of all the minute causes of waste, and rendered them conducive to the general good. Of this we have a most remarkable instance, in the provision made for preserving the soil, or the coat of ve-

getable

getable mould, spread out over the surface of the earth. This coat, as it consists of loose materials, is easily washed away by the rains, and is continually carried down by the rivers into the sea. This effect is visible to every one; the earth is removed not only in the form of sand and gravel, but its finer particles suspended in the waters, tinge those of some rivers continually, and those of all occasionally, that is, when they are flooded or swollen with rains. The quantity of earth thus carried down, varies according to circumstances; it has been computed, in some instances, that the water of a river in a flood, contains earthy matter suspended in it, amounting to more than the two hundred and fiftieth part of its own bulk*. The soil, therefore, is continually diminished, its parts being transported from higher to lower levels, and finally delivered into the sea. But it is a fact, that the soil, notwithstanding, remains the same in quantity, or at least nearly the same, and must have done so, ever since the earth was the receptacle of animal or vegetable life. The soil, therefore, is augmented from other causes, just as much, at an average, as it is diminished by that now mentioned; and this augmentation evidently can proceed from nothing

---

* See Lehman, Traités de Physf. &c. tom. iii. p. 359. Note.

thing but the conftant and flow difintegration of the rocks. In the permanence, therefore, of a coat of vegetable mould on the furface of the earth, we have a demonftrative proof of the continual deftruction of the rocks ; and cannot but admire the fkill, with which the powers of the many chemical and mechanical agents employed in this complicated work, are fo adjufted, as to make the fupply and the wafte of the foil exactly equal to one another.

104. Before we take leave of the rivers and the plains, we muft remark another fact, often obferved in the natural hiftory of the latter, and clearly evincing the former exiftence of immenfe bodies of ftrata, in fituations from which they have now entirely difappeared. The fact here alluded to is, the great quantity of round and hard gravel, often to be met with in the foil, under fuch circumftances, as prove, that it can only have come from the decompofition of rocks, that once occupied the very ground over which this gravel is now fpread. In the chalk country, for inftance, about London, the quantity of flints in the foil is every where great ; and, in particular fituations, nothing but flinty gravel is found to a confiderable depth. Now, the fource from which thefe flints are derived is quite evident, for they are precifely the fame with thofe contained in the chalk beds, where-

ever

ever thefe laft are found undifturbed, and from
the deftruction of fuch beds they have no doubt
originated. Hence a great thicknefs of chalk
muft have been decompofed, to yield the quantity of flints now in the foil of thefe countries;
for the flints are but thinly fcattered through
the native chalk, compared with their abundance in the loofe earth. To afford, for example, fuch a body of flinty gravel as is found
about Kenfington, what an enormous quantity
of chalk rock muft have been deftroyed?

105. This argument, which Dr Hutton has
applied particularly to the chalk countries,
may be extended to many others. The great
plain of Crau, near the mouth of the Rhone, is
well known, and was regarded with wonder,
even in ages when the natural hiftory of the
globe was not an object of much attention. The
immenfe quantity of large round gravel-ftones,
with which this extenfive plain is entirely covered, has been fuppofed, by fome mineralogifts, to have been brought down by the Durance, and other torrents, from the Alps; but,
on further examination, has been found to be of
the fame kind that is contained in certain horizontal layers of pudding-ftone, which are the bafis of the whole plain. It cannot be doubted,
therefore, that the vaft body of gravel fpread
over it, has originated from the deftruction of
layers

layers of the fame rock, which may perhaps have rifen to a great height above what is now the furface. Indeed, from knowing the depth of the gravel that covers the plain, and the average quantity of the like gravel contained in a given thicknefs of rock, one might eftimate how much of the latter has been actually worn away. Whether data precife enough could be found, to give any weight to fuch a computation, muft be left for future inquiry to determine *.

106. In thefe inftances, chalk and pudding-ftone, by containing in them parts infinitely lefs deftructible than their general mafs, have, after they are worn away, left behind them very une-quivocal marks of their exiftence. The fame has happened in the cafe of mineral veins, where the fubftances leaft fubject to diffolution have remained, and are fcattered at a great diftance from their native place. Thus gold, the leaft liable to decompofition of all the metals, is very generally diffufed through the earth, and is found, in a greater or lefs abundance, in the fand of almoft all rivers. But the native place of this mineral is the folid rock, or the veins and cavities contained in the rock, and from thence it muft have made its way into the foil. This, therefore, is another proof of the vaft ex-tent to which the degradation of the land, and of the

* NOTE XVII.

the rock, which is the bafis of it, has been carried; and confequently, of the great difference between the elevation and fhape of the earth's furface in the prefent, and in former ages.

107. The veins of tin furnifh an argument of the fame kind. The ores of this metal are very indeftructible, and little fubject to decompofition, fo that they remain very long in the ground without change. Where there are tin veins, as in Cornwall, the tin-ftone or tin-ore is found in great abundance in fuch vallies and ftreams as have the fame direction with the veins; and hence the *ftreaming*, as it is called, or wafhing of the earth, to obtain the tin-ftone from it. Now, if it be confidered, that none of this ore can have come into the foil but from parts of a vein actually deftroyed, it muft appear evident that a great wafte of thefe veins has taken place, and confequently of the fchiftus or granite in which they are contained.

108. Thefe leffons, which the geologift is taught in flat and open countries, become more ftriking, by the ftudy of thofe Alpine tracts, where the furface of the earth attains its greateft elevation. If we fuppofe him placed for the firft time in the midft of fuch a fcene, as foon as he has recovered from the impreffion made by the novelty and magnificence of the fpectacle before him, he begins to difcover the footfteps

footsteps of time, and to perceive, that the works of nature, usually deemed the most permanent, are those on which the characters of vicissitude are most deeply imprinted. He sees himself in the midst of a vast ruin, where the precipices which rise on all sides with such boldness and asperity, the sharp peaks of the granite mountains, and the huge fragments that surround their bases, do but mark so many epochs in the progress of decay, and point out the energy of those destructive causes, which even the magnitude and solidity of such great bodies have been unable to resist.

109. The result of a more minute investigation, is in perfect unison with this general impression. Whence is it, that the elevation of mountains is so obviously connected with the hardness and indestructibility of the rocks which compose them? Why is it, that a lofty mountain of soft and secondary rock is no where to be found; and that such chains, as the Pyrenees or the Alps, never consist of any but the hardest stone, of granite for instance, or of those primarary strata, which, if we are to credit the preceding theory, have been twice heated in the fires, and twice tempered in the waters, of the mineral regions? Is it not plain that this arises, not from any direct connection between the hardness of stones, and their height in the at-
                                        mosphere,

mofphere, but from this, that the wafte and *detritus* to which all things are fubject, will not allow foft and weak fubftances to remain long in an expofed and elevated fituation? Were it not for this, the fecondary rocks, being in pofition fuperincumbent on the primary, ought to be the higheft of the two, and fhould cover the primary, (as they no doubt have at one time done), in the higheft as well as the loweft fituations, or among the mountains as well as in the plains.

110. Again, wherefore is it, that among all mountains, remarkable for their ruggednefs and afperity, the rock, on examination, is always found of very unequal deftructibility, fome parts yielding to the weather, and to the other caufes of difintegration, much more flowly than the reft, and having ftrength fufficient to fupport themfelves, when left alone, in flender pyramids, bold projections, and overhanging cliffs? Where, on the other hand, the rock waftes uniformly, the mountains are fimilar to one another; their fwells and flopes are gentle, and they are bounded by a waving and continuous furface. The intermediate degrees of refiftance which the rocks oppofe to the caufes of deftruction, produce intermediate forms. It is this which gives to the mountains, of every different fpecies of rock,

a different habit and expreffion, and which, in particular, has imparted to thofe of granite that venerable and majeftic character, by which they rarely fail to be diftinguifhed.

111. The ftructure of the vallies among mountains, fhews clearly to what caufe their exiftence is to be afcribed. Here we have firft a large valley, communicating directly with the plain, and winding between high ridges of mountains, while the river in the bottom of it defcends over a furface, remarkable, in fuch a fcene, for its uniform declivity. Into this, open a multitude of tranfverfe or fecondary vallies, interfecting the ridges on either fide of the former, each bringing a contribution to the main ftream, proportioned to its magnitude; and, except where a cataract now and then intervenes, all having that nice adjuftment in their levels, (99.) which is the more wonderful, the greater the irregularity of the furface. Thefe fecondary vallies have others of a fmaller fize opening into them; and, among mountains of the firft order, where all is laid out on the greateft fcale, thefe ramifications are continued to a fourth, and even a fifth, each diminifhing in fize as it increafes in elevation, and as its fupply of water is lefs. Through them all, this law is in general obferved, that where a higher valley joins a lower one, of the two angles which

H it

it makes with the latter, that which is obtufe
is always on the defcending fide ; a law that is
the fame with that which regulates the con-
fluence of ftreams running on a furface nearly
of uniform inclination. This alone is a proof
that the vallies are the work of the ftreams ;
and indeed what elfe but the water itfelf, working its way through obftacles of unequal refiftance, could have opened or kept up a communication between the inequalities of an irregular
and alpine furface.

112. Many more arguments, all leading to
the fame conclufion, may be deduced from the
general facts, known in the natural hiftory of
mountains ; and, if the Oreologift would trace
back the progrefs of wafte, till he come in fight of
that original ftructure, of which the remains are
ftill fo vaft, he perceives an immenfe mafs of folid
rock, naked and unfhapely, as it firft emerged
from the deep, and incomparably greater than
all that is now before him. The operation of
rains and torrents, modified by the hardnefs and
tenacity of the rock, has worked the whole into
its prefent form ; has hollowed out the vallies,
and gradually detached the mountains from the
general mafs, cutting down their fides into fteep
precipices at one place, and fmoothing them into gentle declivities at another. From this has
refulted a tranfportation of materials, which, both
for

for the quantity of the whole, and the magnitude of the individual fragments, muft feem incredible to every one, who has not learned to
calculate the effects of continued action, and to
reflect, that length of time can convert accidental into fteady caufes. Hence fragments of rock,
from the central chain, are found to have travelled into diftant vallies, even where many inferior ridges intervene: hence the granite of
Mount Blanc is feen in the plains of Lombardy,
or on the fides of Jura; and the ruins of the
Carpathian mountains lie fcattered over the
fhores of the Baltic *.

113. Thus, with Dr Hutton, we fhall be difpofed to confider thofe great chains of mountains, which traverfe the furface of the globe,
as cut out of maffes vaftly greater, and more
lofty than any thing that now remains. The
prefent appearances afford no data for calculating the original magnitude of thefe maffes, or
the height to which they may have been elevated. The neareft eftimate we can form is,
where a chain or group of mountains, like thofe
of Rofa in the Alps, is horizontally ftratified,
and where, of confequence, the undifturbed pofition of the mineral beds enables us to refer
the whole of the prefent inequalities of the furface to the operation of wafte or decay. Thefe

H 2 mountains,

* NOTE XVIII.

mountains, as they now ſtand, may not inapt-
ly be compared to the pillars of earth which
workmen leave behind them, to afford a meaſure of the whole quantity of earth which they
have removed. As the pillars, (conſidering the
mountains as ſuch), are in this caſe of leſs height
than they originally were, ſo the meaſure furniſhed by them is but a limit, which the quantity ſought muſt neceſſarily exceed.

114. Such, according to Dr Hutton's theory,
are the changes which the daily operations of
waſte have produced on the ſurface of the globe.
Theſe operations, inconſiderable if taken ſeparately, become great, by conſpiring all to the
ſame end, never counteracting one another, but
proceeding, through a period of indefinite extent, continually in the ſame direction. Thus
every thing deſcends, nothing returns upward ;
the hard and ſolid bodies every where diſſolve,
and the looſe and ſoft no where conſolidate.
The powers which tend to preſerve, and thoſe
which tend to change the condition of the earth's
ſurface, are never *in equilibrio ;* the latter are,
in all caſes, the moſt powerful, and, in reſpect
of the former, are like *living* in compariſon of
dead forces. Hence the law of decay is one
which ſuffers no exception : The elements of all
bodies were once looſe and unconnected, and to
the

the fame ftate nature has appointed that they fhould all return.

115. It affords no prefumption againft the reality of this progrefs, that, in refpect of man, it is too flow to be immediately perceived : The utmoft portion of it to which our experience can extend, is evanefcent, in comparifon with the whole, and muft be regarded as the momentary increment of a vaft progreffion, circumfcribed by no other limits than the duration of the world. TIME performs the office of *integrating* the infinitefimal parts of which this progreffion is made up; it collects them into one fum, and produces from them an amount greater than any that can be affigned.

116. While on the furface of the earth fo much is every where going to decay, no new production of mineral fubftances is found in any region acceffible to man. The inftances of what are called petrifactions, or the formation of fto-ny fubftances by means of water, which we fometimes obferve, whether they be ferruginous concretions, or calcareous, or, as happens in fome rare cafes, filiceous ftalactites, are too few in number, and too inconfiderable in extent, to be deemed material exceptions to this general rule. The bodies thus generated, alfo, are no fooner formed, than they become fubject to wafte and diffolution, like all the other hard fubftances in

H 3

nature;

nature ; fo that they but retard for a while the progrefs by which they are all refolved into duft, and fooner or later committed to the bofom of the deep.

117. We are not, however, to imagine, that there is no where any means of repairing this wafte ; for, on comparing the conclufion at which we are now arrived, viz. that the prefent continents are all going to decay, and their materials defcending into the ocean, with the propofition firft laid down, that thefe fame continents are compofed of materials which muft have been collected from the decay of former rocks, it is impoffible not to recognife two correfponding fteps of the fame progrefs ; of a progrefs, by which mineral fubftances are fubjected to the fame feries of changes, and alternately wafted away and renovated. In the fame manner, as the prefent mineral fubftances derive their origin from fubftances fimilar to themfelves ; fo, from the land now going to decay, the fand and gravel forming on the fea-fhore, or in the beds of rivers ; from the fhells and corals which in fuch enormous quantities are every day accumulated in the bofom of the fea ; from the drift wood, and the multitude of vegetable and animal remains continually depofited in the ocean : from all thefe we cannot doubt, that ftrata are now forming in thofe regions, to
                                    which

which nature feems to have confined the powers
of mineral reproduction; from which, after
being confolidated, they are again deftined to
emerge, and to exhibit a feries of changes fimilar to the paft *.

118. How often thefe viciffitudes of decay
and renovation have been repeated, is not for
us to determine: they conftitute a feries, of
which, as the author of this theory has remarked, we neither fee the beginning nor the end;
a circumftance that accords well with what is
known concerning other parts of the economy
of the world. In the continuation of the different fpecies of animals and vegetables that inhabit the earth, we difcern neither a beginning
nor an end; and, in the planetary motions,
where geometry has carried the eye fo far both
into the future and the paft, we difcover no
mark, either of the commencement or the termination of the prefent order †. It is unreafon-
able, indeed, to fuppofe, that fuch marks fhould
any where exift. The Author of nature has not
given laws to the univerfe, which, like the infti-
tutions of men, carry in themfelves the elements
of their own deftruction. He has not permitted, in his works, any fymptom of infancy or of
old age, or any fign by which we may eftimate
either their future or their paft duration. He
may put an end, as he no doubt gave a begin-

H 4   ning,

* Note xix.   † Note xx.

ning, to the prefent fyftem, at fome determinate period ; but we may fafely conclude, that this great *cataftrophe* will not be brought about by any of the laws now exifting, and that it is not indicated by any thing which we perceive.

119. To affert, therefore, that, in the economy of the world, we fee no mark, either of a beginning or an end, is very different from affirming, that the world had no beginning, and will have no end. The firft is a conclufion juftified by common fenfe, as well as found philofophy ; while the fecond is a prefumptuous and unwarrantable affertion, for which no reafon from experience or analogy can ever be affigned. Dr Hutton might, therefore, juftly complain of the uncandid criticifm, which, by fubftituting the one of thefe affertions for the other, endeavoured to load his theory with the reproach of atheifm and impiety. Mr KIRWAN, in bringing forward this harfh and ill founded cenfure, was neither animated by the fpirit, nor guided by the maxims of true philofophy. By the fpirit of philofophy, he muft have been induced to reflect, that fuch poifoned weapons as he was preparing to ufe, are hardly ever allowable in fcientific conteft, as having a lefs direct tendency to overthrow the fyftem, than to hurt the perfon of an adverfary, and to wound, perhaps incurably, his mind, his reputation, or his peace.

By

By the maxims of philofophy, he muſt have
been reminded, that, in no part of the hiſtory
of nature, has any mark been diſcovered, either
of the beginning or the end of the preſent *order ;* and that the geologiſt ſadly miſtakes, both
the objeƈt of his ſcience and the limits of his un-
derſtanding, who thinks it his buſineſs to explain
the means employed by INFINITE WISDOM for
eſtabliſhing the laws, which now govern the
world.

By attending to theſe obvious conſiderations,
Mr Kirwan would have avoided a very illiberal
and ungenerous proceeding ; and, however he
might have differed from Dr Hutton as to the
truth of his opinions, he would not have cen-
ſured their *tendency* with ſuch raſh and unjuſti-
fiable ſeverity.

But, if this author may be blamed for wanting the temper, or negleƈting the rules, of philoſophic inveſtigation, he is hardly leſs culpa-
ble, for having ſo ſlightly conſidered the ſcope
and ſpirit of a work which he condemned ſo
freely. In that work, inſtead of finding the
world repreſented as the reſult of neceſſity
or chance, which might be looked for, if the
accuſations of atheiſm or impiety were well
founded, we ſee every where the utmoſt attention to diſcover, and the utmoſt diſpoſition to
admire, the inſtances of wiſe and beneficent de-
ſign,

fign manifefted in the ftructure, or economy of the world. The enlarged views of thefe, which his geological fyftem afforded, appeared to Dr Hutton himfelf as its moft valuable refult. They were the parts of it which he contemplated with greateft delight; and he would have been lefs flattered, by being told of the ingenuity and originality of his theory, than of the addition which it had made to our knowledge of *final caufes*. It was natural, therefore, that he fhould be hurt by an attempt to accufe him of opinions, fo different from thofe which he had always taught; and if he anfwered Mr Kirwan's attack with warmth or afperity, we muft afcribe it to the indignation excited by unmerited reproach.

120. But to return to the natural hiftory of the earth : Though there be in it no *data*, from which the commencement of the prefent order can be afcertained, there are many by which the exift-ence of that order may be traced back to an anti-quity extremely remote. The beds of primitive fchiftus, for inftance, contain fand, gravel, and other materials, collected, as already fhewn, from the diffolution of mineral bodies; which bodies, therefore, muft have exifted long before the oldeft part of the prefent land was formed. Again, in this gravel we fometimes find pieces of fandftone, and of other compound rocks, by which we are of courfe carried back a ftep farther, fo as to reach

a

a fyftem of things, from which the prefent is the third in fucceffion; and this may be confidered as the moft ancient epocha, of which any memorial exifts in the records of the foffil kingdom.

121. Next in the order of time to the confolidation of the primary ftrata, we muft place their elevation, when, from being horizontal, and at the bottom of the fea, they were broken, fet on edge, and raifed to the furface. It is even probable, as formerly obferved, that to this fucceeded a depreffion of the fame ftrata, and a fecond elevation, fo that they have twice vifited the fuperior, and twice the inferior regions. During the fecond immerfion, were formed, firft, the great bodies of pudding-ftone, that in fo many inftances lie immediately above them; and next were depofited the ftrata that are ftrictly denominated fecondary.

122. The third great event, was the raifing up of this compound body of old and new ftrata from the bottom of the fea, and forming it into the dry land, or the continents, as they now exift *. Contemporary with this, we muft fuppofe the injection of melted matter among the ftrata, and the confequent formation of the cryftallized and unftratified rocks, namely, the granite, metallic veins, and veins of porphyry and whinftone.

* Note xxi.

whinftone. This, however, is to be confidered as embracing a period of great duration; and it muft always be recollected, that veins are found of very different formation; fo that when we fpeak generally, it is perhaps impoffible to ftate any thing more precife concerning their antiquity, than that they are pofterior to the ftrata, and that the veins of whinftone feem to be the moft recent of all, as they traverfe every other.

123. In the fourth place, with refpect to time, we muft clafs the facts that regard the detritus and wafte of the land, and muft carefully diftinguifh them from the more ancient phenomena of the mineral kingdom. Here we are to reckon the fhaping of all the prefent inequalities of the furface; the formation of hills of gravel, and of what have been called tertiary ftrata, confifting of loofe and unconfolidated materials; alfo collections of fhells not mineralized, like thofe in Turaine; fuch petrifactions as thofe contained in the rock of Gibraltar, on the coaft of Dalmatia, and in the caves of Bayreuth. The bones of land animals found in the foil, fuch as thofe of Siberia, or North America, are probably more recent than any of the former *.

124. Thefe phenomena, then, are all fo many marks of the lapfe of time, among which the principles of geology enable us to diftinguifh a
certain

* NOTE XXII.

certain order, fo that we know fome of them to
be more, and others to be lefs diftant, but without being able to afcertain, with any exactnefs,
the proportion of the immenfe intervals which
feparate them. Thefe intervals admit of no
comparifon with the aftronomical meafures of
time; they cannot be expreffed by the revolutions of the fun or of the moon; nor is there
any fynchronifm between the moft recent epochas of the mineral kingdom, and the moft ancient of our ordinary chronology.

125. On what is now faid is grounded another objection to Dr Hutton's theory, namely,
that the high antiquity afcribed by it to the
earth, is inconfiftent with that fyftem of chronology which refts on the authority of the Sacred
Writings. This objection would no doubt be
of weight, if the high antiquity in queftion
were not reftricted merely to the globe of the
earth, but were alfo extended to the human
race. That the origin of mankind does not go
back beyond fix or feven thoufand years, is a
pofition fo involved in the narrative of the Mofaic books, that any thing inconfiftent with it,
would no doubt ftand in oppofition to the
teftimony of thofe ancient records. On this
fubject, however, geology is filent; and the
hiftory of arts and fciences, when traced as
high as any authentic monuments extend, refers

the

the beginnings of civilization to a date not very different from that which has juft been mentioned, and infinitely within the limits of the moft recent of the epochas, marked by the phyfical revolutions of the globe.

On the other hand, the authority of the Sacred Books feems to be but little interefted in what regards the mere antiquity of the earth itfelf; nor does it appear that their language is to be underftood literally concerning the *age* of that body, any more than concerning its *figure* or its *motion*. The theory of Dr Hutton ftands here precifely on the fame footing with the fyftem of COPERNICUS; for there is no reafon to fuppofe, that it was the purpofe of revelation to furnifh a ftandard of geological, any more than of aftronomical fcience. It is admitted, on all hands, that the Scriptures are not intended to refolve phyfical queftions, or to explain matters in no way related to the morality of human actions; and if, in confequence of this principle, a confiderable latitude of interpretation were not allowed, we fhould continue at this moment to believe, that the earth is flat; that the fun moves round the earth; and that the circumference of a circle is no more than three times its diameter.

It is but reafonable, therefore, that we fhould extend to the geologift the fame liberty of fpeculation,

culation, which the aftronomer and mathematician are already in poffeffion of; and this may be done, by fuppofing that the chronology of Moses relates only to the human race. This liberty is not more neceffary to Dr Hutton than to other theorifts. No ingenuity has been able to reconcile the natural hiftory of the globe with the opinion of its recent origin; and accordingly the cofmologies of Kirwan and De Luc, though contrived with more mineralogical fkill, are not lefs forced and unfatisfactory than thofe of Burnet and Whifton.

126. It is impoffible to look back on the fyftem which we have thus endeavoured to illuftrate, without being ftruck with the novelty and beauty of the views which it fets before us. The very plan and fcope of it diftinguifh it from all other theories of the earth, and point it out as a work of great and original invention. The fole object of fuch theories has hitherto been, to explain the manner in which the prefent laws of the mineral kingdom were firft eftablifhed, or began to exift, without treating of the manner in which they now proceed, and by which their continuance is provided for. The authors of thefe theories have accordingly gone back to a ftate of things altogether unlike the prefent, and have confined their reafonings, or

their

their fictions, to a crifis which never has exifted but once, and which never can return. Dr Hutton, on the other hand, has guided his invefligation by the philofophical maxim, *Caufam naturalem et affiduam quærimus, non raram et fortuitam.* His theory, accordingly, prefents us with a fyftem of wife and provident economy, where the fame inftruments are continually employed, and where the decay and renovation of foffils being carried on at the fame time in the different regions allotted to them, preferve in the earth the conditions effential for the fupport of animal and vegetable life. We have been long accuftomed to admire that beautiful contrivance in nature, by which the water of the ocean, drawn up in vapour by the atmofphere, imparts, in its defcent, fertility to the earth, and becomes the great caufe of vegetation and of life; but now we find, that this vapour not only fertilizes, but creates the foil; prepares it from the folid rock, and, after employing it in the great operations of the furface, carries it back into the regions where all its mineral characters are renewed. Thus, the circulation of moifture through the air, is a prime mover, not only in the annual fucceffion of the feafons, but in the great geological cycle, by which the wafte and reproduction of entire continents is circumfcribed. Perhaps a more ftriking view than this, of the wifdom

dom that prefides over nature, was never prefented by any philofophical fyftem, nor a greater addition ever made to our knowledge of final
caufes. It is an addition which gives confiftency
to the reft, by proving, that equal forefight is exerted in providing for the whole and for the
parts, and that no lefs care is taken to maintain
the conftitution of the earth, than to preferve
the tribes of animals and vegetables which dwell
on its furface. In a word, it is the peculiar excellence of this theory, that it afcribes to the
phenomena of geology an order fimilar to that
which exifts in the provinces of nature with
which we are beft acquainted ; that it produces feas and continents, not by accident, but by
the operation of regular and uniform caufes ;
that it makes the decay of one part fubfervient
to the reftoration of another, and gives ftability
to the whole, not by perpetuating individuals,
but by reproducing them in fucceffion.

127. Again, in the detail of this theory, and
the ample induction on which it is founded, we
meet with many facts and obfervations, either
entirely new, or hitherto very imperfectly underftood. Thus, the veins which proceed from
maffes of granite, and penetrate the incumbent
fchiftus, had either efcaped the obfervation of
former mineralogifts, or the importance of the
phenomenon had been entirely overlooked. Dr

I   Hutton

Hutton has defcribed the appearances with great accuracy, and drawn from them the moft intereffing conclufions. At the junction of the primary and fecondary ftrata, the facts which he has noted had been obferved by others ; but no one I think had fo fully underftood the language which they fpeak, or had fo clearly perceived the confequences that neceffarily follow from them. He is the firft who diftinctly pointed out the characters which diftinguifh whinftone from lava, and who explained the true relation that fubfifts between thefe fubftances. He alfo difcovered the induration of the ftrata, in contact with veins of whin, and the charring of the coal in their vicinity. His theory alfo enabled him to determine the affinity of whinftone and granite to one another, and their relation to the other great bodies of the mineral kingdom.

To the obfervations of the fame excellent geologift, we are indebted for the knowledge of the general and important fact, that all the hard fubftances of the mineral kingdom, when elevated into the atmofphere, have a tendency to decay, and are fubject to a difintegration and wafte, to which no limit can be fet but that of their entire deftruction; that no provifion is made on the furface for repairing this wafte, and that there, no new foffil is produced ; that the formation of all the varied fcenery which the

furface

furface of the earth exhibits, depends on the operation of caufes, the momentary exertions of which are familiar to us, though we knew not before the effects which their accumulated action was able to produce. Thefe are facts in the natural hiftory of the earth, the difcovery of which is due to Dr Hutton ; and, fhould we lay all further fpeculation afide, and confider the theory of the earth as a work too great to be attempted by man, we muft ftill regard the phenomena and laws juft mentioned, as forming a folid and valuable addition to our knowledge.

128. If we would compare this theory with others, as to the invifible agents which it employs, we muft confider, that fire and water are the two powers which all of them muft make ufe of, fo that they can differ from one another only by the way in which they combine thefe powers. In Dr Hutton's fyftem, water is firft employed to depofite and arrange, and then fire to confolidate, mineralize, and laftly, to elevate the ftrata ; but, with refpect to the unftratified or cryftallized fubftances, the action of fire only is recognifed. The fyftem having leaft affinity to this is the Neptunian, which afcribes the formation of all minerals to the action of water alone, and extends this hypothefis even to the unftratified rocks. Here, therefore, the action of fire is entirely excluded ; and the Neptunifts

I 2 have

have certainly made a great facrifice to the love of truth, or of paradox, in rejecting the affiftance of fo powerful an auxiliary *.

129. In the fyftems which employ the agency of the latter element, we are to look for a greater refemblance to that of Dr Hutton, though many and great marks of diftinction are eafily perceived. In the cofmologies, for example, of LEIBNITZ and BUFFON, fire and water are both employed, as well as in this; but they are employed in a reverfe order. Thefe philofophers introduce the action of fire firft, and then the action of water, which is to invert the order of nature altogether, as the confolidation of the rocks muft be pofterior to their ftratification. Indeed, the theory of Buffon is fingularly defective: befides inverting the order of the two great operations of ftratification and confolidation, and of courfe giving no real explanation of the latter, it gives no account of the elevation, or highly inclined pofition of the ftrata; it makes no diftinction between ftratified and unftratified bodies, nor does it offer any but the moft unfatisfactory explanation of the inequalities of the earth's furface. This fyftem, therefore, has but a very diftant refemblance to the Huttonian theory †.

130. The fyftem of LAZZARO MORO has been remarked as approaching nearer to this theo-

ry

ry than any other; and it is certain, that one very important principle is common to them both. The theory of the Italian geologist was chiefly directed to the explanation of the remains of marine animals, which are found in mountains far from the sea; and it appears to have been suggested to him by the phenomena of the *Campi Phlegræi*, and by the production of the new island of *Santorini* in the Archipelago. He accordingly supposes, that the islands and continents have been all raised up, like the above-mentioned island, from the bottom of the sea, by the force of volcanic fire: that these fires began to burn under the bottom of the ocean, soon after the creation of the world, when as yet the ocean covered the whole earth : that they at first elevated a portion of the land ; and in this primitive land no shells are found, as the original ocean was destitute of fish. The volcanoes continuing to burn, under the sea, after the creation of animated nature, the strata that were then raised up by their action were full of shells and other marine objects ; and, from the violence with which they were elevated, arose the contortions and inclined position which they frequently possess *.

I 3   This

---

* Dé Crostacei, et degli altri Marini Corpi, che si trovano su' Monti : di Ant. Lazzaro Moro. Vinezia. 1740.

This fyftem is imperfect, as it makes no peculiar provifion for the confolidation of the ftrata, which, according to it, as well as the Neptunian fyftem, muft be afcribed to the action,
not of fire, but of water. No account is given
of the mineralization of the fhells found in the
ftrata, or of the difference between them and
the fhells found loofe at the bottom of the fea;
and no diftinction is made between ftratified
and unftratified fubftances. But, with all this,
Lazzaro Moro has certainly the merit of having
perceived, that fome other power than that
which depofited the ftrata, muft have been employed for their elevation, and that they have
endured the action of a difturbing force.

131. From this comparifon it appears, that
Dr Hutton's theory is fufficiently diftinct, even
from the theories which approach to it moft
nearly, to merit, in the ftricteft fenfe, the appel-
lation of *new* and *original*. There are indeed
few inventions or difcoveries, recorded in the
hiftory of fcience, to which nearer approaches
were not made before they were fully unfolded.
It therefore very well deferves to be diftinguifhed by a particular name; and, if it behoves us
to follow the analogy obferved in the names of
the two great fyftems, which at prefent divide
the opinions of geologifts, we may join Mr Kirwan in calling this the PLUTONIC SYSTEM. For
my

my own part, I would rather have it characterized by a lefs fplendid, but jufter name, that of
the HUTTONIAN THEORY.

132. The circumftance, however, which gives
to this theory its peculiar character, and exalts it
infinitely above all others, is the introduction
of the principle of preffure, to modify the effects
of heat when applied at the bottom of the fea.
This is in fact the key to the grand enigma of
the mineral kingdom, where, while one fet of
phenomena indicates the action of fire, another
fet, equally remarkable, feems to exclude the
poffibility of that action, by prefenting us with
mineral fubftances, in fuch a ftate as they could
never have been brought into by the operation
of the fires we fee at the furface of the earth.
Thefe two claffes of phenomena are reconciled
together, by admitting the power of compreffion
to confine the volatile parts of bodies when heat
is applied to them, and to force them, in many
inftances, to undergo fufion, inftead of being
calcined or diffipated by burning or inflammation. In this hypothefis, which fome affect to
confider as a principle gratuitoufly affumed, there
appears to me nothing but a very fair and legi-
timate generalization of the properties of heat.
Combuftion and inflammation are chemical pro-
ceffes, to which other conditions are required,
befides the prefence of a high temperature. The

I 4   ftate

ftate of the mineral regions makes it reafonable
to prefume, that thefe conditions are wanting
in the bowels of the earth, where, of confequence, we have a right to look for nothing but
expanfion and fufion, the only operations which
feem effential to heat, and infeparable from the
application of it, in certain degrees, to certain
fubftances. Though this principle, therefore,
had no countenance from analogy, the admirable
fimplicity, and the unity, which it introduces
into the phenomena of geology, would fufficiently juftify the application of it to the theory of
the earth.

As another excellence of this theory, I may,
perhaps, be allowed to remark, that it extends
its confequences beyond thofe to which the author of it has himfelf adverted, and that it
affords, which no geological theory has yet done,
a fatisfactory explanation of the fpheroidal figure of the earth *.

133. Yet, with all thefe circumftances of originality, grandeur, and fimplicity in its favour,
with the addition of evidence as demonftrative
as the nature of the fubject will admit, this
theory has probably many obftacles to overcome,
before it meet the general approbation. The
greatnefs of the objects which it fets before us,
alarms the imagination; the powers which it
fuppoles to be lodged in the fubterraneous regions,

* NOTE xxv.

gions; a heat which has fubdued the moft refractory rocks, and has melted beds of marble
and quartz ; an expanfive force, which has fold-
ed up, or broken the ftrata, and raifed whole
continents from the bottom of the fea ; thefe
are things with which, however certainly they
may be proved, the mind cannot foon be fami-
liarifed. The change and movement alfo, which
this theory afcribes to all that the fenfes declare
to be moft unalterable, raife up againft it the
fame prejudices which formerly oppofed the belief in the true fyftem of the world ; and it affords a curious proof, how little fuch prejudices are fubject to vary, that as ARISTAR-
CHUS, an ancient follower of that fyftem, was
charged with impiety for moving the everlafting
VESTA from her place, fo Dr Hutton, nearly on
the fame ground, has been fubjected to the very
fame accufation. Even the length of time
which this theory regards as neceffary to the revolutions of the globe, is looked on as belonging to the marvellous; and man, who finds
himfelf conftrained by the want of time, or of
fpace in almoft all his undertakings, forgets,
that in thefe, if in any thing, the riches of nature reject all limitation *.

The evidence which muft be oppofed to all
thefe caufes of incredulity, cannot be fully underftood without much ftudy and attention.

It

* NOTE XXVI.

It requires not only a careful examination of
particular inſtances, but comprehenſive views
of the whole phenomena of geology ; the compariſon of things very remote with one another ; the interpretation of the *obſcure* by the
luminous, and of the *doubtful* by the *deciſive* appearances.   The geologiſt muſt not content himſelf with examining the inſulated ſpecimens of
his cabinet, or with purſuing the nice ſubtleties
of mineralogical arrangement ; he muſt ſtudy
the relations of foſſils, as they actually exiſt ;
he muſt follow nature into her wildeſt and moſt
inacceſſible abodes ; and muſt ſelect, for the
places of his obſervations, thoſe points, from
which the variety and gradation of her works
can be moſt extenſively and accurately explored.
Without ſuch an exact and comprehenſive ſurvey, his mind will hardly be prepared to reliſh
the true theory of the earth.   " *Naturæ enim*
vis atque majeſtas omnibus momentis fide caret,
ſi quis modo partes atque non totam complectatur
animo *.*"

134. If indeed this theory of the earth is as
well founded as we ſuppoſe it to be, the lapſe
of time muſt neceſſarily remove all objections to
it, and the progreſs of ſcience will only develope
its evidence more fully.   As it ſtands at preſent,

* PLIN. Hiſt. Nat. lib. vii. cap. i.

fent, though true, it muſt be ſtill imperfect;
and it cannot be doubted, that the great principles of it, though eſtabliſhed on an immoveable baſis, muſt yet undergo many modifications, requiring to be limited, in one place, or to
be extended, in another. A work of ſuch variety and extent cannot be carried to perfection
by the efforts of an individual. Ages may be
required to fill up the bold outline which Dr
Hutton has traced with ſo maſterly a hand ; to
detach the parts more completely from the general maſs ; to adjuſt the ſize and poſition of
the ſubordinate members ; and to give to the
whole piece the exact proportion and true colouring of nature.

This, however, in length of time, may be expected from the advancement of ſcience, and
from the mutual aſſiſtance which parts of knowledge, ſeemingly the moſt remote, often afford
to one another. Not only may the obſervations
of the mineralogiſt, in tracts yet unexplored,
complete the enumeration of geological facts ;
and the experiments of the chemiſt, on ſubſtances not yet ſubjected to his analyſis, afford
a more intimate acquaintance with the nature
of foſſils, and a meaſure of the power of thoſe
chemical agents to which this theory aſcribes
ſuch vaſt effects : but alſo, from other ſciences,
leſs directly connected with the natural hiſtory

of

of the earth, much information may be received. The accurate geographical maps and furveys which are now making ; the foundings ; the obfervations of currents ; the barometrical meafurements, may all combine to afcertain the reality, and to fix the quantity of thofe changes which terreftrial bodies continually undergo. Every new improvement in fcience affords the means of delineating more accurately the face of nature as it *now* exifts, and of tranfmitting, to future ages, an account, which may be compared with the face of nature as it fhall *then* exift. If, therefore, the fcience of the prefent times is deftined to furvive the phyfical revolutions of the globe, the HUTTONIAN THEORY may be confirmed by hiftorical record ; and the author of it will be remembered among the illuftrious few, whofe fyftems have been verified by the obfervations of fucceeding ages, fupported by facts unknown to themfelves, and eftablifhed by the decifions of a tribunal, flow, but infallible, in diftinguifhing between truth and falfehood.

NOTES

NOTES and ADDITIONS.

NOTES and ADDITIONS.

NOTE I. § 2.

Origin of calcareous rocks.

134. IT has been afferted, that Dr Hutton went further than is ftated at § 2., and maintained all calcareous matter to be *originally* of animal formation. This pofition, however, is fo far from being laid down by Dr Hutton, that it belongs to an inquiry which he carefully avoided to enter on, as being altogether beyond the limits of philofophical inveftigation.

He has indeed no where treated of the *firft origin* of any of the earths, or of any fubftance whatfoever, but only of the transformations which bodies have undergone fince the prefent laws of nature were eftablifhed. He confidered this laft as all that a fcience, built on experiment and obfervation, can poffibly extend to; and willingly left, to more prefumptuous inquirers, the tafk of carrying their reafonings beyond the boundaries of nature, and of unfolding the properties of the chaotic fluid, with as much minutenefs of detail, as if they were defcribing

fcribing the circumftances of a chemical procefs which they had actually witnessed.

The idea of calcareous matter which really belongs to the Huttonian Theory, is, that in all the changes which the terraqueous globe has undergone in paft ages, this matter exifted, as it does now, either in the form of limeftone and marble, or in the compofition of other ftones, or in the ftate of corals, fhells, and bones of animals. It may be true, that there is no particle of calcareous matter, at prefent exifting on the furface of the earth, that has not, at fome time, made a part of an animal body; but of this we can have no certainty, nor is it of any importance that we fhould. It is enough to know, that the rocks of marble and limeftone contain in general marks of having been formed from materials collected at the bottom of the fea; and of this a fingle cockle-fhell, or piece of coral, found included in a rock, is a fufficient proof with refpect to the whole mafs of which it makes a part..

The principal object which Dr Hutton had in view when he fpoke of the maffes of marble and limeftone, as compofed of the calcareous matter of marine bodies *, was to prove, that they had been all formed at the bottom of the

---

* Theory of the Earth, vol. i. p. 23, 24.

the fea, and from materials there depofited. His
general conclufion is, " that all the ftrata of the
earth, not only thofe confifting of fuch calcareous maffes, but others fuperincumbent upon
thefe, have had their origin at the bottom of
the fea, by the collection of fand and gravel, of
fhells, of coralline and cruftaceous bodies, and
of earths and clays varioufly mixed, or feparated
and accumulated. This is a general conclufion,
well authenticated by the appearances of nature,
and highly important in the natural hiftory of
the earth *."

135. In his Geological Effays, Mr Kirwan fays,
that " fome geologifts, as Buffon, and of late Dr
Hutton, have excluded calcareous earth from
the number of the primeval, afferting the maffes
of it we at prefent behold to proceed from fhell-
fifh. But, in addition to the unfounded fuppofition, that fhell-fifh, or any animals, poffefs the
power of producing any fimple earth, thefe philofophers fhould have confidered, that, before
the exiftence of any fifh, the ftony maffes that
inclofe the bafon of the fea, muft have exifted ;
and, among thefe, there is none in which calcareous earth is not found. Dr Hutton endeavours to *evade* this argument, by fuppofing the
world we now inhabit to have arifen from the

K   ruins

---

* Theory of the Earth, vol. i. p. 26.

ruins and fragments of an anterior, without pointing at any original. If we are thus to proceed *in infinitum*, I shall not pretend to follow him ; but, if he stops any where, he will find the same argument equally to occur *."

The argument here employed would certainly be conclusive against any one, who, in disputing about the *first origin* of things, should deny that the calcareous is as ancient as any other of the simple earths. But this has nothing to do with Dr Hutton's speculations, which, as has been just said, never extended to the *first origin* of substances, but were confined entirely to their changes ; so that what he asserts concerning the calcareous rocks, is no more than that those which we now see have been formed from loose materials, deposited at the bottom of the sea. It was not therefore in order to *evade* Mr Kirwan's argument, as the preceding passage would lead us to believe, that he supposed the world which we now inhabit to have arisen from the ruin and waste of an anterior world ; but it was because this seemed to him a conclusion which necessarily followed from the phenomena of geology, and it was a conclusion that he had deduced long before he heard of Mr Kirwan's objections to his system. Instead of an *evasion*, therefore,

---

* Geol. Essays, p. 13.

therefore, any one who confiders the fubject fairly, will fee, in Dr Hutton's reafoning, nothing but the caution of a philofopher, who wifely confines his theory within the fame limits by which nature has confined his experience and obfervation.

It is neverthelefs true, that Dr Hutton has fometimes exprefled himfelf as if he thought that the prefent calcareous rocks are all compofed of animal remains *. This conclufion, however, is more general than the facts warrant; and, from fome incorrectnefs or ambiguity of language, is certainly more general than he intended. The idea of calcareous rocks, on which he argues throughout his whole theory, is precifely that which is ftated in the preceding article.

Note II. § 6.

Origin of coal.

136. The vegetable origin of coal feems to be fufficiently proved by the reafoning in § 5. and 6.; and that reafoning will appear ftill more fatisfactory, from what is faid at § 28. and 29. concerning the confolidation of this foffil. Dr Hutton has treated both of the matter of coal

K 2   and

---

* Theory of the Earth, vol. i. p. 23.

and of its confolidation, Part. I. Chap. 8. of his Theory of the Earth *.

The notion, however, that coal is of vegetable origin, is not peculiar to this theory, but has been for fome time the prevailing opinion. Buffon fuppofes this mineral to be formed from vegetable and animal fubftances, the oil and fat of which have been converted into bitumen by the action of acids †. A fundamental miftake, however, is committed by this author, and by M. GENSANNE, (author of the natural hiftory of Languedoc), on whofe obfervations he greatly relies, in confidering coal as confifting of bitumen united to earth, thus omitting the only ingredient effential to coal, namely the carbon or charcoal. This may truly be confidered as the effential part, becaufe coal may exift without bitumen, as in the inftance of blind-coal, but not without charcoal.

Another theory of coal, very analogous to Dr Hutton's, is that of ARDUINO, profeffor of mineralogy at Venice, in which he fuppofes it formed from vegetable and animal remains from the land and fea, but chiefly from the latter ‡.

This

---

* Vol. i. p. 558, &c.

† Hift. Nat. des Mineraux, tom. i. p. 429. 4to edit.

‡ Saggio Fifico-mineralogico del Sig. Giov. Arduino; Atti di Siena, tom. v, p. 228, 281, &c.

This theory of coal is contained in Dr Hutton's, in which the animal and vegetable remains muft be fuppofed to come both from the earth and the fea. It feems to be without any good reafon that Arduino confiders the fea as the chief fource of thefe materials. His remarks, however, are very ingenious, and deferving of attention.

Thefe accounts of the origin of coal are all nearly the fame ; it is in what relates to the diftinction between the common coal, in which there is no ligneous ftructure, and thofe varieties of it in which that ftructure is apparent, and again in explaining the confolidation of both, that the theory, laid down here, is peculiar.

137. Some other mineralogifts refer one of the ingredients of coal to the vegetable kingdom, but not the other. Unable to refift the conviction which arifes from the fibrous ftructure of parts of ftrata, and even entire ftrata of coal, they have fuppofed, that wood, which had been fomehow buried in the earth, or perhaps depofited at the bottom of the fea, had become impregnated with bitumen, which laft, however, they confider as of mineral origin. This appears to be the opinion of Lehman, and alfo of fome very late writers. There feems, however, to be hardly lefs reafon for referring the origin of one part of coal to the vegetable or animal kingdom

K 3   than

than another. The two laſt are certainly capable
of furniſhing both the carbonic and bituminous
parts ; and therefore, to derive theſe from different ſources, is at leaſt a very unneceſſary com-
plication of hypotheſes.

138. Another explanation of coal, very different from any of the preceding, has lately been
advanced and ſet up in oppoſition to the Huttonian Theory. Mr Kirwan *, the only mineralogiſt, I believe, who has attempted to derive both
the carbonic and bituminous matter of coal from
the mineral kingdom, diſtinguiſhes between
wood-coal and mineral-coal, and gives a theory
entirely new of the formation of the latter.
Wood-coal is that in which the ligneous ſtructure is ſo apparent, as to leave no doubt of its
vegetable origin ; mineral coal is that in which
no ſuch ſtructure can be diſcovered, and is the
ſame which Dr Hutton derives from the vegetable juices, and other remains, comminuted, diſ-
perſed, carried into the ſea, and there precipitated, ſo as to unite with different proportions of
earth, and to become afterwards mineralized.

Theſe two ſpecies of coal, which the Huttonian theory conſiders as gradations of the ſame
ſubſtance, Mr Kirwan regards as perfectly diſtinct, conſtituting two minerals, of an origin
and

* Geol. Eſſays, eſſay vii. p. 290.

and formation entirely different. He therefore endeavours to afcertain the diftinguifhing characters of each, confidered geologically.

139. But here the leading diftinction, implied in all the reft, that the two kinds of coal are never found in the fame bed, but always in different fituations, and with different laws of ftratification, is exprefsly contradicted by matter of fact. Coal, as is faid above, with its ligneous texture quite apparent, and coal with no fuch ftructure vifible, are often found in the fame feam, are brought up from the fame mine, and united in the fame fpecimen. I have a fpecimen from a bed of coal, in the Ifle of Sky, found under a bafaltic rock, confifting of a ligneous part, which graduates into one in which there is no veftige of a fibrous texture, and in which the furface is fmooth and gloffy, with a fracture almoft vitreous. The upper part of the fpecimen is therefore perfect wood-coal, and the under part perfect mineral-coal, in the language of Mr Kirwan; at the fame time that the tranfition from the one to the other is made by infenfible degrees. This fpecimen, were it perfectly folitary, is fufficient to prove the identity of the two fpecies of coal we are now fpeaking of, and to fhew, that the difference between them is accidental, not effential. The fpecimen, however, is far from being folitary; the number of fimi-

lar

lar appearances is fo great, as hardly to have efcaped the obfervation of any mineralogift.   Mr
Kirwan admits, that wood-coal is often found under bafaltes*; but what is effential to be remarked is, that, in this inftance, we have both the
wood-coal, and the common mineral-coal, lying
under that rock, and the one paffing gradually
into the other.   It appears, indeed, that many of
the facts which Mr Kirwan produces, in treating
of what he calls *carboniferous* foils, are quite inconfiftent with the diftinction he would make
between wood-coal and mineral-coal †.

140. It is, however, true, that there are inftances in which the wood-coal, or foffil-wood,
as it is ufually called, forms entire beds, quite
unconnected with the ordinary coal, and ftratified in fome refpects differently.   Such is the
Bovey coal in Devonfhire, the wood coal in the
north of Ireland, and perhaps the Surturbrandt of
Iceland.   With refpect to the Bovey coal, it does
by no means anfwer to one of Mr Kirwan's remarks, viz. that late obfervations have afcertained,
that no fuch parallelifm of the beds, as in mineral-coal, nor even any diftinct number of ftrata,
is found.   In the Bovey coal, the number of
ftrata is very well defined, by beds of clay regularly interpofed ; but as to the extent of thefe
beds,

---

* Geol. Effays, p. 310.   † *ibid.* p. 311.

beds, the coal having been worked only at one
place, and by an open pit, without any extenfive
fubterraneous excavation, nothing is known with
certainty.

In the Bovey coal too, I muft obferve, though
its beds have the ligneous ftructure very diftinct,
the clay interpofed between thefe beds, which
is but little indurated, contains a great deal of
coaly matter, in the form of thin flakes, inter-
fperfed through it. So far as I know, there are
no mineral veins nor fhifts, nor any bed of indurated ftone, that accompany this coal; fo that,
though one cannot doubt of its vegetable origin,
fome doubt may be entertained concerning
the nature of the mineralizing operations, to
which it has been fubjected. The confideration
of thefe, however, does not belong to the prefent
argument; and the peculiarities of this femi-
mineralized coal, as it may be called, have
nothing to do with the general queftion, whether wood-coal and mineral-coal are the fame
fubftance; about which queftion, if the gradations are properly confidered, I think, no reafonable doubt can remain.

141. One of Mr Kirwan's objections to the
vegetable origin of coal, is founded on this fact,
that there is, in the mufeum at Florence, a cel-
lular fandftone, the cells of which are filled with
genuine mineral coal. " Could this, (adds he)
have

have been originally wood * ?"   The anſwer to the interrogatory propoſed here as a *reductio ad abſurdum*, is, that moſt undoubtedly it may have been wood.   Sandſtone with charred wood, that is, with wood-coal in it, is not an uncommon phenomenon in coal countries.   I have ſeen a ſpecimen of this kind from the Hales Quarry, near Edinburgh, conſiſting of a piece of charred wood, imbedded in ſandſtone ; the wood was much altered, but the remains of its fibrous ſtructure were diſtinctly viſible.   This affords a perfect commentary on the ſpecimen in the Florence cabinet.

142. If then it be granted, as I think it muſt, that the two kinds of coal we have been ſpeaking of are of the ſame origin, it is not very neceſſary to enter on a refutation of Mr Kirwan's theory with reſpect to either of them.   His account of the formation of mineral-coal, however, is ſo ſingular, that it cannot be paſſed over without remark.

Mr Kirwan ſuppoſes, 1mo, That natural carbon was originally contained in many mountains of the granite and porphyritic order, and alſo in ſiliceous ſchiſtus ; and might, by diſintegration and decompoſition, be ſeparated from the ſtony particles.   2do, That both petrol and carbon are often contained in trap, ſince hornblend, which

---

* Geol. Eſſays, p. 321.

which has lately been found to contain carbon, very frequently enters into its compofition.

" My opinion adds he) is, that coal mines, or ftrata of coal, as well as the mountains in which they are found, owe their origin to the difintegration of primeval mountains, either now totally deftroyed, or whofe height and bulk, in confequence of fuch difintegration, are confiderably leffened ; and that thefe rocks, anciently deftroyed, contained moft probably a far larger proportion of carbon and petrol than thofe of the fame denomination now contain, fince their difintegration took place at fo early a period *.

" By the decompofition of thefe mountains, the feltfpar and hornblend were converted into clay ; the bituminous particles, thus fet free, reunited, and were abforbed, partly by the argil, but chiefly by the carbonaceous matter, with which they have the greateft affinity. The carbonic and bituminous particles, thus united, being difficultly mifcible with water, and fpecifically heavier, funk through the moift, pulpy, incoherent argillaceous maffes, and formed the loweft ftratum," &c.

Such is Mr Kirwan's theory of the formation of coal, and nobody I think will difpute the originality of it.

143. To

---

* Geol. Effays. p 328, &c.

143. To enter on a formal refutation of an opinion so loaded with objections, would be a task as irksome as unnecessary. A few observations will suffice.

The notion of the great degradation of mountains, involved in this hypothesis, is the part of it to which I am least disposed to object. But I cannot help reminding Mr Kirwan, that the effects of waste are not supposed less in this, than in Dr Hutton's theory; and that he has assumed the very principle, of which that theory makes so much use, though he has reserved to himself, as it should seem, the right of denying it, when it does not accord with his system. It is indeed worth while to compare what is said concerning the degradation of mountains, in the above quotations, and still more fully in the book itself, with what is advanced concerning their indestructibility, in another passage of the same volume * :

" All mountains are not subject to decay; for instance, scarce any of those that consist of red granite. The stone of which the Runic rocks are formed, have withstood decomposition for two thousand years, as their characters evince," &c.

" Basaltic pillars, in general, bid defiance to decay," &c. He goes on to deny every step of the degradation of land, by which it is wasted, carried

---

* Page 436.

carried into the fea, and fpread out over its bottom, though all thefe are neceffary *poftulata* in
his theory of the formation of coal. One can
be at no lofs about eftimating the value of a
fyftem, in which fuch grofs inconfiftencies make
a neceffary part.

144. The quantity of hornblend and filiceous
fchiftus, neceffary to be decompofed, in order to
produce the coal ftrata prefently exifting, is
enormous, and would lead to an eftimate of what
is worn away from the primeval mountains, far
exceeding any thing that Dr Hutton has fuppofed. It is true, that Mr Kirwan, never at all
embarraffed about preferving a fimilitude between nature as fhe is now, and as fhe was heretofore, lays it down, that the part of the primeval mountains which is worn away, contained
much more carbon than the part which is left
behind. This, however, is an arbitrary fuppofition; and fince, in this fyftem, fuch fuppofitions are fo eafily admitted, why may we not
conceive, in the primeval mountains, a more
copious fource of carbonic matter than hornblend or filiceous fchiftus? We have but to
imagine, that the *diamond* exifted among thefe
mountains in fuch abundance, as to conftitute
large rocks. This ftone being made up of
pure, or highly concentrated carbon, the ada-
mantine fummits of a fingle ridge, by their
decompofition,

decompofition, might afford a carbonic bafis, fufficient for the coal beds of all the furrounding plains.

145. We may alfo object to Mr Kirwan, that the filiceous part of the mountains has not been chemically diffolved; it has been only abraded and worn away. Mechanical action has reduced the quartz to gravel and fand, but has not produced on it any chemical change. The carbon, therefore, could not be let loofe. Experiment, indeed, might be employed, to determine whether the filiceous matter of the fecondary, and of the primary ftrata contains this fubftance in the fame proportion.

Again, a more fatal fymptom can hardly be imagined in any theory, than that, when the circumftances of the phenomena to be explained are *a little* changed, the theory is under the neceffity of changing *a great deal*. Now, this is what happens to Mr Kirwan's theory, in the attempt made to explain by it the ftratum of coal defcribed in the *Annales de Chimie* *, as cutting a mountain of argillaceous ftrata in two, at about three-fourths of its height. This ftratum, Mr Kirwan fays, muft have been formed by *tranfudation* from the fuperior part of the mountain †. Befides that this is a gratuitous fuppofition of a thing,

---

* Tom. xi. p. 272.   † Geol. Effays, p. 338.

thing, without example, it involves in it an abfurdity, which becomes evident the moment the
queſtion is aſked, What occupied the place of
the coal-bed before the tranſudation from the
upper part of the mountain? Has the *liquid
coal*, as it percolated through the upper ſtrata,
expelled any ſubſtance from the place it now
occupies? or has it been powerful enough to
raiſe up, or to float, as it were, the upper part
of the mountain?

The ſituation of this bed of coal is not ſingular, and its formation is eaſily explained on Dr
Hutton's theory. It is part of a ſtratum of coal,
which has been depoſited, like all others, at the
bottom of the ſea; from whence certain cauſes,
of very general operation, have raiſed it up, together with the attending ſtrata: theſe ſtrata have ſince been all cut down, and worn away
by the operations of the ſurface; and the mountain, with the coal ſtratum in the middle of it, is
a part of them which has been left behind. There
is no wonder, that a coal ſtratum ſhould be
found alternating with others, in a mountain,
any more than in the bowels of the earth, and
no more need of a ſeparate explanation *.

146. After

---

* This ſtratum of coal, which is deſcribed by HAS-
SENFRATZ, is remarkable for being in a mountain which
reſts immediately on primary ſchiſtus and granite.

146. After all, it may be afked, for what purpofe is it that fo many incongruous and ill-fupported hypothefes are thus piled on one another? is it only to avoid afcribing the carbonic and bituminous matter of coal to a fubftance in which we know with certainty that fuch matter refides in great abundance, in order to derive it from other fubftances, in which a fubtle analyfis has fhewn, that it exifts in a very fmall proportion? Such reafoning is fo great a trefpafs on every principle of common fenfe, not to fay of found philofophy, that, to beftow any time on the refutation of it, is, in fome degree, to fall under the fame cenfure.

NOTE III. § 7.

Primitive mountains.

147. The enumeration of the different kinds of primary fchiftus, at § 7., is not propofed as at all complete. It will be lefs defective, however, if we add to it *talcofe fchiftus*, and *lapis-ollaris* or *potftone* *.

148. The rocks called here by the name of primary, were firft diftinguifhed, as forming the

basis

---

* Kirwan's Mineralogy, vol. i. p. 155.

bafis of all the great chains of mountains, and
as conftituting a feparate divifion of the mineral
kingdom, by J. G. LEHMAN, director of the
Pruffian mines. See his work, intituled, *Effai
d'une Hiftoire Naturelle de Couches de la Terre* *.
Thefe rocks were regarded by Lehman as parts
of the original *nucleus* of the globe, which had
undergone no alteration, but remained now fuch
as they were at firft created ; and, agreeably to
this fuppofition, he beftowed on them, and on the
mountains compofed of them, the name of primitive. He remarks, neverthelefs, their diftribution into beds, either perpendicular to the horizon, or highly inclined, and the fuper-pofi-
tion of the fecondary, and horizontal ftrata.
However mineralogifts may now differ in their
theories from Lehman, they muft confider this
diftinction as a great ftep in the fcience of geology, and very material to the right arrangement of the natural hiftory of the earth.

149. Several mineralogifts have agreed with
him in the fuppofition, that thefe rocks are a part
of the original ftructure of the globe, and prior to
all organized matter. Of this number is PAL-
LAS † ; and alfo De Luc, who applies the term

L   *primordial*

---

* Tom iii. p. 239, &c. The French tranflation is in
1759, but the original preface is dated at Berlin 1756.

† Obfervations fur la Formation des Montagnes.

primordial to the rocks in queſtion, and conſiders them as neither ſtratified nor formed by
water *. In his ſubſequent writings, however,
he admits their formation from aqueous depoſition, as the Neptuniſts do in general, but holds
them to be more ancient than organized bodies.

150. Pini, profeſſor of natural hiſtory at Mi-
lan, has denied the ſtratification of primitive
mountains, in a memoir on the mineralogy of
St Gothard, and in another on the revolutions
of the globe †. His reaſonings are oppoſed by
Saussure ‡, and are certainly, in many reſpects,
very open to attack. They proceed on a compariſon between the diviſion of rocks, by what
is called the planes of their ſtratification, and
their diviſion by tranſverſe fiſſures; two things,
which he thinks ſo much alike, that they ought
not to be referred to different cauſes; and, as
the one cannot be regarded as the effect of aqueous depoſition, ſo neither ſhould the other. This
is a very fallacious argument, becauſe it confounds two things that are eſſentially different;
and,

---

* Lettres Phyſ. ſur l'Hiſtoire de la Terre, tom. ii.
p. 06.

† Memoria ſulle Rivoluzione del Globo Terreſtre;
Memorie della Societa Italiana, tom. v. p. 222, &c.

‡ Voyages aux Alpes, tom. iv. § 1881.

and, inftead of inquiring about a matter of fact, inquires about its caufe. The truth is, that the difpute has arifen from not diftinguifhing the granite from the fchiftus mountains, and from involving both under the name of primitive. M. Pini feems to be in the right, when he holds the granite of St Gothard to be unftratified ; but it is without any good reafon, that he would extend the fame conclufion to the fchiftus of that mountain. CHARPENTIER, and Sauffure, in his laft two volumes, contend even for the ftratification of granite *.

As the confent, if not univerfal, is very general for the ftratification of the primary fchiftus, and the fact itfelf abundantly obvious, in almoft all the inftances I have ever met with, I have not confidered it as neceffary to enter here into any argument on this fubject.

NOTE IV. § 8.

Primary ftrata not primitive.

151. An account of the facts referred to § 8., may be found in Hutton's Theory, vol. i.

L 2   p. 332,

---

* See NOTE xv. on Granite.

p. 332, &c. To what is there said, of the
shells contained in the primary limestone of
Cumberland, I must add, that I have since had
an opportunity of verifying the conjecture, that
the limestone rock, in which the shells were
found, near the head of *Coniston* Lake, is part of
the same body of strata, where shells were found,
in a quarry between Ambleside and Low-wood.
The limestone of that quarry contains several marine objects ; it is in strata declining about 10°
from the perpendicular, toward the S. E., and
forms a belt, stretching across the country from
N. E. to S. W.

In a quarry where the argillaceous schistus,
on the south side of this limestone belt, is worked
for pavement, are impressions of what I think
may safely be accounted marine objects ; they
have the form of shells, are much indurated,
and full of pyrites. They seem to be of the same
kind with the impressions said to be found in a
slate quarry, near the village of Mat in Switzerland *.

Another spot, affording instances of shells in
primary limestone, is in Devonshire. On the
sea shore on the east side of Plymouth Dock,
opposite to Stonehouse, I found a specimen of
schistose micaceous limestone, containing a shell
of

* Hutton's Theory, vol. i. p. 327.

of the bivalve kind : it was ftruck off from the
folid rock, and cannot poffibly be confidered as
an adventitious foffil.

Now, no rocks can be more decidedly primary than thofe about Plymouth. They confift of
calcareous ftrata, in the form either of marble
or micaceous limeftone, alternating with varieties of the fame fchiftus, which prevails through
Cornwall to the weft, and extends eaftward into
Dartmoor, and on the fea-coaft, as far as the
Berry-head. Thefe all interfect the horizontal
plane, in a line from eaft to weft nearly ; they
are very erect, thofe at Plymouth being elevated
to the north.

Though, therefore, the remains of marine
animals are not frequent among the primary
rocks, they are not excluded from them ; and
hence the exiftence of fhell-fifh and zoophytes,
is clearly proved to be anterior to the formation
even of thofe parts of the prefent land which are
juftly accounted the moft ancient.

152. The rocks which contain fand or gravel,
or which are of a granulated texture, muft alfo be
confidered as carrying in themfelves a teftimony
of the moft unequivocal kind, of their being
derived from the *detritus* and wafte of former
rocks. Now, the fact ftated in the text, concerning fand found in fchiftus, moft juftly accounted primary, might be exemplified by actual

L 3   reference

reference to many fpots on the earth's furfacc. A few fuch will be fufficient in this place.

St Gothard is a central point, in one of the greateft tracts of primary mountains on the face of the earth, yet arenaceous ftrata are found in its vicinity. Between Ayrolo and the Hofpice of St Gothard, Sauffure found a rock, compofed of an arenaceous or granular pafte, including in it hornblend and garnets. He is fomewhat un-willing to give the name *gres* to this ftone, which M. Beffon had done; but he neverthe-lefs defcribes it as having a granulated ftruc-ture *.

Among the moft indurated rocks that com-pofe the mountains of this ifland, many are are-naceous. Thus, on the weftern coaft of Scot-land, the great body of high and rugged moun-tains on the fhores of Arafaig, &c. from Ardna-murchan to Glenelg, confifts, in a great mea-fure, of a granitic fandftone, in vertical beds. This ftone fometimes occupies great tracts; at other times it is alternated with the micaceous, or other varieties of primary fchiftus; it occurs, likewife, in feveral of the iflands, and is a fof-fil which we hardly find defcribed or named by the writers on mineralogy. Much, alfo, of

a

---

* Voyages aux Alpes, tom. iv. § 1822.

a highly indurated, but granulated quartz, is found in feveral places in Scotland, in beds or ftrata, alternated with the common fchiftus of the mountains. Remarkable inftances of this may be feen on the north fide of the ferry of Bala-chulifh, and again on the fea-fhore at Cullen. At the latter, the ftrata are remarkably regular, alternating with different fpecies of fchiftus. At the former, the quartz is fo pure, that the ftone has been miftaken for marble.

Thefe examples are perhaps fufficient; but I muft add, that in the micaceous and talcofe fchifti themfelves, thin layers of fand are often found, interpofed between the layers of mica or talc. I have a fpecimen, from the fummit of one of the higheft of the Grampian mountains, where the thin plates, of a talcky or afbeftine fubftance, are feparated by layers of a very fine quartzy fand, not much confolidated.

The mountain from which it was brought, confifts of vertical ftrata, much interfected by quartz veins. It is impoffible to doubt, in this inftance, that the thin plates of the one fubftance, and the fmall grains of the other, were depofited together at the bottom of the fea, and that they were alike produced from the degradation of rocks, more ancient than any which now exift.

L 4

153. In

153. In the Neptunian fyſtem, as improved by WERNER, an attempt is made to take off the force of fuch inſtances as are produced in § 8, 9, and 151, &c. by diſtinguiſhing rocks, as to their formation, into three different orders, the primitive, the intermediate, and the fecondary, or, to fpeak more properly, into primary, fecondary, and tertiary. The fame mineralogiſt diſtinguiſhes, among the materials of thefe rocks, between what he terms chemical and mechanical depoſites. By mechanical depoſites, are underſtood fand, gravel, and whatever bears the mark of fracture and attrition; by chemical depoſites, thofe which are regularly cryſtallized, or which have a tendency to cryſtallization, and in which the action of mechanical caufes cannot be traced. This diſtinction is founded in nature, and proceeds on real and palpable differences; but the application made of it to the three kinds of ſtrata juſt enumerated, feems by no means entitled to the fame praife.

The primitive rocks contain, it is faid, none but chemical depoſites, and are entirely compofed of them: the intermediate contain a mixture of both, and alfo fome veſtiges of organized bodies: the fecondary conſiſt almoſt entirely of the mechanical, or of the remains of fuch bodies, with little of the chemical. The firſt of thefe, then, are held to contain no mark or veſ-
                                        tige

tige whatfoever of any thing more ancient than themfelves, and are, in the ftricteft fenfe, primeval, or formed of the firft materials, depofited by the immenfe ocean which originally encompaffed the globe.

After them were formed the intermediate, moftly confifting of chemical depofites, but containing alfo fome animal remains, and fome fpoils from the land, fubjected to the various kinds of deftruction, which even then made a part of the order of nature. Thefe rocks, it is alleged, are chiefly argillaceous, are lefs indurated than the primary, and not interfected by veins of quartz.

The fecondary were formed from the remains of the other two, and contain more mechanical depofites than any other.

This fketch of what I underftand to be Werner's opinion concerning the different formation of the ftrata, is chiefly taken from a view of his fyftem, in the *Journal de Phyfique* for 1800.

154. The main objection to the diftinction here made between the primary and the intermediate ftrata, is founded on the facts that have been juft ftated. The fandftone of St Gothard is from a country having every character of a primary one in the higheft perfection. The inftances I have mentioned from the Highlands of Scotland, are from mountains, lefs elevated indeed

indeed than the Alps, but where the rock is micaceous, talcose, or filiceous, in planes erect to the horizon, and interfected by veins of quartz. The fhells from Plymouth are from a rock, that Werner would, I think, admit to be truly primitive. Thofe from the lakes, alfo, are from the centre of a country, occupied by porphyry, fchorl, hornftone-fchiftus, and many others, about the order of which there can be no difpute. It is true, that in this tract there are argillaceous ftrata, of the kind that might be accounted intermediate, were they not interpofed among thofe that are certainly primary ; and this very intermixture fhews, how little foundation there is for the diftinction attempted to be made between the formation of the one and of the other. If there is any principle in mineralogy, which may be confidered as perfectly afcertained, it is, that rocks fimilarly ftratified, and alternated with one another, are of the fame formation.

Hence we conclude, that there is *no order of ftrata yet known*, that does not contain proofs of the exiftence of more ancient ftrata. We fee nothing, in the ftrict fenfe, primitive. It muft be underftood, that what is here faid has no reference to granite, which I do not confider as a ftratified rock, and in which neither the remains of organized bodies, nor fand, have I believe

believe been ever found; though fome inftances will be hereafter mentioned, where granite contains fragments of other ftones, viz. of different kinds of primary fchiftus.

To the inftances of fand involved in primary fchiftus, I might have added many from the rocks of that order on the coaft of Berwickfhire, of which mention is fo often made in thefe Illuftrations; but I wifhed to draw the evidence from thofe rocks that are moft unequivocally primary, and to which the Wernerian diftinction of *intermediate* could not poffibly be applied.

If any one affert, as M. de Luc has done, that fand is a chemical depofite, a certain mode of cryftallization which quartz fometimes affumes, let him draw the line which feparates fand from gravel; and let him explain why quartz, in the form of fand, is not found in mineral veins, in granite, nor in bafaltes, that is, in none of the fituations where the appearances of cryftallization are moft general and beft afcertained.

NOTE V. § 10.

Tranfportation of the materials of the ftrata.

155. The great tranfportation or *travelling* of the materials of the ftrata, fuppofed by Dr Hutton,

ton, has been treated as abfurd by fome of his opponents, particularly De Luc and Kirwan. Thefe philofophers feem not to have obferved, that their own fyftem, and indeed every fyftem which derives the fecondary ftrata from the primary, involves a tranfportation of materials, hardly lefs than is fuppofed in the Huttonian theory, and a degradation of the primeval mountains, in many inftances much greater. To form fome notion of this degradation, it muft be recollected, that the primeval mountains, which furnifhed the materials of the fecondary ftrata in the plains, cannot have ftood in the place now occupied by thefe plains. This is obvious; and therefore we muft neceffarily regard the fecondary ftrata as derived from the primitive mountains which are the neareft to them, and of which a part ftill remains. This part is fufficient to define the bafe of the original mountains; and the quantity of the fecondary ftrata which furround them may help us to make fome eftimate of their height. Let us take, for inftance, the extenfive tract of fecondary country about Newcaftle, where coal mines have been funk through a fucceffion of fecondary ftrata, to the depth of more than a thoufand feet. This fecondary country may be confidered as comprehending almoft the whole of the counties of Northumberland and Durham, and probably as

extending

extending very far under the part of the German Ocean which washes their coasts; and the whole strata composing it must be derived, on the hypothesis we are now considering, from the Cheviot Hills, on one side, and from those in the high parts of Westmoreland and Cumberland on the other, comprehending the Alston-Moor Hills, and the large group of primary mountains, so well known from the sublime and romantic scenery of the *Lakes*. Now, the mountains which stood on this base, had not only to supply the materials for the tract already mentioned, on the east, but had also their contingent to furnish to the plains on the west and north; the Cheviots to Roxburghshire and Berwickshire; the Northumberland mountains to the coal strata about Whitehaven, and along the sea-coast to Lancashire. On the whole, we shall not exceed the truth, if we suppose, that the secondary strata, at the feet of the above mountains, are six or seven times more extensive than the base of the mountainous tract. If then we take the medium depth of these secondary strata to be one thousand feet, it is evident, that the mass of stone which composes them, if it were placed on the same base with the primitive mountains, would reach to the height of six thousand feet. This is supposing the mass to preserve the breadth of its base uniformly to the

the fummit ; but if it be fuppofed to taper, as mountains ufually do, we muft multiply this fix thoufand by three, in order to have the height of thefe primeval mountains, which, therefore, were originally elevated not lefs than eighteen thoufand feet: in height, therefore, they once rivalled the Cordelieras, and are now but poorly reprefented by the hills of Skidaw and Helvellyn. It were eafy to fhew, that this eftimate is ftill below the refult that ftrictly follows from the Neptunian hypothefis ; but it is unneceffary to proceed further, than to prove, that the principle of the degradation of mountains, is involved in that hypothefis to an exceffive and improbable degree ; and that the fupporters of it, have either been guilty of the inconfiftency of refufing to Dr Hutton the moderate ufe of a principle, which they themfelves employ in its utmoft extent, or of not having fufficiently adverted to the confequences of their own fyftem.

156. The formation of fecondary ftrata from the degradation of the contiguous mountains, on clofe examination, is fubject to many other difficulties of the fame kind. Mountains of fecondary ftrata, and nearly horizontal, are found in this ifland of the height of three thoufand feet. Such are Ingleborough, Wharnfide, and perhaps fome others on the weft of Yorkfhire. The whole

whole chain, indeed, for fecondary mountains, is of great elevation. The ftrata are of lime-ftone, and of a very coarfe-grained fandftone, alternating with it. No mountains can more clearly point out, that the ftrata of which they confift were once continued quite acrofs the vallies which now feparate them; and hence, if the materials of thofe ftrata were indeed furnifhed from any contiguous primitive mountains, the latter muft have been, out of all proportion, higher than any mountains now in Britain.

157. Thus, a great degradation of the primitive mountains, and of courfe a great travelling of their materials, is proved to make a neceffary part of the Neptunian theory. The extent of this travelling or tranfportation may be rendered more evident, if we apply a fimilar mode of reafoning to larger portions of the globe. The north-weft of Europe furnifhes us an inftance of a very extenfive tract of fecondary country, comprehending the greater part of Britain, the whole of Flanders and Holland, part of Germany, the northern provinces of France, and probably the bed of the German Ocean, at leaft for a great extent. Within this circle almoft all is fecondary, and on the fides of it all round are placed ridges or groups of primitive mountains, namely, the mountains of Auvergne,

at

at leaft in part, and going round by the eaft, the Alps, the Vofges, the Hartz, the Highlands and Weftern Iflands of Scotland, the hilly coun-tries of Cumberland, Wales and Cornwall. This zone of primitive mountains, on the fuppo-fition of the Neptunifts, muft have rifen up in the form of iflands in the great ocean, that ori-ginally covered the earth, forming a kind of circular Archipelago, including in its bofom a fea, which was from feven to five hundred miles in diameter. Over the whole of this extent, the *detritus* of the above mountains muft have been carried, in order to form the flat in-terjacent countries which are now expofed to our view. Such then, even on their own fuppofi-tion, is the extent to which the Neptunifts muft admit that the materials of the primeval moun-tains were tranfported by the ocean.

158. This tranfportation of materials, may not be fo great as that which is involved in Dr Hutton's theory, but is fuch as fhould make the enemies of his fyftem confider, how nearly the principles they *muft* introduce, agree with thofe that they *would* reject. This is one fact out of many, which fhews, that there is at prefent a much nearer agreement between the fyftems of geology, than between their au-thors.

159. To

159. To these facts, demonstrating the great transportation of fossils in some former conditions of the globe, we may add another, recognised by all mineralogists. The animal *exuviæ* contained in limestone and marble, are often known to belong to seas, extremely remote from the countries where they are now found. In the chalk-beds of England, in the limestones of France, a great proportion of the petrifactions belong to the tropical seas, and appear to have been brought from the vicinity of the equator. Buffon observes, that of the fossil shells found in France, it has been disputed, whether the foreign are not more numerous than the native ; and, though he is himself of opinion that they are not, it is evident that they must bear a considerable proportion to the whole *. In the petrifactions of Monte Bolca, near Verona, where the impressions of fish are preserved between the laminæ of a calcareous schistus, one hundred and five different species have been enumerated, of which thirty-nine are from the Asiatic seas, three from the African, eighteen from those of South, and eleven from those of North America †. Similar observations have been made on the marine plants, and the impressions of vegetables, found in rocks, in different parts of

M   Europe.

---

* Buffon, Théorie de la Terre, art. 8.

† Saussure, Voyages aux Alpes, tom. iii. § 1535.

Europe.   At St Chaumont, near Lyons, is found
an argillaceous fchiftus, covering a bed of coal,
every lamina of which is marked with the impreffions of the ftem, leaf, or other part of fome
plant ; and it happens, fays M. FONTENELLE,
by an unaccountable deftination of nature, that
not one of thefe plants is a native of France.
They are all ferns of different fpecies, peculiar
to the Eaft Indies, or the warmer climates of
America.   Here alfo was found the fruit of a
tree, which grows only on the coafts of Malabar
and Coromandel *.

The fame holds of the bodies of amphibious
animals which now make a part of the foffil
kingdom.   The head and the bones of croco-
diles have been found in the ifland of Shepey,
at the mouth of the Thames ; and the remains
of an animal of the fame fpecies, but of a variety now peculiar to the Ganges, have been
difcovered in the alum rocks on the coaft of Yorkfhire †.   Thefe proofs of the tranfportation of
materials

---

* Mém. de l'Acad. des Sciences, 1718, p. 3. and 287 ;
and 1721, p. 89, &c.

† Phil. Tranf. vol. l. p. 688.   CAMPER denies that the
remains here mentioned belong to the crocodile, or any
amphibious animal, and refers them to the balæna.   He
paffes the fame judgment on thofe foffil bones from St Peter's Mount, near Maeftrich, which have been fuppofed to
belong.

materials by the sea, have the advantage of involving nothing hypothetical, and of being equally addreſſed to the geologiſts of every perſuaſion.

On this ſubjeċt I cannot help obſerving, that
the accurate compariſon of the animal exuviæ
of the mineral kingdom, with their living arche-
types, is not merely a curious inquiry, but is
one that may lead to important conſequences,
concerning the nature and direċtion of the forces which have changed, and are continually
changing, the ſurface of the earth.

160. Theſe remarks I have thought it proper
to add to the proofs of the compoſition of the
preſent from former ſtrata, in order to ſhew, that
the great tranſportation of materials involved in
that ſuppoſition, is not only conformable to the
hypotheſis of the Neptuniſts concerning the ſecondary ſtrata, but is alſo proved by the moſt
direċt evidence, independently of all hypotheſis.
All this reaſoning regards the ancient ſtate of

M 2   the

---

belong to the crocodile ; he looks on them as belonging to
whales, though of an unknown ſpecies. In this Mount, ſo
famous for its petrifaċtions, he finds many ſpecimens of
bones, which he thinks belong to the turtle. Phil. Tranſ.
vol. lxxvi. p. 443. The opinion of an author, ſo well
ſkilled in comparative anatomy, muſt be regarded as of
great weight : if it takes from our argument in one part,
it adds to it in another, and the acquiſition of the turtle
makes up abundantly for the loſs of the crocodile.

the globe. Whether ſuch a travelling of ſtony bodies makes a part of the ſyſtem now actually carrying on, will be conſidered in another place *.

Note vi. § 13.

Mr Kirwan's notion of precipitation.

161. The Neptuniſt who has provided the means of diſſolving the materials of the ſtrata, has only performed half his work, and muſt find it a taſk of equal difficulty to force this power-ful menſtruum to part with its ſolution. Mr Kirwan, aware in ſome degree of this diffi-culty, has attempted to obviate it in a very ſin-gular way. Firſt, he aſcribes the ſolution of all ſubſtances in water, or, in what he calls the chaotic fluid, to their being finely pulveriſed, or created in a ſtate of the moſt minute diviſion. Next, as to the depoſition, the ſolvent being, as he acknowledges, very inſufficient in quantity, the precipitation took place, (he ſays), on that account the more rapidly.

If he means by this to ſay, that a precipitation without ſolution would take place the ſooner the more inadequate the menſtruum was to diſ-ſolve the whole, the propoſition may be true ; but

---

* See Note xix.

but will be of no ufe to explain the cryftallization of minerals, (the very object he has in view),
becaufe to cryftallization, it is not a bare fubfidence of particles fufpended in a fluid, but it is
a paffage from chemical folution to non-folu-
tion, or infolubility, that is required.

If, on the other hand, he means to fay, that the
folution actually took place more quickly, and
was more immediately followed by precipitation,
becaufe the quantity of the menftruum was infufficient, this is to affert, that the weaker the
caufe, the more inftantaneous will be its effect.

Of two propofitions, the one of which is nu-
gatory, and the other abfurd, it is not material to
inquire which the author had in view.

Note VII. § 16.

Compreffion in the mineral regions.

162. It is worthy of remark, that the effects
afcribed to compreffion in the Huttonian Theory, very much refemble thofe which Sir Isaac
Newton fuppofes to be produced in the fun and
the fixed ftars by that fame caufe. " Are not,"
fays he, " the fun and fixed ftars great earths,
vehemently hot, whofe heat is conferved by the
greatnefs of the bodies, and the mutual action

and

and reaction between them, and the light which they emit ; *and whofe parts are kept from fuming away, not only by their fixity, but alfo by the vaft weight and denfity of the atmofpheres incumbent upon them, and very ftrongly compreffing them *."*

163. The fact, of water boiling at a lower temperature under a lefs compreffion, is fufficient to juftify the fuppofition, that bodies may be made by preffure to endure extreme heat, without the diffipation of their parts, that is, without evaporation or combuftion. A further *poftulatum* is introduced in Dr Hutton's theory, namely, that compound bodies, fuch as carbonat of lime, when the compreffion prevents their feparation, may admit of fufion, notwithftanding that the fixed part may be infufible when feparated from the volatile. This affumption is fupported by the analogical fact of the fufion of the carbonat of barytes, as mentioned in the text.

164. In a region where the action of heat was accompanied with fuch compreffion as is here fuppofed, there could be no fire, properly fo called, and no combuftion : this is admitted by Dr Hutton, and it is therefore a fallacious argument which is brought againft his theory, from the impoffibility of fire being maintained

in

---

* Newton's Optics, Query 11.

in the bowels of the earth.   This impoffibility
is precifely what he fuppofes ; and yet Mr Kirwan's arguments are directed, not againft the
exiftence of heat in the interior of the earth,
but againft the exiftence of burning and inflammation.

After taking notice *, that Sauffure had fucceeded, though with extreme difficulty, in melting a particle of limeftone, fo fmall as to be vifible only with a microfcope, " what (adds he)
muft have been the heat neceffary to melt whole
mountains of this matter ?   Judging by all that
we at prefent know of heat, fuch a high degree
could only be produced by the pureft air, acting
on an enormous quantity of combuftible matter.
Now, EHRMAN obferved, that the combuftion
of two hundred and eighty cubic inches of air,
acting on charcoal, was not able to effect the
fufion of one grain of Carrara marble ;   from
whence it is apparent, that all the air in the atmofphere, nor in ten atmofpheres, would not
melt a fingle mountain of this fubftance, of any
extent, even if there were a fufficient quantity
of inflammable matter for it to act upon.   Judging alfo of fubterraneous heat by what we know
of that of volcanoes, no fuch heat exifts : the
higheft they in general produce, is that requi-
fite for the fufion of the volcanic glafs called

M 4   obfidian,

---

* Geol. Effays, p. 453.

obfidian, which Sauffure found not to exceed
115° of Wedgewood; but bafaltine, which requires 140° of Wedgewood, is never melted in
the lavas of Ætna.   How little capable, then,
would volcanic heat be to effect the fufion of
Carrara marble, which, according to the fame
excellent author, would require a heat of upwards of 6300° of Wedgewood, if this pyrometer could extend fo far ?   And in what circumftances does Dr Hutton fuppofe this aftonifhing
heat to have exifted, and even ftill to exift,
under the ocean, in the bowels of the earth,
where neither a fufficient quantity of pure air,
nor of combuftible matter, capable of fuch
mighty effects, can, with any appearance of probability, be fuppofed to exift ; and, without
thefe, fuch degrees of heat cannot even be imagined, without flying into the region of chimeras."

165. Now, this reafoning is not applicable
to Dr Hutton's hypothefis of fubterraneous heat,
becaufe it is grounded on experiments, where
that very feparation of the volatile and fixed
parts takes place, which is excluded in that
hypothefis.   When limeftone or marble is expofed to fuch heat as is here mentioned, or
even to heat of a degree vaftly inferior, the
carbonic gas is expelled, and the body is reduced to pure lime ; from the refractory nature
of which, as we learn from the fact relative

to

to barytes, mentioned above, no conclufion can be drawn as to the infufibility of the fame fubftance, when combined with the carbonic gas. The Carrara marble may require a heat of 6300° of Wedgewood, to melt it in the open air, where the carbonic gas efcapes from it; but under fuch a preffure as would retain this gas, it cannot be inferred, that it might not melt with the heat of a glafs-houfe furnace. In like manner, it may be true, that two hundred and eighty cubic inches of air, acting on charcoal, cannot effect the fufion of one grain of this marble, after its fixed air is driven off from it; but we cannot from thence draw any inference, applicable to a cafe where the carbonic gas is retained, and where the action of heat is independent of atmofpheric air.

Nothing, therefore, can be more inconclufive than this reafoning, as it proceeds on the fuppofition, that Dr Hutton's fyftem admits propofitions, which in fact it exprefsly denies.

166. Of the production and maintenance of heat, in circumftances fo different from thofe of ordinary experience, we can hardly be expected to give any explanation; but we are not entitled, merely on that account, to doubt of the exiftence of fuch heat. Mr Kirwan thinks otherwife: " Judging," he fays, " from all we at prefent know of heat, fuch a high degree of it, (as will melt limeftone), could only be produced by the pureft

rest air, acting on an enormous quantity of combustible matter. Without these, such degrees
of heat cannot even be imagined, without flying into the region of chimeras *."

Now, in the first place, the high degree of
temperature which is here understood, is probably not neceſſary to the purpoſes of mineralization, as has juſt been shewn ; and, in the ſecond place, it is not FIRE, in the uſual ſenſe of
the word, but HEAT, which is required for that
purpoſe ; and there is nothing *chimerical* in ſuppoſing, that nature has the means of producing
heat, even in a very great degree, without the
aſſiſtance of fuel or of vital air. Friction is a
ſource of heat, unlimited, for what we know, in
its extent, and ſo perhaps are other operations,
both chemical and mechanical ; nor are either
combuſtible ſubſtances, or vital air, concerned
in the heat thus produced. So alſo the heat of
the ſun's rays in the focus of a burning glaſs,
the moſt intenſe that is known, is independent
of the ſubſtances juſt mentioned ; and, though
that heat certainly could not calcine a metal,
nor even burn a piece of wood, without oxyge-
nous gas, it would doubtleſs produce as high a
temperature in the abſence as in the preſence
of that gas.

It

---

* Geol. Eſſays, p. 454.

It is true, that it is not by the folar rays that
fubterraneous heat is produced ; but ftill, from
this inftance, we fee, that there is no incongrui-
ty in fuppofing the production of heat to be independent of combuftible bodies, and of vital air.
We are indeed, in all cafes, ftrangers to the origin of heat : philofophers difpute, at this moment, concerning the fource of that which is
produced by burning ; and much more are they
at a lofs to determine, what upholds the light
and heat of the great luminary, which animates
all nature by its influence. If we would form
any opinion on this fubject, we fhall do well
to attend to the fuggeftions of that great philofopher, who was hardly lefs diftinguifhed from
others by his doubts and conjectures, than by
his moft rigorous and profound inveftigations.
" May not great, denfe, and fixed bodies, when
heated beyond a certain degree, emit light fo
copioufly, as, by the emiffion and reaction of
its light, and the reflections and refractions of
its rays within its pores, to grow ftill hotter, till
it comes to a certain period of heat, fuch as is
that of the fun ?   And, are not the fun and fixed ftars great earths, vehemently hot, whofe heat
is conferved by the greatnefs of the bodies, and
the mutual action and re-action between them
and the light which they emit * ?"

167 Some

---

* Newton's Optics, *ubi fuprà.*

167. Some recent experiments, seem to make the suggestions in this query applicable to an opaque body like the earth, as well as to luminous bodies, such as the sun and fixed stars. The radiation of heat, where there is no light, was first rendered probable by the experiments of M. PICTET of Geneva * ; and the only objections to which the conclusions from those experiments seemed liable, are removed by the late very important discoveries of Dr HERSCHEL †. From these it appears, that heat is capable of refraction and reflection, as well as light, so that it is not absurd to suppose, that *the heat of great, dense, and fixed bodies, may be conserved by the grea ness of the bodies, and the mutual action and reaction between them and the heat which they emit.*

The existence of subterraneous heat is still further rendered probable from the researches of MAIRAN, which tend to shew, that there is another source of terrestrial heat besides the influence of the solar rays ‡.

Whatever be the truth with regard to these conjectures, it is certain, that the first and original source of heat is independent of burning. Burning is an *effect* of the concentration of heat ;
and

---

* Essai sur le Feu.

† Phil. Transf. 1800. p. .84.

‡ Mém. de l'Acad. des Sciences, 1765. p. 143.

and though, by a certain reaction, it has the power of continuing and augmenting that heat, it never can be regarded as its primary and material cause. When, therefore, we suppose a source of heat, independent of fire and of burning, we suppose what certainly exists in nature, though we are not informed of the manner of its existence, nor of its place, otherwise than from considering the phenomena of the mineral kingdom.

168. Lastly, we are not entitled, according to any rules of philosophical investigation, to reject a principle, to which we are fairly led by an induction from facts, merely because we cannot give a satisfactory explanation of it. It would be a very unsound view of physical science, which would induce one to deny the principle of gravitation, though he cannot explain it, or even though the admission of it reduces him to great metaphysical difficulties. If indeed a downright absurdity, or inconsistency with known and established facts, be involved in any principle, it ought not to be admitted, however it may seem calculated to explain other appearanes. If, for instance, Dr Hutton held, that combustion was carried on in a region where there was no vital air, we should have said, that he admitted an absurdity, and that a theory founded on such *postulata* was worse than chimerical. But, if the only thing imputable

imputable to him is, that, being led by induction to admit the fufion of mineral fubftances in the bowels of the earth, he has affumed the exiftence of fuch heat as was fufficient for this fufion, though he is unable to affign the caufe of it, I believe it will be found, that his fyftem only fhares in an imperfection, which is common to all phyfical theories, and which the utmoft improvement of fcience will never completely remove.

169. Thus, then, we are led, it muft be allowed, into the *region of hypothefis and conjecture*, but by no means into that of *chimeras*. Indeed, the reproach of flying into the latter region, may be faid to come but ill from one, who has trode fo often the *crude confiftence* of the chaos, and who delights to dwell beyond the boundaries of nature. By fojourning there long, it is not impoffible that the eye may become fo accuftomed to fantaftic forms, that the figures and proportions of nature fhall appear to it deformed and monftrous.

NOTE VIII. § 24.

Sparry ftructure of calcareous petrifactions.

170. When the fhells and corals in limeftone are quoted by mineralogifts, it is not always
considered

confidered in what ftate they are found. In
general, they have a fparry ftructure, very different from that of the original fhell or coral,
of which, however, they retain the figure with
wonderful exactnefs, though probably fometimes altered in fize. Though fparry, they are
often foliated, and preferve their animal, in conjunction with their mineral, texture. Now, this
cryftallization is a mark of fome operation,
quite different from any that can be afcribed
to the water in which thefe bodies had their
origin, and by which they were brought into
their place. They were impervious to water; and it cannot be faid that their fparry
ftructure has been derived from the percolation
of that fluid, carrying new calcareous matter
into their pores. We can account for the
change produced in them, I think, only by
fuppofing them to have been foftened by heat,
fo as to permit their parts to arrange themfelves anew, and to affume the characteriftic
organization of mineral fubftances.

All fhells have not the change effected on
them that is here referred to; thofe in chalk,
for inftance, retain very much their original
form in all refpects. This is what we might
expect from the very different degree of intenfity, with which the mineralizing caufe has
acted on chalk, and on limeftone or marble. In
general, it is in the hardeft and moft confolidated

ted limeſtone, that the marine objects are moſt completely changed into ſpar.

It would be exceedingly intereſting to examine, whether any of the phoſphoric acid remains united to ſhells of either of theſe kinds. We might moſt readily expect it to be united, in a certain degree, to the ſhells that are leaſt mineralized.

This experiment would enable us alſo to appreciate the force of Mr Kirwan's argument againſt the finer marbles, ſuch as the Carrara, containing ſhells *. This argument proceeds on an experiment, mentioned in the *Turin Memoirs* for 1789, from which it appears, that no phoſphoric acid is found in pure limeſtone; and its abſence, Mr Kirwan ſays, cannot be attributed to fuſion, as phoſphoric acid is indeſtructible by heat.

He calls this a demonſtration; but, in order to entitle it to that name, it will be neceſſary, firſt, to prove, that phoſphoric acid exiſts in thoſe limeſtones which evidently conſiſt of ſhells in a mineralized ſtate. If theſe are found without phoſphoric acid, it is evident that the preceding argument fails entirely. If they are found to contain that acid, it will then no doubt afford a probability, though not a demonſtration, that Carrara

---

* Geol. Eſſays, p. 458.

Carrara marble does not directly originate from shells.

That nature has some procefs, by which the above acid is feparated from the earth of bones, and probably alfo from the earth of fhells, is evident from the ftate in which the bones are found in the caves of Bayreuth. Thofe that are the moft recent, and leaft petrified, contain moft of the phofphoric acid. Where the petrifaction has proceeded far, that acid is not found.

171. Among many of the ftrata, fuch a fluidity has prevailed, as to enable fome of the fub-ftances included in them to cryftallize. Calca-reous fpar and filiceous cryftals are often found in ftratified rocks, forming veins of fecretion, or lining clofe cavities, included on all fides by the uncryftallized rock. In the inftances of gneifs, and many fpecies of marble, almoft the whole matter of the ftratum is cryftallized. This union of a ftratified and cryftallized ftructure in the fame fubftance, has a great affinity to that union of the cryftallized with the *organic* ftruc-ture of fhells and corals which has juft been mentioned ; and both are doubtlefs to be refer-red to the fame caufe.

N   Note

NOTE IX. § 31.

Petroleum, &c.

172. According to the theory of coal laid down above, its two chief materials, charcoal and bitumen, being furnished by the vegetable and animal kingdoms, both of the land and of the sea, have formed with one another a new combination, by the action of subterraneous heat; but have also, in some cases, been separated by that same action, where the degree of compression necessary for their union, happened to be wanting. The carbonic part, when thus separated from the bituminous, forms an infusible coal, which burns without flame: the bituminous part, when separated from the carbonic, is found in the various states of naphtha, petroleum, asphaltes, and jet.

The great resemblance of infusible or blind coal, to the residuum obtained by the distillation of bituminous coal; and again, the coincidence of the bitumens just named, with the volatile part, or the matter brought over by such distillation, are strong arguments in favour of this theory. The other facts in the natural history of coal, serve to confirm the same conclusion; but it must be confessed, that what

we

we know of the pure bitumens, except the circumſtance juſt mentioned, is of a more ambiguous nature, and may be reconciled with different
theories. The drops of petroleum contained
within the cavities of the limeſtone, mentioned
at § 31., are however ſtrong facts in confirmation
of Dr Hutton's opinions, and they are furniſhed
by the ſubſtances purely bituminous. A careful
examination would probably make us acquainted
with others of the ſame kind, for limeſtone is very
often the matrix in which petroleum and aſphaltes are contained. The greateſt mine of aſphaltes in Europe, that in the *Val de Travers*, in
the territory of Neufchâtel, is in limeſtone, from
which, though it in ſome places exudes, it is in
general extracted by the application of heat.
The ſtrata for ſeveral leagues are impregnated
with bitumen ; and, if examined with attention, would probably afford ſpecimens ſimilar
to thoſe which have juſt been mentioned.

173. It is a general remark, that, where petroleum is found, on digging deeper, they come
to aſphaltes ; and, at a depth ſtill greater, they
diſcover coal. This probably does not hold invariably ; but it is certain, that moſt of the
fountains of petroleum are in the neighbourhood
of coal ſtrata. Petroleum and aſphaltes are
found in great abundance in Alſace, in a bed of
ſand, between two beds of clay or argillaceous
ſchiſtus.

schistus, and the same country also affords coal *.
This is true likewise of the fossil-pitch of Coal-
Brookdale ; and of the petroleum found in St
Katharine's well, near Edinburgh.   Auvergne †
contains abundance of fossil-pitch, which exudes,
in the warm season, from a rock impregnated
with it through its whole mass.   There are
also coal strata in the same country, not far
distant.

A very satisfactory observation relating to
this subject, has lately been communicated from
a country, with whose natural history we were
till of late entirely unacquainted.   In the Bur-
mha empire, petroleum is dug up in an argillaceous earth, from the depth of seventy cubits.
This argillaceous earth, or schistus, lies under a
bed of freestone ; and under all, about one hundred and thirty cubits from the surface, is a bed
of coal ‡.

174. In the petroleum lake of the Island of
Trinidad, described *Phil. Transf.* 1789, the petroleum evidently exudes from the rock, and is
collected in a variety of springs in the bottom,
after which it hardens, and acquires the consistency

---

* Encyclopédie, mot, *Asphalte.*

† Voyage en Auvergne, par Legrand, tom. i. p. 351.

‡ Asiatic Researches, vol. vi. art. 6. p. 130.

ency of pitch. The manner, therefore, in which petroleum exifts in the ftrata, is very confiftent with the idea of its having been introduced in the form of a hot vapour.

Even amber appears to have fome relation to coal. It is found in the unconfolidated earth in Pruffia and Pomerania; but I am not fure whether this earth is *travelled* or not. In the fame earth where the amber is found, there is often a mixture of coaly matter, which burns in the fire; it is apparently fibrous, and has been confidered as a kind of foffil-wood *.

Thefe circumftances make out a connection between the purer bitumens and ordinary coal; but do not, it muft be acknowledged, eftablifh any thing with refpect to the more immediate relation, fuppofed in this theory to exift between them and blind-coal. It is probable, indeed, that, to difcover any facts of that kind, the natural hiftory of both fubftances muft be more carefully examined; the natural hiftory of blind-coal, in particular, has hitherto been but little attended to.

175. A fact is mentioned by Mr Kirwan, which muft not be regarded as lefs valuable for being adverfe to this theory. It is, that neither petroleum, nor any foffil bitumen, is found in the vicinity of the Kilkenny coal, as might be ex-

N 3   pected,

---

* Buffon, Hift. Nat. des Mineraux, tom. ii. p. 5.

pected, if that coal was deprived of its bituminous part by fubterraneous diſtillation *. This, however, admits of explanation.   Though a general connection, on the above hypotheſis, might be expected between bitumens and infuſible coal, we cannot look for it in every inſtance. The heat which drove off the bitumen from one part of a ſtratum of coal, may only have forced it to a colder part of the ſame ſtratum; and thus, in ſeparating it from one portion of carbonic matter, may have united it to another. Blind-coal may therefore be found where no bitumen has been actually extricated.   In like manner, bitumen may have been ſeparated, where the coal was not reduced to the ſtate of coak, as a part of the bitumen only may have been driven off, and enough left to prevent the coal from becoming abſolutely infuſible.

It ſhould be conſidered too, if the bitumen was really ſeparated, and forced, in the ſtate of vapour, into ſome argillaceous or limeſtone ſtratum, that this ſtratum may have been waſted and worn away long ago, ſo that the bitumen it contained may have entirely diſappeared.   It does not therefore neceſſarily follow, that, wherever we find blind-coal, there alſo we ſhould diſcover ſome of the purer bitumens.

NOTE

---

* Geol. Eſſays, p. 473.

Note x. § 37.

The height above the level of the sea at which the marks of aqueous deposition are now found.

176. We have two methods of determining the *minimum* of the change which has happened to the relative level of the sea and land; or for fixing a limit, which the true quantity of that change muft neceffarily exceed. The one is, by obferving to what height the regular ftratification of mountains reaches above the prefent level of the fea; the other is, by determining the greateft height above that level, at which the remains of marine animals are now found. Of thefe two criterions, the firft feems preferable, as the fact on which it proceeds is moft general, and leaft fubject to be affected by accidental caufes, or fuch as have operated fince the formation of the rocks. The refults of both, however, if we are careful to felect the extreme cafes, agree more nearly than could have been expected.

177. The mountain Rofa, in the Alps, is entirely of ftratified rocks, very regularly difpofed,

N 4

and

and nearly horizontal *.   The higheft fummit of this mountain is, by Sauffure's meafurement, 2430 toifes, or 14739 Englifh feet, above the level of the fea, or lower than the top of Mont Blanc only by 20 toifes, or 128 feet †.   This is, I believe, the higheft point on the earth's furface, at which the marks of regular ftratification are certainly known to exift; for though, by the account of the fame excellent mineralogift, Mont Blanc itfelf is ftratified, yet, as the rock is granite, the ftratification vertical, and fomewhat ambiguous, it is much lefs proper than Mont Rofa for afcertaining the limit in queftion.

178. Again, in the new continent, we have an inftance of fhells contained in a rock, not much lower than the fummit of Mont Rofa. This is one defcribed by Don ULLOA, near the quickfilver mine of Guanca Velica, in Peru. The height at which a fpecimen of thefe fhells, given by Ulloa to M le GENTIL, was found, was 2122⅓ toifes, or 14190 feet Englifh, above the level of the fea ‡.   This height agrees with the preceding, within 549 feet, a quantity comparatively fmall.

179. The

---

* Voyages aux Alpes, tom. iv. § 2138.

† Ibid. § 2135.

‡ See Hift. Acad. des Sciences, 1770. Phyf. Générale, No. 7.

179. The laft of the facts juft mentioned is curioufly commented on by Mr Kirwan. As he has proved, he fays, that the mountains higher than 8500 feet were all formed before the creation of fifh, it follows, that the fhells found at Guanca-Velica, muft have been carried there by the deluge *. Now, without objecting to the proof here referred to. (though it feems very open to objection), it is fufficient to remark, that, if the fhells at Guanca Velica were carried there by the deluge, or any other caufe that operated after the formation of the rock of which the mountain confifts, they can make no part of that rock, but muft lie, like other adventitious foffils, loofe and detached on the furface, or at moft externally agglutinated to the ftone. This, however, is certainly not the fact ; for, in the account juft quoted, we read, that Don Ulloa told M. le Gentil, " qu'il avoit détaché ces coquilles d'un banc fort épais." This feems plainly to indicate, that the fhells were included in a bed of rock. But, granting that the expreffion is a little ambiguous, on turning to the *Mémoires Philofophiques* of the fame author, the difficulty is completely removed, and it is made evident, that thefe fhells are in fact integrant parts of the rock. " On voit dans ces montagnes-là, (about Guanca-

* Geol. Effays, p. 54,

Guanca-Velica, and particularly at that in which
is the quickſilver mine), des coquilles entières,
petrifiées et enfernıées au milieu de la roche,
que les eaux de pluie mettent à decouvert.   Ces
coquilles font corps avec la pierre ; mais malgré
cela, on remarque que la partie qui fut coquille,
ſe diſtingue par la couleur, la ſtruͨture, la qua-
lité de la matière de tout autre corps pierreux
qui l'enferme, et du maſſif qui s'eſt fixé entre
les deux ecailles *," &c. He goes on to ſay,
that one can diſtinguiſh marks of theſe ſhells
having been worn, before they were included in
the ſtone.

180. Thus it appears, that whatever proof
any foſſil-ſhell affords, that the rock in which
it is found was formed under the ſea, the
ſame is afforded by the foſſil-ſhells of Guanca Velica ; and we are, therefore, perfeͨtly entitled to conclude, that the relative level of
the ſea and land has changed, ſince the formation of the latter, by more than 14000 feet.
The height aſſumed in § 37. is therefore much
under the truth ; and the water, for which the
Neptuniſts muſt provide room in ſubterraneous
caverns, might very well have been ſtated at
more

---

* Mém. Philoſophiques de Don Ulloa, Diſcours xvi.
vol. i. p. 364.

more than a five-hundredth part of the whole mass of the earth.

Thus also the argument by which the Neptunists would connect the creation of fish with the beginning of the secondary mountains, falls entirely to the ground. Indeed, it is strange that Mr Kirwan should have supposed it possible, that the shells in question were loose and unconnected with the rock, and had continued so, ever since the deluge, in such elevated ground, where the torrents wear and cut down the mountains with unexampled violence, and have hollowed out *Quebradas* so much deeper and more abrupt than the glens or vallies among other mountains. He had not, I believe, seen the passage I have quoted from Ulloa ; but the circumstances did not warrant the shells in question to be regarded as extraneous and adventitious fossils. A geologist should have known better than to suppose this possible. When we see VOLTAIRE ascribing to accidental causes the transportation of those shells which he had been told were often found among the Alps, we can excuse in a Poet and a Wit, that ignorance of the facts in mineralogy, which concealed from him the extreme absurdity of his assertion ; but when a Chemist or Mineralogist talks and reasons in the same manner, we cannot consider him as entitled to the same indulgence.

NOTE

Note XI. § 42.

Fracture and dislocation of the strata.

181. The greatest part of the facts relative to the fracture and dislocation of the strata, belongs to the history of veins. The instances of *slips*, where no new mineral substance is introduced between the separated rocks, are what properly belong to this place. The frequency of these, and their great extent, are well known wherever mines have been wrought. In some of them no opening is left, but the slipped strata remain contiguous; in other cases, there is introduced an unconsolidated earth, often a clay, which may be supposed to have come from above, and very probably to have been carried down by the water. In some such cases, however, there are not wanting appearances, which show the matter in the slip to have been forced up from below, as we find it to contain substances which could not have come from the surface *.

182. A

---

* Unconsolidated earth contained between the sides of a rock that has slipped, is frequent in Cornwall, and is called a *Fleukan*.

182. A very remarkable fact of this kind occurred not long ago, in digging the Huddersfield
canal in Yorkſhire ; and a very diſtinct account
of it is given in the *Philoſophical Tranſactions*,
by the engineer who directed the work.   In
carrying a tunnel into the heart of a hill, the
miners came to what is called in the deſcription
a *fault*, *throw*, or *break*, or what we have here
called a ſhift, which was filled with *ſhale* ſet on
edge, mixed with ſofter earth, and in ſome places with ſmall lumps of coal.   The fault or
ſpace filled with theſe materials, was in general
about four yards broad, and lay nearly in the
direction of the tunnel, ſo that a conſiderable
extent of it was viſible.   Beſide the ſhale, it
contained a *rib* of limeſtone, about four feet
thick, which run parallel to the ſides of the *fault*,
and about four feet from the ſouthern margin
of it.   On each ſide of this rib were found balls
of limeſtone, promiſcuouſly ſcattered, and of various ſizes, from an ounce to one hundred pounds
weight.   The balls, when broken, were found
to contain ſome pyrites near their edges ; they
were not perfectly globular, but flattened on the
oppoſite ſides, and ſimilar to one another *.
At the time when the account was written, about
ſeventy yards of the *rib* had been diſcovered.

183. Now,

---

* Phil. Tranſ. 1796. p. 350.

183. Now, it is certain, that neither this rib of limeſtone, nor the balls that accompanied it, can have come from above, as there is no lime-ſtone within twenty miles of the place where they were found. They muſt, therefore, have been forced up from below, and no doubt be-long to ſome limeſtone ſtrata, which lie there at a great depth under the ſurface. The length of this fragment of rock, which, from the ac-count, one muſt ſuppoſe to have been entire, conveys no mean idea, either of the intenſity or regularity of the force by which it was brought into its preſent ſituation. In veins, it is not un-common to meet with ſtones that appear to have come from a greater depth : but this is probably the moſt remarkable inſtance of the ſame phe-nomenon, which has appeared in a mere ſlip, and none, I think, can ſpeak a language leſs liable to be miſunderſtood.

184. I ſhall here mention another mark of violent fracture, that has been obſerved in rocks of breccia or pudding-ſtone, which, though not of the ſame kind with the preceding, and of a nature quite peculiar, belongs rather to this place than any other. In rocks of the kind, juſt mentioned, it ſometimes happens, that con-ſiderable portions are ſeparated from one ano-ther, as if by a mathematical plane, which had cut right acroſs all the quartzy pebbles in its way.

way. None of the pebbles is drawn out of its
focket, that is, out of the cement that furrounds
it, but is divided in two with a very fmooth and
even fracture. The pebbles, in the inftances
which I have feen, were of quartz, and other
fpecies of primary and much indurated rock.

Lord WEBB SEYMOUR and I obferved pudding-ftone rocks, exhibiting inftances of this
fingular kind of fracture, near Oban, in Argyle-
fhire, about three years ago. The phenomenon
was then entirely new to us both ; but I have
fince met with an inftance of the fame kind in
Sauffure's laft work. As the fact is of fo particular a kind, I fhall ftate it in his own words :
The place was on the fea fhore, near the little
town of Alaffio, between Nice and Genoa.

" En paffant entre ces blocs de breche, j'ad-
mirai quelques-uns d'entr'eux, d'une grandeur
confidérable, et taillés en cubes, avec la plus
parfaite régularité. Il y avoit ceci de remar-
quable, c'eft que l'action de la pefanteur, qui avoit
taillé ces cubes en rompant leurs couches, avoit
coupé tous les cailloux des breches à fleur de la
furface de la pierre, auffi nettement que fi c'eût
été une maffe molle qu'on eût tranchée verti-
calement avec un rafoir. Cependant parmi ces
cailloux, la plupart calcaires, il s'en trouvoit de
très durs, de petrofilex, par exemple, même de
jade,

jade, qui étoient tranchées tout auffi nettement
que les autres *."

185. This defcription is no doubt accurate,
though it involves in it fomething of theory, viz.
that the fracture was made by the weight of
the ftone.   This may indeed be true ; the operation probably belongs altogether to the furface, and is one with which the powers of the
mineral regions are not directly concerned.   The
phenomenon, however, appears to me, on every
fuppofition, very difficult to explain.   In the fpecimen which I brought from Oban, the fmalleft
pieces of ftone are cut in two, as well as the largeft. The confolidation and hardnefs of the mafs
are very great, and the connection of the different fragments fo perfect, that it is no wonder the
whole fhould break as one ftone.   But ftill, that
the fracture fhould be fo exactly in one plane,
and without any fhattering, is not a little enigmatical ; if it is indeed a fracture, it muft be the
confequence of an immenfe impulfe, very fuddenly communicated.

Note

* Voyages aux Alpes, tom. iii. § 1371.

Note xii. § 43.

Elevation and inflexion of the strata.

186. The evidence of the different formation of the primary and secondary strata, and of the changes which the former have undergone, is best seen at the points where those strata come into contact with one another. Dr Hutton was not the first who observed these junctions, though the first who rightly interpreted the appearances which they exhibit. He has mentioned observations of this sort by De Luc on the confines of the Hartz ; by the author of the *Tableau de la Suisse*, at the pass of Yetz ; by Voight, in Thuringia ; and Schreiber, at the mountain of Gardette *.

The leading facts to be remarked, are,

i. The vertical or very upright position of the primary or lower strata.

ii. The superstratification of the secondary, in a position nearly horizontal, so as to be at right angles to those on which they rest.

iii. The interposition of a breccia between them ; or, as happens in many cases, the transition of the lowest of the secondary beds into a

O   breccia,

---

* Theory of the Earth, vol. i. from p. 410. to 453.

breccia, containing fragments fometimes worn, fometimes angular, of the primary rock.

This laſt is a phenomenon extremely general, and all our fubfequent information confirms Dr Hutton's anticipations concerning it. " It will be very remarkable," he fays, " if fimilar appearances, (fuch as thofe of the breccia defcribed by Voight), are always found upon the junction of the Alpine with the level countries *." Sauffure, in a part of his work, not publifhed when Dr Hutton wrote this paffage, has atteſted the generality of the faƈt with refpeƈt to the whole Alps, from the Tyrol to the Mediterranean : " Un fait que l'on obferve fans aucune exception, ce font les amas de débris, fous la forme de blocs, de breches, de poudingues, de grés, de fable, ou amoncelés, et formant des montagnes, ou des collines, difperfée fur le bord exterieur, ou même dans les plains qui bordent la chaine des Alpes †."

This paffage is perfeƈtly decifive as to the generality of the faƈt, that the Alps, from the Tyrol to the Mediterranean, are bordered all round by pudding-ſtones or breccias. At the fame time, it is neceffary to remark, that M. Sauffure, by enumerating loofe blocks and fand, along with pudding-ſtones, breccias and grit, confounds together things which are extremely different, and which

---

* Theory of the Earth, vol. i. p. 448.

† Voyages aux Alpes, tom. iv. § 2330.

which have had their origin at periods extremely
remote from one another. The confolidated
rocks of breccia, pudding-ftone and grit, though
they are indications of wafte, have received
their prefent character at the bottom of the fea :
the loofe blocks of ftone, the fand and gravel, on
the other hand, are the effects of the wafte now
going forward on the furface of the land, and
are the materials out of which rocks of the three
kinds juft mentioned may hereafter be compofed.
If fo fkilful a mineralogift as Sauffure is guilty
of fuch inaccuracy, it muft be afcribed to the
confufion neceffarily arifing from the fyftem
which he followed, and not to his own want of
difcrimination.

187. The fame phenomenon, of a breccia cir-
cumfcribing the primary mountains, is met with
in Scotland ; and the Grampians, wherever they
are bounded by fecondary ftrata, whether on
the fouth or north, afford examples of it. The
breccia generally confifts of the fragments of the
primary rock, moft commonly rounded, but
fometimes alfo angular, united by a cement of
fecondary formation, and the whole difpofed in
horizontal beds. It was on the conftancy of this
accompaniment of the primary ftrata, and on
the great quantity of highly polifhed gravel often included in thefe breccias, that Dr Hutton
grounded the hypothefis of the double raifing

O 2   up

up and letting down of the ancient ftrata. See § 43.

188. As the fpots where the primary and fe-condary rocks may be feen in contact with one another are of great importance in geology, and prefent to the fenfes the moft ftriking monuments of the high antiquity and great revolutions of the globe, it may be ufeful to point out fuch of them as have been obferved in this ifland. To thofe which Dr Hutton has defcribed, I have a few more to add, the refult of fome geological excurfions, which I made in company with the Right Honourable Lord WEBB SEYMOUR, to whofe affiftance I have been much indebted in the profecution of thefe inquiries.

189. The moft fouthern junction which we obferved is at Torbay, where the ancient fchiftus which prevails along the coaft, from the Land's End to that point, receives a covering of red horizontal ftandftone, the fame which compofes the greater part of Devonfhire. The fpot where the immediate contact is vifible, is on the fhore, a little to the fouth of Paynton; and one circumftance, which among many others ferves to diftinguifh the different formation of the two kinds of rock, is, that the fchiftus, which is elevated here at an angle of about 45°, is full of quartz veins, which veins are entirely confined

fined to it, and do not, in as far as we could obferve, penetrate into the fandftone, in a fingle
inftance. It is probable, that on the north fhore
of the bay, the fame line of junction is vifible :
we faw it at Babicomb Bay, ftill more to the
northward.

190. From this place, the fecondary ftrata of
different kinds prevail without interruption,
along the coaft of the Britifh Channel, and of
the German Ocean, as far as Berwick upon
Tweed, and for fome miles beyond it. The
fea-coaft then interfects a primary ridge, the
Lammermuir Hills, which traverfes Scotland
from eaft to weft, uniting, near the centre of the
country, with the metalliferous range of Lead-
hills, and afterwards with the mountains of Galloway. The fection which the fea-coaft makes
of the eaftern extremity of this ridge, is highly
inftructive, from the great difturbance of the
primary ftrata, and the variety of their inflexions. The junction of thefe ftrata with the
fecondary, on the fouth fide, is near the little
fea-port of Eyemouth, but the immediate contact is not vifible.

On the north fide of the ridge, the junction is
at a point called the *Sictar*, not far from Dun-
glafs, the feat of Sir James Hall, Baronet. By
being well laid open, and diffected by the working of the fea, the rock here difplays the relation between the two orders of ftrata to great

O 3 advantage.

advantage. Dr Hutton himſelf has deſcribed this junction; *Theory of the Earth*, vol. i. p. 464.

191. From the point juſt mentioned, the ſecondary ſtrata continue as far as Stonehaven, where the ſouthern chain of the Grampian mountains is interſected by the ſea-coaſt. Here a great maſs of pudding-ſtone appears to lie on the primary ſtrata, but their immediate contact has not been obſerved.

192. Going along the coaſt toward the north, the next junctions which we ſaw were on the ſhore, one near Gardenſton, and another near Cullen, in Banff-ſhire. The latter is very diſtinct; it is about a mile to the weſtward of the rocks called *The Three Kings*, where a red ſandſtone, the lower beds of which involve much quartzy gravel, lies horizontally upon very regular, upright, and highly indurated ſtrata. Some of theſe ſtrata are micaceous, and others of the granulated quartz, mentioned in § 152.

193. This laſt is, I believe, the moſt northern junction which has been obſerved in our iſland. The weſtern coaſt furniſhes ſeveral more, which however are not all viſible. The line of ſeparation, between the primary ſchiſtus of the Grampians and the ſandſtone which covers it, is interſected at its weſtern extremity by the Frith of Clyde, not far from Ardencaple in Dunbartonſhire. The two kinds of ſtone can be

traced

traced within a few yards of each other, but not to the actual contact : the beds of fandftone neareft the fchiftus form as ufual a breccia, loaded with fragments of the primary rock. The fecondary rock, which begins here, continues for about fifty miles fouth, to Girvan in Ayrfhire, where the primary fchiftus again rifes up, but is not feen in contact with the fecondary. It extends to the Mull of Galloway and the fhores of the Solway Frith.

The Ifle of Arran, however, not far diftant from this part of the coaft, contains a junction at its northern extremity, where fecondary ftrata of limeftone lie immediately on a primary micaceous fchiftus. This is defcribed by Dr Hutton, and was the firft phenomenon of the kind which he had an opportunity of examining *. The junction is vifible but at one fpot, and is not feen fo diftinctly as in fome of the inftances juft mentioned ; but the great quantity of pudding-ftone near it, renders it more interefting than it would be otherwife. As the greater part of this little ifland is furrounded by fecondary ftrata, other junctions might be expected to be vifible.

194. On the coaft of England and Wales, from the Solway Frith to the Land's End, though there are feveral alternations from fecondary to primary

O 4 mary

---

* Theory of the Earth, vol. i. p. 429.

mary ſtrata, I know not that any of them have been obſerved. At St Bride's Bay, in Pembrokeſhire, the primary and ſecondary ſtrata are ſeen very near their junction ; but the precſe line I believe is not viſible. The coal-pits in the ſecondary ſtrata, approach here within a few hundred yards of the primary. The ſecondary ſtrata which commence at this place, occupy both ſides of the Briſtol Channel, and meet the Corniſh ſchiſtus, which extends acroſs the north of Devonſhire to the Quantock Hills, in a line that may be looked for on the ſea coaſt, ſomewhere between Watchett and Minehead.

195. Beſides the ſea-coaſt, the beds of rivers may be expected to afford information on this ſubject. To the inſtances I have mentioned, I have accordingly two others from the inland country to be added. One of them is from the river Jed, a little way above Jedburgh, where the ſecondary ſtrata are ſeen lying horizontally on the primary, a ſection of both being made by the bed of the river. The phenomena here are very diſtinct, and ſtrongly marked : Dr Hutton has deſcribed and repreſented them in a plate *. He has mentioned another junction, not far from this, which he ſaw in the Tiviot. Both theſe belong to the ſame primary ridge with the Siccar Point.

196. I

---

* Theory of the Earth, vol. i. p. 430.; alſo plate 3.

196. I fhall mention only one other, which was difcovered by Lord Webb Seymour and myfelf, at the foot of the high mountain of Ingleborough, in Yorkfhire. As we went along the Afkrig road from Ingleton, about a mile and a half from the latter, an opening appeared in the fide of the hill, on the right, about one hundred yards from the road, formed by a large ftone, which lay horizontally, and was fupported by two others, ftanding upright. On going up to the fpot, we found it was the mouth of a fmall cave, the ftone lying horizontally, being part of a limeftone bed, and the two upright ftones, vertical plates of a primary argillaceous fchiftus. The limeftone bed, which formed the roof of the cave, was nearly horizontal, declining to the fouth-eaft ; the fchiftus nearly vertical, ftretching from north-weft by weft, to fouth-eaft by eaft. The fchiftus, though clofe in contact with the limeftone, feemed to contain nothing calcareous, and did not effervefce with acids in the flighteft degree.

As this cave is at the foot of Ingleborough, a cold wind, 24° below the temperature of the external air, which iffued from the mouth of it, might very well be fuppofed to come from the inmoft receffes of that mountain. Ingleborough, which confifts entirely of ftrata of limeftone and grit, nearly horizontal, and alternating with one another, rifes to the height of 1800 or 2000 feet above

above the ſpot where we now ſtood. This, I believe, is the greateſt thickneſs of ſecondary ſtrata
that has ever been obſerved incumbent on the
primary, and it is therefore a geological fact
highly deſerving of attention. The country all
round, to a very great extent, is compoſed of
limeſtone, with a few beds of grit interpoſed,
and forming, beſide Ingleborough, ſome other
high mountains, ſuch as Wharnſide and Penni-
gant, all reſting, it is probable, on the ſame
foundation.

At the ſpot juſt deſcribed, no breccia appeared to be interpoſed between the primitive and
ſecondary rock; but we found a breccia at another point of the ſame junction, not far diſtant. This was at a caſcade, in the river
Greata, called Thornton Force, about two miles
and a half from the place juſt mentioned. The
Greata here precipitates itſelf from a horizontal rock of limeſtone; and, after a fall of a-
bout eighteen or twenty feet, is received into
a baſon which it has worked out in the primary ſchiſtus. This ſchiſtus is in beds almoſt perpendicular; it exactly reſembles that
which has juſt been deſcribed, and ſtretches
nearly in the ſame direction. On the ſouth ſide
of the river a breccia was ſeen, lying upon the
ſchiſtus, or rather, it might be ſaid, that the
loweſt beds of limeſtone contained in them many rounded fragments of ſtone, which, on compariſon,

parifon, refembled exactly the fchiftus underneath. The primary rock itfelf is here feven or
eight hundred feet above the level of the fea.

The fame fchiftus, fomewhat lower down the
valley, and nearer to Ingleton, appears in large
quantities, and is quarried for flate. Here, however, the immediate junction of the limeftone
and fchiftus does not appear.

I have dwelt longer on the defcription of thefe
appearances than on any others of the fame kind,
becaufe, from the great mafs of fecondary ftrata
which here covers the primary, the circumftances are fuch as we cannot expect to fee very
often exemplified.

197. The Lakes of Cumberland are much vifited
by travellers ; and it may be worth remarking,
on that account, that, as the fite of thefe lakes
is a patch of primary country, bounded on all
fides by fecondary, fo, in the rivers that run
from the lakes, fuch junctions as we are now
treating of may be expected to be found. Under Dun-Mallet, on the fide toward Ulles Water, we obferved a breccia, which was in horizontal layers, and feemed to lie on the primary
fchiftus, fo that the whole hill is perhaps a piece
of more indurated breccia, or fecondary rock,
which has refifted the wearing and wafhing
down of the rivers better than the reft.

198. After afcertaining the fact of the difturbance of the ftrata, and their removal from their
original

original pofition, it is of confequence to inquire into the direction of the force by which thefe changes have been produced. Now, if the difturbed or elevated ftrata, were every where in planes, without bending or finuofity, it might perhaps be hard to determine, whether that force had acted in the direction of gravity, or in the oppofite. Either fuppofition would account for the appearances ; and, as gravity is a known force, providing we can find fome place fit to receive the matter impelled downward by it, its action would furnifh the moft probable folution of the difficulty.

It is on this principle that the Neptunian fyftem proceeds, imagining, that certain great caverns or vacuities having been opened in the interior of the globe, a great part of the waters which formerly covered its furface, retired into them, and much of the folid rock alfo funk down at the fame time. In this way, one extremity of a ftratum has been elevated, while the other has been depreffed, and a certain inclination to the horizon has been given to the whole of it. Thus one caufe ferves two purpofes ; the vacuities in the interior of the earth account, both for the depreffion of the fea, and the elevation of the land ; and the Neptunifts, if the phenomena were all fuch as have been now ftated, might boaft of a felicity of explanation, not very ufual in their fyftem.

                                                    But

But this appearance of fuccefs vanifhes, when the elevation and difturbance of the ftrata are more minutely examined, and are found to include waving and inflexion, in a great variety of forms. It then becomes evident, that the beds of rock, at the time when they were difturbed from their horizontal pofition, had not their prefent hardnefs and rigidity, but were, in a certain degree at leaft, foft and flexible. Without thefe qualities, they could not have received, as they have often done, the curvature of a circle, not many feet, nay, not many inches, in diameter ; nor could they have been bent into fuperficies, with their curvature in oppofite directions, fo that the fame furface is in one part convex, and in another concave, on the fame fide, with a line of contrary flexure interpofed. Thefe are appearances, not reconcilable with the mere falling in, and breaking down of indurated rocks.

199. The inflexions and wavings that we are here fpeaking of, though not peculiar to the primary ftrata, are found moft frequently among them, and are perfectly familiar to every one who has travelled among mountains with any view to the ftudy of geology. The following are a few inftances of this phenomena, out of a great number which might be produced.

Sauffure,

Sauffure, in defcribing the rout from Geneva to Chamouny, mentions many remarkable in-ftances of the bending of the ftrata, and parti-cularly where the fmall ftream of Nant d'Ar-penaz forms a cafcade, by falling over the face of a perpendicular limeftone rock. The ftrata of this rock are bent into circular arches, ex-tremely regular, and with their concavity turned to the left. What deferves particularly to be remarked, is, that a mountain behind the caf-cade has its ftrata bent in a direction oppofite to the former, or with their concavity to the right. There is no doubt that the ftrata of both rocks are the fame, fo that a vertical fection of them would give a curve, in the figure of an S *. Thefe circumftances are mentioned by Sauffure, and from them we may infer this other proper-ty of thefe ftrata, that their fection by a hori-zontal plane, muft exhibit a fyftem of ftraight lines, probably all parallel to one another.

The fame mineralogift defcribes the calcareous ftrata which compofe the mountain Axenberg, on the fide of the Lake of Lucerne, as having from top to bottom of the mountain the form of the letter S compreffed (*écrafée*), with their curva-ture in fome places very great. Thefe inflexions

---

* Voyages aux Alpes, vol. i. § 472.; alfo, Theory of the Earth, vol. ii. p. 30.

ions are repeated several times, and often in contrary directions; the layers are sometimes broken, where their curvature is greatest *.

On the side of the same lake, is another instance of bent strata, in a mountain, of which the beds are horizontal in the lower part, but are bent at one end upwards, in the form of the letter C. The horizontal part is of great extent, and the rock is also calcareous †.

The *Montagne de la Tuile*, near Montmelian, receives its name from the beds of rock being incurvated in form of a tyle ‡. Among secondary mountains, the same kind of phenomena are observed, though less frequently, and with less variety of inflexion. The chain of Jura is secondary, and the beds which compose it are of limestone, or of grit: they are bent in such a manner, that in a transverse section of the mountain, each layer would have the figure of a parabola §.

200. The Pyrenees furnish abundance of phenomena of the same kind, as we learn from the *Essai sur la Mineralogie des Pyrénées.* The

calcareous

---

* Voyages aux Alpes, tom. iv. § 1935.

† *Ibid.* § 1937.

‡ *Ibid.* vol. iii. § 1182, and plate i.

§ *Ibid.* tom. 1. § 334.

calcareous ftrata of the valley of Afpe, reprefented plate v. of that work, deferve particularly to be remarked.

201. Our own ifland abounds with examples
of the bending and inflexion of the ftrata, efpecially the primary, and many of them very much
refembling thofe in the Alpes and Pyrenees.
On the top of the mountain of *Ben-Lawers*, in
Perthfhire, there is a rock, the face of which
exhibits a fection of a great number of thin
equidiftant layers, bent backwards and for-
wards, like thofe defcribed by Sauffure; and
this unequivocal proof of the rock having
once exifted in the ftate of a flexible and
tenacious pafte, is rendered more ftriking, by
the great elevation of the fpot, and the ruggednefs and induration, both of the ftone itfelf, and of every thing that furrounds it. Many other mountains in this tract confift of a
fchiftus, which is talcofe rather than micaceous, and fubject, in a remarkable degree, to
the fort of finuofity and inflexion here treated
of.

The appearances of the primary ftrata on the
coaft of Berwickfhire, have been already mentioned, as affording much valuable inftruction
in geology. They alfo exemplify the waving
and inflexion of the ftrata on a large fcale, and
with great variety. A fection of fome of them

is

is given by Dr Hutton, in his *Theory of the Earth*, vol. i., from a drawing made by Sir James Hall. The nature of the curve fuperficies into which the fchiftus is bent, is the better underftood from this, that, befides tranfverfe fections from north to fouth, the deep indentures which the fea has made, and the projecting points of rock, exhibit many longitudinal fections, in a direction from eaft to weft.

202. The dock-yards at Plymouth are in feveral places cut out of a folid rock of primary fchiftus, fingularly incurvated. The inflexions are feen there to great advantage, being exhibited in three fections, at right angles to one another, tranfverfe, longitudinal and horizontal.

203. From thefe inftances, to which it were eafy to add many more, two conclufions may be drawn. The firft of thefe is very obvious, viz. that the ftrata muft have been pliant and foft when they acquired their prefent form. The bending of an indurated bed of ftone into an arch of great curvature, and without fracture, as in the preceding examples, is a phyfical impoffibility. Sauffure has indeed obferved a fracture to accompany the bending, in one or two cafes; but it is an uncommon phenomenon, and, where it happens, muft no doubt be underftood to indicate an imperfect flexibility. Now, if it be granted that the ftrata were at any time

P   foft

foft and flexible, fince their complete formation, it will be found impoffible to deny their having been foftened by the application of heat.

204. The fecond conclufion, alluded to above, refults from a property, which belongs very generally, if not univerfally, to the inflexions of the ftrata. This confifts in their curvature being fimple, or in one dimenfion only, like a cylindric fuperficies, not double, or in two dimenfions, like the fuperficies of a fphere or fpheroid. This may be otherwife expreffed, by faying, that the fections of the bent ftrata, by a horizontal plane, are ftraight lines, parallel to one another. On this account, every fuch ftratum feems as if it were bent over an axis, and the axes of all thefe different bendings, for a great extent of country, are nearly parallel.

The truth of this is evident, where the ftrata are feen both tranfverfely and longitudinally. It holds remarkably of the primary fchiftus on the coaft of Berwickfhire; where the beds of rock, if cut tranfverfely, by a vertical plane, exhibit the figures of very complicated curves, with various *maxima* and *minima*, and points of contrary flexure; but, if they are cut by a horizontal plane, the fection will produce nothing but ftraight lines, nearly parallel.

205. The

205. The conftancy of the direction of the primary ftrata, when eftimated by their inter-fection with the horizontal plane, is often very remarkable. Their elevation and flexure are fubject to great and fudden changes, fo as to pafs not only from greater to lefs, but from one fide to the oppofite, within a fmall diftance; but the horizontal line in which they *ftretch*, ufually preferves the fame bearing to a great extent. The general direction of the primary ftrata, in the fouth part of Scotland, is from E. N. E. to W. S. W.; and the fame is nearly true of thofe which compofe the ridge of the Grampians on the north, and the hills of Cum-berland and Weftmoreland toward the fouth, though between the fchiftus of thefe three tracts, there is no communication at the furface, each being entirely feparated from the one next it, by the interpofition of fecondary ftrata. I have already mentioned the obfervations of Lord Webb Seymour and myfelf, at the foot of Ingle-borough; and it appears from them, that the vertical fchiftus on which that mountain refts, though it ftill preferves an eaftern and weftern direction, varies feveral points from that of the more northern ftrata. The ftrata of Wales re-turn more to the firft-mentioned direction, and thofe of Devonfhire and Cornwall agree with it very nearly. In all this, it will be eafily con-

ceived,.

ceived, that I do not mean to ſpeak with abſolute preciſion, or to deny the exiſtence of great
local irregularities.   The reſult given is only a
kind of average, deduced from obſervations
hardly ſuſceptible of great exactneſs, and not
yet ſufficiently multiplied to give to the concluſion all the accuracy it may attain.

206. This tendency of the primary ſtrata to
take a uniform direction, has alſo been obſerved
in other countries. Sauſſure remarked in the
Alps, that the beds of ſchiſtus are generally parallel to the chains of mountains compoſed of
them * ; and this remark is probably applicable to all mountains conſiſting of primary ſtrata.
The general direction, therefore, of the ſchiſtus
of the Alps, muſt be confined between W. 10° S.
and W. 40° S. In the Pyrenees, the direction
of the ſtrata is about W. N. W †. If Sauſſure's
rule may be depended on, the ſchiſtus of the
Altaic, and moſt of the other great chains in
the old continent, are in directions that run conſiderably to the ſouth of weſt. The Ourals,
and perhaps ſome other of the northern chains,
are however entirely different. In the Ourals,
as we learn not only from the general direction of
the chain, but from a ſection of it in the 10th volume

---

* Voyages aux Alpes, tom. i. § 577.

† Eſſai ſur le Mineralogie des Pyrenées.

lume of the Nova Acta of Peterſburgh, (tab. 12.),
the direction of the ſtrata is nearly from N. to S.
This laſt is probably the direction in the great
chains of South America; ſo that the uniformity
of direction in the primary ſtrata, which ſome
mineralogiſts would extend to thoſe of the whole
earth, is certainly imaginary, though there can
be no doubt that it extends over very large portions of the earth's ſurface *.

207. The

---

* It is perhaps unneceſſary to obſerve, that the two
propoſitions, that the interſections of the ſtrata with the
horizon are parallel lines; and that they are lines which
preſerve the ſame bearing with reſpect to the points of
the compaſs; are nearly the ſame thing for tracts of
moderate extent, but for large portions of the earth's
ſurface are extremely different. If, for inſtance, the
belt of primary vertical ſchiſtus, which traverſes the
ſouth of Scotland, were to be produced eaſtward in the
ſame plane, from its northern extremity, where its direction is E. N. E. and its latitude 55°.57′, it would
cut the meridian always leſs obliquely as it advanced,
till, having increaſed its longitude about 26°.28′, it
would be at right angles to the meridian, and its direction of conſequence due eaſt and weſt. This would
happen in the parallel of 58°.51′, (on the ſhore of the
Gulf of Finland, near Revel), the ſtrata being now extended about 880 G. miles from the Siccar Point. Con-
verſely, vertical ſtrata, having the ſame bearing with
reſpect

207. The tendency of the primary ſtrata to remain ſtraight in the horizontal direction, and to be bent in the vertical, is a phenomenon which points very directly to the cauſes from whence it has ariſen. A ſurface of ſimple curvature, or a ſurface ſtraight in one direction, is what

---

reſpect to the meridian, may be in planes very much inclined to one another. A ſtratum which bears eaſt and weſt in Cornwall, and one that does the ſame at the eaſt end of the Altaic chain, will be in planes, which, if produced, would cut one another at right angles. All this is ſufficiently plain from the doctrine of the ſphere, and is mentioned here, merely as a caution to prevent too haſty concluſions from being drawn from any correſpondence of bearing among the ſtrata of remote countries.

For the ſake of thoſe who would deduce the medium bearing of any body of ſtrata from a number of obſervations, it may be proper to take notice, that the true average is not to be found by ſimply taking an arithmetical mean among all the obſervations. A more exact way is to work by the traverſe table, as in keeping a ſhip's reckoning, (ſuppoſing the diſtance run to be always unity), and to compute from the obſerved bearings the amount of all the ſouthing or northing, and alſo of all the eaſting or weſting. The ſum of all the latter, divided by the ſum of all the former, is the tangent of the angle which the general direction of the ſtrata makes with the meridian.

what the application of forces to different points
of a plane, which is flexible, though with a certain degree of rigidity, will naturally produce.
The fuppofition, therefore, that thefe ftrata were
once flat and horizontal, and were impelled upward from that fituation before they had become rigid or hard, will explain their having
the kind of curvature which removes them as
little as poffible from their original condition.
But no other hypothefis affords any reafon why
they fhould have that curvature more than any
other. From the falling in of roofs of caverns,
we might expect fracture and diflocation, without
any order or regularity ; but certainly no bending or finuofity, nor any fymmetrical arrangement. If, as fome mineralogifts allege, the curvature, as well as inclination of the ftrata, arofe from
the irregularities of the bottom on which they
were depofited, why is the former in one dimenfion only, and why is it not in every direction,
like that of hills and valleys, or the actual furface
of the earth ? Or, laftly, if the whole ftructure
of the primitive mountains is an effect of cryftallization, and if thefe mountains are now fuch as
they have ever been from the time of their confolidation, whence is it, that, in their bendings
the law juft mentioned is fo conftantly obferved ? Indeed, the idea of afcribing the inflexions of the ftrata to cryftallization, though fuggefted

gefted by Sauffure *, and fince become a favourite fyftem with feveral mineralogifts, appears to
me in the higheft degree unfatisfactory and il-
lufive. The purpofe for which cryftallization
is here introduced, is not to give a fpecific
figure to a particular fubftance, but to arrange
the fubftances which it has formed and figured, according to certain rules; a work which
we know not how it is to perform, and in
which we have no experience of its power.
Accordingly, this principle does not account,
in any way whatever, for the circumftances
which attend the inflexion of the ftrata, for
the fimple curvature which they affect, nor for
that parallelifm of their layers, which, in all
their bendings, is fo accurately preferved. It
does, indeed, fo little ferve to explain thefe
facts, that, were the appearances completely
reverfed; did the ftrata affume the moft complex, inftead of the moft fimple curvature;
inftead of equidiftant, were they converging,
or alternately receding and approaching to one
another; the theory of cryftallization might
be equally applied to them. The ftate of the
phenomena is a matter of perfect indifference
to fuch a theory as this : all things are explained by it with the fame facility ; the ftraight and
the

---

* Voyages aux Alpes, tom. i. § 475.

the crooked, the fquare and the round, the moveable and the immoveable. Is it not evident
that fuch an explanation is a mere word ; or, if
any thing more than a word, an expreffion of
our ignorance, fo awkward and indirect, as to
deprive us of whatever credit might have been
gained by a plain and candid avowal of it ?

It fhould never be forgotten, that a theory
which accounts for *any thing*, and a theory which
accounts for *nothing*, ftand precifely on the fame
footing, and ought to be banifhed from all parts
of philofophy, as they have been from thofe
fciences which are juftly honoured with the name
of accurate. The animated orbs of Ariftotle, and
the vortices of Des Cartes, have long ceafed to be
mentioned in phyfical aftronomy ; the firft, becaufe they accounted for every thing alike ; the
fecond, becaufe, when they accounted for one
thing, they never could be made to account for
another. Both theories, therefore, have very
properly been rejected ; and, when geology
fhall undergo a fimilar purification, the principle we have been confidering will not be the
only facrifice required of the Neptunian fyftem.

208. An appearance obferved in fome kinds
of primary fchiftus, which clearly indicates their
depofition by water, and in planes very different
from thofe in which we now fee them, though
it might have been introduced before, is alfo
much

much connected with the prefent argument. This appearance confifts of fmall wavings or undulæ on the furface of the plates of fchiftus, precifely fimilar to thofe marks which are left by the fea on a gently inclining beach of fand, at the ebbing of the tide. All the fpecies of fchiftus do not feem to afford inftances of thefe wavings. The rocks which do fo, are, I think, chiefly of the argillaceous kind, but often highly indurated; fo that the laminæ containing the impreffions are not to be torn afunder but with great difficulty. Inftances of it abound in the fchiftus of Berwickfhire, and are alfo not unfrequent in that of Galloway. All muft agree about the agent which produced thefe marks; it could be no other than the fea; but it muft have been the fea acting on loofe, fmall and round particles, lying on a furface which was nearly horizontal.

209. Dr Hutton's theory is no where ftronger, than in what relates to the elevation and inflexion of the ftrata; points in which all others are fo egregioufly defective. The phenomena to be connected are here extremely various, and even in appearance contradictory: the horizontality of one part of the ftrata; the inclined or vertical pofition of another; the perfect planes in which one fet are extended; the breaking and diflocation

diflocation found in a fecond ; the inflexion and
finuofity of a third ; and almoft every where the
utmoft rigidity and induration, combined with
appearances of the greateft foftnefs and flexibility ; the prefervation of a parallelifm of fuperficies in the midft of fo much irregularity,
and the affumption of a determinate fpecies of
curvature, under circumftances the moft diffimilar ; all thefe appearances were to be connected
with one another, and with the confolidation of
the ftrata, and this is done by the twofold hypothefis, of aqueous depofition, and the action of fubterraneous heat.   When thefe circumftances are
fairly confidered, and when the fhifts which other
fyftems are put to on this occafion are remembered, I think it will be granted, that few
attempts at generalization have been more fuccefsful, than that which is here made by the
Huttonian Theory.

210. To the fact of the elevation of the ftrata, the ftudy of geology is much indebted. The
ftratified form of a great proportion of the
earth's furface, gives to minerals that organization and regularity, which makes their difpofition an object of fcience, and their inclined pofition ferves to bring that organization into view,
from far greater depths than we can ever reach
by artificial excavations. If, for inftance, the termination of ftrata, that make with the horizon
an

an angle of 30°, lying one over another, is seen
for a horizontal diſtance of two miles ; then it
is certain, that if theſe ſtrata have that extent
under ground, which may be reaſonably ſuppoſed, the thickneſs of the whole maſs, meaſured by a line perpendicular to its ſtratification, is half the horizontal diſtance, or amounts
to one mile. It would alſo require a pit to be
ſunk from the uppermoſt of theſe ſtrata, to the
depth of (2 miles × tan 30°, =) 6093 feet, before it could interſect the undermoſt ; and
therefore, if we ſuppoſe the ſame ſtratum to preſerve the ſame character for the extent of ſome
miles, we obtain the ſame information from in-
ſpecting the edge-ſeams, and ſee in reality as
far into the bowels of the earth, as if we had
ſunk a perpendicular ſhaft to the depth of 6000
feet.

In general, the length of the horizontal line
drawn acroſs the ſtrata, from the loweſt in poſition to the higheſt, multiplied into the ſine of
the inclination of the ſtrata to the horizon, gives
the thickneſs of the whole, meaſured perpendicularly to the plane of the ſtratification : and
the ſame horizontal diſtance, multiplied into the
tangent of the inclination, gives the actual depth
at which the loweſt ſtratum would meet a perpendicular to the horizon, drawn from the higheſt extremity of the upper ſtratum.

In

In many cafes, the extent of ftratified materials admitting of fuch an examination as this,
is much greater than has now been fuppofed.
M. Pallas defcribes a range of hills on the
fouth-eaft fide of the peninfula of the Tauride,
which is cut down perpendicularly toward the
fea, and offers a complete fection of the parallel
beds of a primary, or, as he calls it, an ancient
limeftone, inclined at an angle of 45° to the horizon ; and this fection continues for the length of
130 *verſts*, or about 86 Englifh miles. The
beds are fo regular, that M. Pallas compares
them to the leaves of a book *. The height of
thefe hills does not exceed 1200 feet, but the
real height of the uppermoft ftratum above the
undermoft, is $86 \times \sqrt{\frac{1}{2}} = 86 \times \frac{5}{7} = 61$ miles
nearly.

If therefore we conceive that there is no fhift
in all this great fyftem of ftrata, we in reality
are enabled, by means of it, to fee no lefs than
61 miles into the interior of the earth, nearly
a 65th part of the radius of the globe. It is
true, that we can hardly fuppofe fo great a body
of ftrata to have been raifed without fhifting,
fo that we muft diminifh this depth confiderably ; but were it reduced even to one-half, it
will

* See Nova Acta Acad. Petropol. tom. x. (1792,)
p. 257.

will appear, that men fee much farther into the interior of the globe than they are aware of, and that geologifts are reproached without reafon for forming theories of the earth, when all that they can do is but to make a few fcratches on its furface. Art indeed can do little more; but nature fupplies the deficiency, and makes difcoveries to the attentive obferver, on the fame great fcale with her other operations.

The fimpleft account that can be given of the vaft body of parallel and highly inclined ftrata juft mentioned, is, that it confifts of the ends of horizontal ftrata, or of ftrata not greatly inclined, that have been forced up when they were all foft and flexible. This is a much more conceivable fuppofition than Pallas's, viz. that the greater part of this mafs has funk down into fome vaft cavern in the interior of the earth.

NOTE

Note XIII. § 53.

Metallic Veins.

211. The large specimens of native iron found
in Siberia and Peru, mentioned above, § 51.,
are among the moft curious facts in the natural
hiftory of metals. It has been doubted, however, by fome, whether they really belong to
natural hiftory, or are not rather to be accounted artificial productions. If they had been
found in the heart of rocks, or in the midft of
metallic veins, no doubt of this fort could poffibly have been entertained; but, as they lie
quite on the furface, in the middle of flat countries, and at a diftance from any known vein of
metal, the conjecture that they may be artificial,
and the remains of the iron founderies of ancient and unknown nations, is at firft fight not
entirely deftitute of probability. This probability, however, will appear to be the lefs, the
more carefully the fpecimens are examined.
The metal is too perfect, and the maffes too
large, to have been melted in the furnaces, or to
have been tranfported by the machinery, of a
rude people. The fpecimen in South America
weighs 300 quintals, or about 15 tons, and is

foft

foft and malleable *. The Siberian fpecimen, defcribed by Pallas, is alfo very large; it is foft and malleable, and full of round cavities, containing a fubftance, which, on examination, has been found to be chryfolite †. Now, it is certainly quite impoffible, that, in an artificial fufion, fo much chryfolite could have come by any means to be involved in the iron; but, if the fufion was natural, and happened in a mineral vein, the iron and the chryfolite were both in their native place, and their meeting together has nothing in it that is inexplicable.

212. Some circumftances in the defcription of the fpecimen in South America, fuch as the impreffions of the feet of men and of birds on its furface, are not to be accounted for on any hypothefis, and certainly require more careful inveftigation. It is faid, that this iron is very little fubject to ruft, and the analyfis of a piece of it by Proust makes it probable, that it owes this quality to its union with nickel ‡. It appears, alfo, that the country of Chaco, where this fpecimen was found, affords many others of the fame kind, one of which is mentioned in the defcription above referred to. That
                                                    country

---

* Phil. Tranf. 1788. p. 37. alfo p. 183, &c.

† Kirwan's Mineralogy, vol. ii. art. Native Iron.

‡ Annales de Chimie, tom. xxxv. Meffidor, p. 47.

country lies on the eaſt ſide of the Plata, and is
a plain, extremely level, and of vaſt extent,
without any appearance of mineral veins; but
ſuch veins may neverthelefs exiſt undiſcovered,
in a tract ſubject to periodical inundations, and
where the native rock is covered with alluvial
earth and gravel to a great depth. The veins may
be waſhed away, and the more durable ſubſtances, ſuch as thoſe pieces of native iron, may be
left behind ; and, though they muſt be of a formation extremely ancient, according to this hypotheſis, they may not have been very long on
the ſurface.

213. Specimens of native iron have been
found, lefs remarkable than the preceding for
their ſize, but in circumſtances that excluded
all idea of artificial fuſion. Of this ſort was
MARGRAAF's ſpecimen of native iron, the firſt of
the kind that was known ; it conſiſted of ſmall
bits of ſoft and malleable iron, found in the
heart of a brown iron-ſtone *. This makes it
certain, that native iron is a natural production,
and the mere circumſtance of great magnitude,
in the ſpecimens before mentioned, does not entitle us to doubt of their having that ſame origin. It is a circumſtance, beſides, not in the
leaſt material to this argument ; the ſmalleſt

Q　　　　　　piece

---

* Kirwan's Mineralogy, vol. ii. p. 156.

piece of native iron being as much a proof of
fufion as the greateft; and the fpecimen of
Margraaf being juft as conclufive in favour of
the Huttonian Theory, as thofe of Pallas or De
Celis, fuppofing their reality as mineral productions to be completely eftablifhed.   A metal
malleable and ductile, in ever fo fmall a quantity, cannot be the refult of precipitation from
a menftruum, without a very particular combination of circumftances.   Such a metal, on the
other hand, can be readily produced by igneous
fufion; fo that here the negative and affirmative
parts of the inductive argument may both be
regarded as complete.

214. Mr Kirwan, in order to account for the
magnitude of the two large fpecimens mentioned
above, fuppofes, that fmall pieces of native iron
(about the formation of which he appears to
have no difficulty), have been originally agglutinated by petroleum, and left bare, when the
furrounding ftony or earthy maffes either wi-
thered or were wafhed off*.   This is no doubt
the moft fingular of all the opinions which have
been advanced on the fubject; and, as it bor-
rows nothing from analogy, it admits of no
proof, and requires no refutation.   None but a
chemift of eminence could have ventured with
                                                    impunity

* Geol. Effays, p. 405.

impunity on an affertion fo inconfiftent with all the phenomena and principles of his fcience.

215. A remark of the fame author, on the fubject of the native gold found in the county of Wicklow in Ireland, is entitled to more atten-tion. " That thefe lumps of native gold," he fays, " were never in fufion, is evident from their low fpecific gravity, and the grains of fand found in the midft of them. I found the fpe-cific gravity of a lump of the fize of a nutmeg to be only 12800, whereas, after fufion, it be-came 18700 *."

This argument is plaufible; but, I think, neverthelefs inconclufive. The fand found in the gold, accounts, at leaft in part, for its lightnefs. It is only by repeated fufions that any of the metals is brought to its utmoft pu-rity and higheft fpecific gravity; and on no fuppofition can the melting of gold in the mineral regions, be very likely to feparate it from heterogeneous fubftances. That quartzy fand fhould be found in it, after fuch a procefs, is naturally to be expected. The impreffions which the quartz cryftals have left on the Wicklow gold, would be received as a full proof of the fufion of that metal, if geologifts always regu-

Q 2   lated

---

* Geol. Effays, p. 402.

lated their theories by the principles which determine the belief of ordinary men.

216. Don Rubin de Celis, in the paper referred to above, mentions some maſſes of ſilver found at Quantajaia, and alſo ſome duſt of platina, in terms that excite a ſtrong deſire to have more information concerning them. They are conſidered by him as effects of volcanic fire; ſo we may conclude, that they contain evident marks of fuſion, and would in this ſyſtem be aſcribed to that heat, from which volcanic fire is but a partial and accidental derivation.

217. The ſtate alſo in which gold and ſilver are often found pervading maſſes of quartz, and ſhooting acroſs them in every direction, furniſhes. a ſtrong argument for the igneous origin, both of the metal and the ſtone. From ſuch ſpecimens, it is evident, that the quartz and the metal cryſtallized, or paſſed from a fluid to a ſolid ſtate, at the ſame time; and it is hardly leſs clear, that this fluidity did not proceed from ſolution in any menſtruum: For the menſtruum, whether water or the *chaotic fluid*, to enable it to diſſolve the quartz, muſt have had an alkaline impregnation; and, to enable it to diſſolve the metal, it muſt have had, at the ſame time, an acid impregnation. But theſe two oppoſite qualities could not reſide in the ſame ſubject; the acid and alkali would unite together, and,

if

if equally powerful, form a neutral falt, (like fea-falt), incapable of acting either on the metallic or the filiceous body. If the acid was moft powerful, the compound falt might act on the metal, but not at all upon the quartz ; and if the alkali was moft powerful, the compound might act on the quartz, but not at all on the metal. In no cafe, therefore, could it act on both at the fame time. Fire or heat, if fufficiently intenfe, is not fubject to this difficulty, as it could exercife its force with equal effect on both bodies.

218. The fimultaneous confolidation of the quartz and the metal is indeed fo highly improbable, that the Neptunifts rather fuppofe, that the ramifications in fuch fpecimens as are·here alluded to, have been produced by the metal diffufing itfelf through *rifts* already formed in the ftone *. But it may be anfwered, that between the channels in which the metal pervades the quartz, and the ordinary cracks or fiffures in ftones, there is no refemblance whatever : That a fyftem of hollow tubes, winding through a ftone, (as the tubes in queftion, muft have been, according to this hypothefis, before they were filled by the metal), is itfelf far more inconceivable than the thing which it is intended to explain ;

Q 3 and

* Geol. Effays, p. 401.

and laftly, that if the ftone was perforated by
fuch tubes, it would ftill be infinite to one that
they did not all exactly join, or inofculate with
one another.

219. The compenetration, as it may be called, of two heterogeneous fubftances, has here
furnifhed a proof of their having been melted
by fire. The inclufion of one heterogeneous
fubftance within another, as happens among the
fpars and drufens, found fo commonly in mineral veins, often leads to a fimilar conclufion.
Thus, from a fpecimen of chalcedony, including
in it a piece of calcareous fpar, Dr Hutton has
derived a very ingenious and fatisfactory proof,
that thefe two fubftances were perfectly foft at
the fame time, and mutually affected each other
at the moment of their concretion *.

Each of thefe fubftances has its peculiar form,
which, when left to itfelf, it naturally affumes ;
the fpar taking the form of rhombic cryftals,
and the chalcedony affecting a mammalated ftructure, or a fuperficies compofed of fpherical fegments, contiguous to one another.   Now, in the
fpecimen under confideration, the fpar is included in the chalcedony, and the peculiar figure
of each is impreffed on the other; the angles and
planes of the fpar are indented into the chalcedony,

---

* Theory of the Earth, vol. i. p. 93.

dony, and the fpherical fegments of the chalcedony are imprinted on the planes of the fpar.
Thefe appearances are confiftent with no notion
of confolidation that does not involve in it the
fimultaneous concretion of the whole mafs; and
fuch concretion cannot arife from precipitation
from a folvent, but only from the congelation
of a melted body. This argument, it muft be
remarked, is not grounded on a folitary fpecimen, (though if it were it might ftill be perfectly conclufive), but on a phenomenon of which
there are innumerable inftances.

220. According to this theory, veins were
filled by the injection of fluid matter from below; and this account of them, which agrees fo
well with the phenomena already defcribed, is
confirmed by this, that nothing of the fubftances
which fill the veins is to be found any where at
the furface. It is not with the veins as with
the ftrata, where, in the loofe fand on the fhore,
and in the fhells and corals accumulated at the
bottom of the fea, we perceive the fame materials of which thefe ftrata are compofed. The
fame does not equally hold of metallic veins:
" Look, fays Dr Hutton, into the fources of our
mineral treafures? Afk the miner from whence
has come the metal in his veins? Not from the
earth or air above, nor from the ftrata which
the vein traverfes: thefe do not contain an atom

of

of the minerals now confidered. There is but one place from whence thefe minerals may have come ; this is the bowels of the earth ; the place of power and expanfion ; the place from whence has proceeded that intenfe heat, by which loofe materials have been confolidated into rocks, as well as that enormous force, by which the regular ftrata have been broken and difplaced *."

221. The above is a very juft and natural reflection ; but if, inftead of interrogating the miner, we confult the Neptunift, we will receive a very different reply. As this philofopher never embarraffes himfelf about preferving a uniformity in the courfe of nature, he will tell us, that though it may be true, that neither the air, the upper part of the earth's furface, nor even the fea, contain at prefent any thing like the materials of the veins, yet the time was when thefe materials were all mingled together in the chaotic mafs, and conftituted one vaft fluid, encompaffing the earth ; from which fluid it was, that the minerals were precipitated and depofited in the clefts and fiffures of the ftrata.

222. It is alleged, in proof of this hypothefis, that mineral veins are found to be lefs rich as they go farther down, whereas they ought to be richer, if they were filled by the projection of melted

---

* Theory of the Earth, vol. i. p. 130.

melted matter from below. But the fact, that
mines are lefs rich as they defcend farther,
though it may hold in fome inftances, is not general, and may therefore be fuppofed to arife
from local caufes, fuch as are, in refpect of us,
accidental, and beyond the limits to which our
theories can be expected to reach. Thus the
mines of Mexico and Peru are faid to be fubject to the preceding rule; but in the mines
of Derbyfhire and Cornwall, the very contrary
is underftood to take place. Befides, what we
are pleafed to call the riches of a mine, are
riches relatively to us, and relatively to a diftinction which nature does not recognife. The fpars
and veinftones which are thrown out in the rubbifh of our mines, may be as precious in the eyes
of nature, as conducive. to the great objects of
her economy, and are certainly as characteriftic
of mineral veins, as the ores of filver or gold, to
which we attach fo great a value. Unlefs the
former are in fmaller quantity, or lefs highly
cryftallized at great than at fmall depths, which
I believe is not alleged, no conclufion can be
drawn from fubftances, which occupy in general but a fmall proportion of any vein, and, in
their diffemination through it, do not feem to
be always guided by the fame law.

223. Again, if the veins were filled by depofition from above, we ought to difcover in them
fuch

fuch horizontal ftratification as is the effect of
depofition from water, and we fhould perceive
no marks of the materials having been introduced with violence into their place. The Neptunifts cannot object to the trial of their theory
by thefe two facts.

As to the firft, it is acknowledged, that there
is a certain regular difpofition of the fubftances
in mineral veins, as ftated § 59, but it is one
which has hardly any thing in common with
the real phenomena of ftratification. It confifts in the diftribution of the principal fubftances in coats parallel to the fides of the vein, each
fubftance forming a feparate coat. In a vein,
for inftance, containing quartz, fluor, calcareous
fpar, lead, &c. we might expect to find a lining
of quartz cryftals, applied immediately to the
walls of the mine, and following exactly the
irregularities of their furface ; next, perhaps,
a coat of fluor, then of calcareous fpar, and laft of
lead-ore in the centre of the vein, the fame order being obferved on the oppofite fide. Thefe
fucceffive coats, it is material to remark, are not
in planes, but in uneven furfaces, of which the
inequalities are evidently determined by thofe
of the walls, that is, of the rock which forms
the fides of the vein ; neither are they horizontal, but are parallel to the walls, whether thefe
be perpendicular or inclined. Here, therefore,
there

there is no appearance of the action of that ftatical law which has directed the arrangement
of the other ftrata, and which tends to make the
plane of every ftratum depofited by water perpendicular to the direction of gravity. The
coating of the veins has therefore been performed under the conduct of fome other power than
that which prefides over aqueous depofition.
If, as the Neptunifts maintain, the materials in
the veins were depofited by water, in the moft
perfect tranquillity, it is wonderful that we do
not find thofe materials difpofed in horizontal
layers, acrofs the vein, inftead of being parallel
to its fides; and it feems very unaccountable,
that the common ftrata, depofited as we are told
while the water was in a ftate of great agitation, have fo rigoroufly obeyed the laws of hydroftatics, (§ 38.), and acquired a parallelifm in
the planes of their ftratification, which approaches fo often to geometrical precifion; while
the materials of the veins, in circumftances fo
much more favourable for doing the fame, have
done nearly the reverfe, and taken a pofition,
often at right angles to that which hydroftatical
principles require. This is a paradox which
the Neptunian fyftem has created, and which
therefore it is not very likely to refolve.

224. Mere words fhould have little power to
miflead, in a fcience which treats of fenfible objects,

jects, such as are always easily subjected to the examination of sight or of touch; yet there is some appearance as if the Neptunists were misled in this, and other instances, by the term *stratification*. Though an incrustation on the perpendicular face of a rock has very little affinity to a stratum, such as we are accustomed to see deposited by water, yet the same name being once imposed on both, mineralogists have proceeded to reason concerning them, as if they were precisely the same thing, and were both to be ascribed to the same cause. Indeed, every perpendicular or highly-inclined bed of stone, is inexplicable as an effect of aqueous deposition, in a system, unprovided, as the Neptunian is *, with the means of raising up such beds from a horizontal into a vertical position. This observation may also be extended to all cases of vertical stratification. Water cannot directly arrange its deposites in planes highly inclined, and therefore I have often wondered to see the Neptunists contending so eagerly for the stratification of certain rocks, such as granite, which, being vertical, or highly inclined, was much less friendly to their system than the entire absence of all stratification would have been. I was disposed to admire their candour, when the use

---

* See preceding note.

ufe which they made of the fact convinced me, that I ought only to wonder at their inconfequential reafoning. The Huttonian Theory is, indeed, the only one which poffeffes the means of reconciling the elevation of the ftrata with their horizontal depofition, and which is entitled to confider ftratification, in whatever plane it may be, as originally the work of the ocean. The geologifts who attach themfelves exclufively to the action of water, will never be able to extend the dominion of that element fo far as Dr Hutton has done, by combining it with fire.

225. But, though the Neptunian fyftem were provided with engines, powerful enough to raife up ftrata from a level to a vertical plane, this would avail nothing in the prefent inftance; fince, on no fuppofition, can the incruftations on the perpendicular fides of a vein have ever been horizontal. On no fuppofition, therefore, can thefe incruftations be received as a proof of aqueous depofition : it may indeed be certainly inferred from them, that the matter which they confift of was fluid at the time of their formation; but the abfence of all appearance of a horizontal difpofition, in any part of the vein, amounts nearly to a demonftration, that this fluidity did not proceed from folution in a menftruum. We muft therefore conceive the coats to have been formed during the refrigeration of the melted

melted matter injected from the mineral regions into the clefts and fiffures of the ftrata (§ 59.).

226. Mineral veins, particularly at their interfections with one another, contain abundant marks of the moft violent and repeated difturbance, (§ 56). Not to mention that they owe their firft formation to the fracture and difplacing of rocks already confolidated, it appears, that they have originated at very different periods, and that the birth of each has been accompanied with convulfions, which fhook the foundations of the earth. In Cornwall, for inftance, the principal veins, and thofe which they diftinguifh particularly by the name of *Lodes*, have nearly the fame direction with the ftrata or vertical fchiftus, extending from about E. N. E. to W. S. W. Thefe, however, are often interfected nearly at right angles by other mineral veins, called *Crofs Courfes*, and this hardly ever happens without the latter moving, or, as it is called, *heaving* the former out of their direction. This plainly indicates, that the crofs courfes are of later origin than the others, and that their formation was accompanied with fuch a force, as muft, in many inftances, have moved the whole body of rock which conftitutes the promontory of Cornwall, and probably much more, for feveral yards, in a horizontal direction. Sometimes, alfo, both the longitudinal and

and the crofs vein are forced out of their place by a third. Thefe difturbances arife not only from mineral veins, but from veins of porphyry and granite, the production of which has been attended with no lefs violence than of the others.

227. What is here faid of Cornwall, is the hiftory, in fome degree, of all mineral countries whatever. The great horizontal *tranflation* which has thus accompanied the formation of veins; the movement impreffed on fuch vaft bodies of rock, and the frequent renewal of thefe immenfe convulfions; are not to be explained by the mild and tranquil dominion of the watery element. They require the utmoft power that is known any where to exift, and were it not for the admonitions of the volcano and the earthquake, we might doubt if even fubterraneous heat itfelf poffeffed an energy adequate to thefe aftonifh-ing effects.

228. From the *heaving* of one vein by ano-ther, it is evident, that there was a force of pro-trufion in the direction of one of them, that acted at the time of its formation. This force cannot be accounted for on the fuppofition that veins were produced by the mere fhrinking of the ftrata; for the rocks could not, in that cafe, have been rent afunder, and impelled forward at the fame time. It appears moft likely, that fif-

fures

fures in the ftrata were made, at leaft in many
inftances, and the matter poured into them,
nearly at the fame time, both being effects of
the fame caufe, the expanfive force of fubterraneous heat.

229. It is remarked, at § 56., that the fhifting
of the ftrata is beft obferved where the veins
make a tranfverfe fection of beds of rock, confiderably inclined to the horizon. It is alfo
true, that in fome cafes the near approach of
the ftrata to the level, may make the fhifts produced by the veins very eafy to be difcovered.
Thus in Derbyfhire, where the mineral veins
are in fecondary ftrata, nearly horizontal, there
is almoft no inftance in which the correfponding ftrata are not obferved to be on different levels, on the oppofite fides of the fame vein.

230. The fact defcribed by De Luc, and referred to as § 55., may, for what we know of it,
admit of being explained in two ways. The
great wedge of rock which appears to be infulated between two branches of the fame vein,
may either be a mafs that has been broken off,
and fuftained by the melted matter that flowed
all around it ; or, it may be a mafs of rock contained between two veins that are in reality
diftinct, and of different formation. Whether
this laft fuppofition is the truth, would probably
be evident from a careful examination of both

parts

parts of the vein ; as fome difference of character cannot fail to be the confequence of different formation.   If no fuch difference is obferved, the two branches muft be fuppofed to belong to the fame vein, and the only probable
explanation of the infulation of fo large a mafs
of rock will be by the firft-mentioned fuppofition.   This fact, therefore, notwithftanding the
great attention M. De Luc has beftowed on it,
ftill requires further examination, before it can
be decided whether it inclines to the Huttonian
Theory, as on the firft fuppofition, or is, as on
the latter hypothefis, equally balanced between
it and the *Wernerian.*

231. Whatever be the cafe with this fact, the
general one of pieces of rock being found infulated in veins, is certainly favourable to the notion of an injected and ponderous fluid having
originally fuftained them.   Where, as happens
in fome inftances, the ftones contained in the
veins have no affinity to any of the rocks above,
they cannot be fuppofed to have come any how
but from below, and to have been carried up by
the matter of the vein.   The inftance from the
flip at the Huddersfield Canal has been already
mentioned.

232. The preceding obfervations have been
principally directed againft that theory of veins
which fuppofes them to have been filled by de-

R   pofition

position from water. There is another theory maintained by some of the Neptunists, that the metals in veins were introduced there by infiltration *. This opinion is sufficiently refuted by the fact, that rarely any metallic ore is found out of the vein, or in the rock on either side of it, and least of all where the vein is richest. This is inconsistent with the notion of the ore being carried into the vein by water percolating through the adjacent rocks, unless some satisfactory reason is assigned, which determined the water to leave the ore in the vein and no where else. Besides, this hypothesis does not account for the formation of the spars and veinstones which fill the vein, and which appear clearly to have been brought there at the same time with the ore, and no doubt by the same cause.

233. The veins, properly so called, are indefinitely extended; but there are also thin plates of spar, and of crystals of different kinds, often found included in rocks, and shut in on all sides, to which the name of veins is commonly applied. These last ought certainly to be distinguished from the former, and may not improperly be called *Plate Veins* or *Lenticular Veins*, the plate or cake of spar of which they consist having very often the form of a lens, though,

as

---

* Geol. Essays, p. 401.

as may be fuppofed, confiderably irregular. Either of thefe terms being derived entirely from
external characters, has the advantage of involving nothing theoretical.

The lenticular veins are certainly not formed
like the ufual mineral veins, by injection, fince
they are fhut in, on all fides, by the folid rock.
When they are found, therefore, in ftratified
rocks, fuch as have not themfelves been melted,
we muft conceive them to be compofed of materials more fufible than the furrounding rock,
fo that they have been brought into fufion by a
degree of heat which the reft of the rock was
able to refift, and, on cooling, have affumed a
fparry ftructure. When they are found in
rocks, of which the whole has been fluid, they
muft be confidered as component parts of that
mafs, which, by an elective attraction, have
united with one another, and feparated themfelves from the fubftances to which they had
lefs affinity.

The veins of this kind feem to be connected
with thofe called in Derbyfhire *Pipe Veins*, in
which the ores of metals are fometimes found.
The pipe veins, indeed, are not in all cafes completely infulated, but fometimes communicate
with the veins properly called mineral. I am
too little acquainted, however, with their natural hiftory, to be able to fay with certainty to

which

which of the two species they ought to be referred.

On Whinstone.

234. To the facts and reasonings given above, I shall, in this note, add a few remarks, tending to shew, that whinstone is not of volcanic, nor of aqueous, but certainly of igneous origin.

It is asserted (§ 62.), that carbonat of lime and zeolite are often contained in whinstone, but never in lava, and that this circumstance may sometimes serve to distinguish these stones from one another. With respect to carbonat of lime, in particular, it seems evident, that this substance cannot enter into the original composition of any lava, because the same heat which melted the lava, would, where there was no greater pressure than the weight of the atmosphere, expel the carbonic acid and produce quicklime. Notwithstanding this, rocks, containing carbonat of lime, have often been considered as lavas, into the pores and cavities of which, calcareous matter having been carried by the infiltration of water, had crystallized into spar. Thus SPALLANZANI,

in

in his account of the Euganean Hills, in Lombardy, defcribes fome of the rocks as abounding at their furface, and even in their interior, with air-bubbles of various fizes, from uch as are hardly perceptible, to fome that are half an inch in diameter; and which, he fays, are all of an oval figure, with their longeft diameters in the fame direction.   This he confiders as a proof that the rock is a genuine lava; for the air-bubbles prove the ftone to have had its fluidity from fire; and by their elongation in the fame direction they prove, that the mafs when fluid was alfo in motion.   Spallanzani adds, that *many of thefe cavities are filled with cryftals of the carbonat of lime, an effect of the infiltration of water* *.

235. Though the argument here advanced for the igneous origin of the rock may be admitted as conclufive, the introduction of calcareous fpar into it by infiltration muft ftill be queftioned.   Lava, except in a ftate of decay or decompofition, is not readily penetrated by water; and, if it were, the filling of cavities with fpar, by means of the water percolating through them, would ftill be fubject to many difficulties, (§ 12.). Befides, whinftone rocks are frequently found

R 3   fo

---

* Voyages dans les deux Siciles, tom. iii. p. 157. Edit. de Faujas de St Fond.

fo full of calcareous fpar, or of zeolite, that they
would become porous to fuch a degree, if the
cavities filled with thefe latter fubftances were
all empty, that they could hardly fuftain their
own weight, and much lefs that of the great maffes
of rock incumbent on them.   In fuch cafes, it is
certain, that the cryftallized fubftances were part
of the original compofition of the rock.   The
truth is, that the infiltration of the water is a mere
gratuitous affumption, introduced for the purpofe of explaining the exiftence of carbonated
lime in a ftone which had endured the action of
intenfe heat ; and this affumption ought of
courfe to be rejected, if the phenomenon can be
explained by a theory, that is in other refpects
conformable to nature.   The fpar, then, may
be confidered as a proof, that the rocks in queftion are to be numbered with thofe unerupted
lavas which have flowed deep in the bowels of
the earth, and under a great compreffing force.
This is the more probable, that the Euganean
Hills, like fome whinftone hills in our own country, have, in certain places, a covering of flaty
and calcareous ftrata incumbent on them, even
at their fummits *, fo that the torrent of melted
ftone, of which they are admitted to confift, cannot have flowed from the mouth of a volcano. I do

not

---

* Phil. Tranf. 1775, p. 34.

not mean to fay, that there are among thefe hills no veftiges of volcanic explofion. I am very far from having *data* fufficient for drawing this conclufion ; but I believe it may be fafely affirmed, that the bulk of them is no more compofed of volcanic lava, than the bafaltes of Staffa, or of the Giant's Caufeway.

236. But, befides the evidence deduced from calcareous fpar and zeolite, againft the rocks containing them being real lava, there are other marks, even lefs equivocal perhaps, that diftinguifh the lavas which we fuppofe to have flowed in the mineral regions, from thofe which have actually flowed on the furface. Thefe are what we collect from the difpofition, the organization, or, as we may fay, the phyfical geography of whinftone countries, unlike, in fo many refpects, to that of volcanic countries. The fhape of whinftone hills ; their large flat terraces, rifing one above another ; their perpendicular faces, and the correfpondence of their heights even at confiderable diftances ; have nothing fimilar to them in the irregular torrents of volcanic lavas. The phenomena of the former are alfo on a fcale of magnitude very far exceeding the latter, and clearly indicate, that though both have been produced by fire, it has been by fire in very different circumftances, and regulated by very different laws. The ftructure of the two kinds of

rock

rock agrees, in many refpects, and fo does their chemical analyfis; but their difpofition and arrangement are fo diffimilar, that they cannot be fuppofed to be of the fame formation.

237. This argument, I believe, was firft ftated by Mr STRANGE, in a letter to Sir JOHN PRINGLE, publifhed in the 65th volume of the *Philofophical Tranfactions* *. That intelligent obferver, after vifiting the countries in Europe moft remarkable either for burning, or for what are accounted, extinguifhed volcanoes, and examining them with a very difcriminating eye, remained convinced, that there are two diftinct fpecies of rock, which both owe their origin to fire; but to fire acting in circumftances and fituations extremely different. The firft is the common volcanic lava; the other, to which he gives the name of a bafaltine rock, comprehends fuch rocks as the Giant's Caufeway, the bafaltes of the Vivarais, of the Euganean Hills, &c. and differs in nothing from that which is called here by the name of whinftone. Mr Strange conceived, that the one of thefe kinds of ftone could, no more than the other, be accounted the work of aqueous depofition, but was led to the diftinction juft mentioned, by obferving the organization and

---

* Account of Two Giants Caufeways in the Venetian State, &c. by John Strange, Efq; Phil. Tranf, vol. lxv. (1775.) p. 5, &c.

and arrangement in the rocks of the latter kind,
and comparing them with the diforder and ruin
that every where mark the footfteps of volcanic
fire. He does not pretend to determine the nature
of the fire to which the bafaltine rocks owe their
formation, nor the circumftances in which it has
acted : he is fatisfied with the negative conclufion, that it is not volcanic ; and his paper affords
a fpecimen of what is perhaps rare in any of the
fciences, and certainly moft rare of all in geology, viz. a philofophic induction carried juft as
far as the facts will bear it out, and not a fingle
ftep beyond that point.

238. Several other hints contained in this paper are highly deferving of notice ; for we not
only find in it the notion of a formation of bafaltic rocks, igneous though not volcanic, but
alfo that of their fimultaneous cryftallization *,
together with the fuggeftion, that granite and
bafalt are of the fame origin †. Thefe opinions had not, I believe, occurred at that
time to any mineralogift except Dr Hutton, nor
had they been communicated by him to any but
a few of his moft intimate friends ; fo that Mr
Strange has without doubt all the merit of a firft
difcoverer. Indeed, without the knowledge of
the

---

* Phil. Tranf. *ubi fupra*, p. 17.
† *Ibid.* p. 36. and 37.

the principle of compreffion, fuch as it is laid
down by Dr Hutton, it was hardly poffible for
him to proceed further than he has done. He
remarked the *unburnt* limeftone that lies on the
tops of fome of the Euganean bafaltes, and feems
to have been aware of the great difficulty, which
it was referved for the Huttonian Theory to overcome. His letter contains alfo fome excellent
general remarks on the rocks of the Vivarais
and Velay, which he had vifited, before Faujas
de St Fond had publifhed his curious and elaborate defcription of thefe countries.

239. The caufe of the peculiar ftructure which
has juft been obferved to diftinguifh whinftone
from volcanic countries, is eafily affigned in the
Huttonian Theory. According to that theory, the
whinftone rocks were formed, in the bowels of
the earth, of melted matter poured into the rents
and openings of the ftrata. They were caft,
therefore, in thofe openings, as in a mould; and
received the impreffion and character of the
rocks by which they were furrounded. Hence
the tabular maffes of whinftone, which when
foft have been interpofed between ftrata, and
compreffed by their weight, fo as almoft to have
themfelves acquired the appearance of ftratification. Hence the perpendicular faces of the fame
rocks, produced by their being abutted when

yet

yet foft, againſt the abrupt ſides of the ſtrata.
The rocks which formed thoſe moulds have, in
many caſes, entirely diſappeared ; in others, a
part ſtill remains, ſurrounding, or even covering,
the baſaltes, as in the Euganean Hills, in thoſe
of the Val di Noto in Sicily, the rocks near
Liſbon *, and in different parts of Great Britain.

Above all, the veins of whinſtone which interſect the ſtrata, are the completeſt proofs of
the theory here given of theſe rocks, and the
moſt inconſiſtent, in all reſpects, with the hypotheſis of their volcanic origin.

240. If theſe *criteria* are applied to what‘are
called extinguiſhed volcanoes, I have no doubt
that many which have been reckoned of that
number, will be found to derive their origin
more directly from the fire of the mineral regions. The baſaltic rocks of the Vivarais, I am
well perſuaded, belong to this claſs ; and I conclude that they do ſo, not only from the account
of them given by Mr Strange, but from the deſcription of Faujas himſelf, who, though under
the influence of the oppoſite theory, ſeems very
fair and accurate in his deſcription of phenomena. The moſt unequivocal mark of real
whinſtone rock, and of a formation in the ſtricteſt

---

* Recherches ſur les Volcains Eteints du Vivarais ;
Lettre de Dolomieu, p. 443.

eft fenfe mineral, is where veins of that kind of
rock interfect the ftrata. Now, in a letter to
Buffon, on the ftreams of lava found in the interior of certain calcareous rocks in the lower
Vivarais, Faujas defcribes what can be accounted nothing elfe but a vein or dike of whinftone,
accompanied with feveral of its moft remarkable
and characteriftic appearances : " Figurez-vous
un courant de lave, de la nature du bafalte noir,
dur et compacte, qui a percé à travers les maffes
calcaires, et s'eft fait jour dans quelques parties,
paroiffant et difparoiffant alternativement : Cette
coulée de matière volcanique s'enfonce fous une
partie de la ville, bâtie fur le rocher ; elle re-
paroit dans la cave d'un maréchal, fe cache et
fe montre encore de temps en temps en defcen-
dant dans le vallon, &c. Ce qu'il y a d'admirable, c'eft que la lave forme deux branches
bien extraordinaires, dont l'une s'éleve fur la
crête du rocher, tandis que l'autre coupe horizontalement de grands bancs calcaires efcarpés,
qui font à découvert, et bordent le chemin.

" Quels efforts n'-a-t-il pas fallu pour forcer
cette lave fe prendre une telle direction, et fe
percer cette fuite de rochers calcaires ? Si cette
longue coulée de lave avoit eu 200 ou 300 toifes
de largeur, je ne ferois pas furpris qu'un torrent de matiere en fufion de ce volume eut pu
produire des effets extraordinaires et violens ;
mais

mais figurez-vous, Monsieur, que dans les en-
droits les plus larges, elle n'a tout-au-plus qu'en-
viron 12 *ou* 15 *pieds ; elle n'en a que* 3 *ou* 4 *dans*
certaines parties *."

This narrow ftream is to be traced acrofs the
ftrata for more than a league and a half; and
the whole appeared to Faujas fo marvellous, that
he fays he almoft doubted the teftimony of his
fenfes. He would have done much better, however, to have doubted the conclufions of his
theory; for it was by them that the phenomena
before him were rendered fo myfterious and incredible. While he continued to regard what
is defcribed above as a ftream of melted lava,
which had defcended from the top of one mountain, and climbed up the fides of the oppofite,
like water in a conduit pipe, piercing occafionally through vaft bodies of folid rock, it is no
wonder that he confidered as marvellous what is
indeed phyfically impoffible. Had his belief in
the volcanic theory permitted him to fee in all
this, not a fuperficial current, but one of indefinite depth, he would have beheld the object
divefted, not of what was curious and interesting, but of what was incredible or abfurd,
and reduced to the fame clafs of things
with mineral veins. That it belongs really to
this clafs, and is no more than a vein or dike

of

---

* Volcains Eteints du Vivarais, p. 328, &c.

of whinſtone, interſecting the ſtrata to an unknown depth, and moſt probably, like other
veins, communicating with the mineral regions,
cannot be doubted by any one who has ſtudied
the ſubject of baſaltine rocks, through any other
medium than the volcanic theory. The ramifications which run from it into the calcareous
rock, contrived, Faujas ſays, juſt as if on purpoſe
to perplex mineralogiſts, is one of the well-
known and characteriſtic appearances of baſaltic veins.

241. It can hardly be doubted, that the lava
deſcribed by the ſame author as heaving up
a maſs of granite *, and including pieces of
it, is a rock of real whinſtone. The ſame
may be ſaid of many others ; and, though I
pretend not to affirm that there is nothing volcanic in the Vivarais, I muſt ſay, that nothing
decidedly volcanic appears in the deſcription of
that country, but many things that are certainly
of a very different origin.

In the preſent ſtate of geological ſcience, a
ſkilful mineralogiſt could hardly employ himſelf better, than in traverſing thoſe ambiguous
countries, where ſo much has been aſcribed to
the ancient operation of volcanic fire, and mark-
ing out what belongs either clearly to the erupted

---

* Volcains Eteints du Vivarais, fol. p. 365, &c.

ed or unerupted lavas, and what parts are of doubtful formation, containing no mark by which they may be referred to the one of thefe any more than to the other. Such a work would contribute very materially to illuftrate the natural hiftory of the earth.

242. One of the moft ingenious attempts to fupport the volcanic theory, is the fyftem of *fubmarine volcanoes*, imagined by the celebrated mineralogift DOLOMIEU. The phenomenon that led to this hypothefis, was what he had obferved in the hills near Lifbon, and ftill more remarkably in thofe of the Val di Noto in Sicily, where the bafaltine rocks had regular ftrata incumbent on them, and in fome cafes interpofed or alternated with them *. It feemed from this evident, that the ftrata were of later formation than the ftone on which they refted ; and as they muft, on every fuppofition, be held to be depofited by water, it was concluded, that the lava which they covered had been thrown out by volcanoes at the bottom of the fea ; that the ftrata had afterwards been depofited on this lava ; and that, in fome cafes, there had been frequent

quent

---

* Mémoire de Deodate de Dolomieu, fur les Volcains Eteints du Val di Noto, en Sicile. Journal de Phyf. tom. xxv. (1784. Septembre.) p. 191.

quent alternations of thefe eruptions and depo-
fitions *.

243. Though this hypothefis does certainly
deliver the fyftem of the Volcanifts from one
great difficulty, it is itfelf liable to infurmountable objections. I fhall juft mention fome of
the principal.

1. The regular and equidiftant ftrata that
we often fee covering the tops of whinftone
or bafaltic rocks, could not have been depofited
in the oblique and very much inclined pofition
which they now occupy.

This is remarkable in the ftrata which cover
the bafaltic rock of Salifbury *Craig*, near Edinburgh, at its northern extremity. The ftrata
are very regular, and muft have been depofited
in a plane nearly horizontal; yet the furface of
the bafaltes on which they now reft is very much
inclined, dipping rapidly to the north-eaft. The
neceffity of a horizontal depofition in ftrata,
which, though not now horizontal, have their
planes

---

* Near Vizini, in the Val di Noto, Dolomieu tells
us, that he counted eleven beds, alternately calcareous
and volcanic, in the perpendicular face of a hill, which
at a diftance appeared like a piece of cloth, ftriped black
and white; *ubi fupra*. In another inftance he faw more
than twenty of thefe alternations. He has fince made
fimilar obfervations in the Vincentine and in Tirol.
Journal de Phyf. tom. xxxvii. (1790), partie 2. p. 200.

planes nearly parallel to one another, has been proved at § 38.

2. If there is any truth in the principles eftablifhed above, even the ftrata themfelves have not been confolidated without the action of fire. By Dolomieu's fyftem, therefore, the confolidation of the ftrata which cover the bafaltes is not accounted for.

3. There are no means furnifhed by the hypothefis of fubmarine volcanoes for bringing the bafalt, and the ftrata which cover it, above the level of the fea. If it is faid that the waters of the fea have been drained off, the objections are all incurred that have been ftated at § 37 *. If it is faid, that the rocks themfelves have been elevated by a force, impelling them upwards, we fay, that the exiftence of fuch a force, when admitted, furnifhes another means of explaining the whole phenomenon, namely, that of the injection of melted matter among the ftrata, the fame that is ufed in the Huttonian Th ory.

4. The phenomena of balfaltic veins are not in the leaft explained by the hypothefis of fubmarine volcanoes. That hypothefis, then, even if the foregoing objections were removed, does

S   not

---

* Dolomieu adopts this fuppofition; he thinks, that the furface of the fea muft have been formerly 500 or 600 toifes above its prefent level. *Ibid.* p. 196.

not ferve to explain all the facts refpecting the rocks of this genus, and wants, of confequence, one of the moft important characters of a true theory. It muft be allowed, however, that it makes a confiderable approach to fuch a theory, and that the fubmarine volcanoes of Dolomieu, have an affinity to the unerupted lavas of Dr Hutton.

244. Though in thefe remarks I have endeavoured to expofe the errors of the volcanic fyftem, I cannot but confider that fyftem as coming infinitely nearer to the truth than the Neptunian. It has the merit of diftinguifhing an order of rocks, which bears no mark of aqueous formation, and in which the cryftallized, fparry, or lava like ftructure, befpeaks their primeval fluidity, and refers their origin to fire. The Neptunian fyftem, on the other hand, ftrives to confound the moft marked diftinction in the mineral kingdom, and to explain the formation, both of the ftratified and unftratified rocks, by the operation of the fame element. Though chargeable with this inconfiftency, it has become the prevailing fyftem of geology ; and the arguments which fupport it are therefore entitled to attention.

245. It will no doubt be thought fingular, that the fame mineralogift, whom we have juft feen exerting his ingenuity in defence of the volcanic

volcanic fyftem, fhould now appear equally ftre-
nuous in defence of the Neptunian. Though
Dolomieu contends for the volcanic origin of
fome bafaltic rocks, he does not admit that all
bafaltes is volcanic, nor even all of igneous formation. Thus he ftates, that he had examined
at Rome fome of the moft ancient monuments
of art, executed in bafaltes, brought from Upper
Egypt, and that he could difcover no mark of
the action of fire in any of them *. On the
contrary, he found that fome of them confifted of green bafaltes, which changes its colour
to a bronze, when expofed even to a moderate heat, and which therefore, he argues,
can never have endured any ftrong action of
fire.

The anfwer to this argument is very plain, if
we admit the effects afcribed by Dr Hutton to
the compreffion which neceffarily takes place in
the mineral regions. If indeed the heat in thofe
regions refembled exactly that of our fires at
the furface, it would not be eafy to deny the
above conclufion, which therefore certainly
holds good againft the volcanic origin of the
Egyptian bafaltes. But there is no reafon why,
under ftrong compreffion, the colouring matter

---

* Journal de Phyfique, tome xxxvii. (1790.) partie 2.
p. 193.

of thefe ftones might not be fixed, and indeftructible by heat, though it can be eafily volatilized or confumed when fuch compreffion is
removed. This argument then is againft the
volcanic ; but not againft what has been called
the *Plutonic* formation of bafaltes.

246. As to the other marks of fire which Dolomieu fought for and did not find in the above-
mentioned ftones, we are not exactly informed
in what they confifted. If the cryftallized or
fpathofe texture that belongs to this defcription
of ftones was wanting, the fpecimens were not
to be confidered as of the real bafaltic or whinftone genus, whatever their name or hiftory may
feem to indicate. If they did poffefs that texture, they had the only mark of an igneous origin that could be expected, fuppofing that origin to have been in the bowels of the earth.
No part, therefore, of the obfervations of this
ingenious mineralogift, can be confidered as inconfiftent with the theory of bafaltic rocks
which has been laid down above.

247. Bergman had before reafoned on this
fubject precifely in the fame manner, but from
better data, as the ftones from which he derived his argument were in their native place :
" Trap," fays that ingenious author, (that is,
whinftone), " is found in the ftratified mountains of Weft Gothland, in a way that deferves
                                          to

to be defcribed. The lower ftratum, which is
feveral Swedifh miles in circuit, (10½ of thefe
miles make a degree), is an arenaceous ftone,
horizontal, refting on granite, and having its
particles agglutinated by clay. The ftratum
above this is calcareous, full of the petrifactions
of marine animals, and above this is the trap.
Thefe three kinds of rock compofe the greater
part of the mountains juft mentioned, though
there are fome other beds, particularly very thin
beds of marl and of clay, which feparate the
middle ftratum, both from that which is under
it and over it, and are frequently fo penetrated
with bitumen that they burn in the fire. This
fchiftus is black; when burnt it becomes red,
and afterwards, when wafhed with water, affords alum. How can it be fuppofed," he adds,
" that the trap has ever been violently heated,
while the fchiftus on which it is incumbent retains its blacknefs, which however it lofes by
the action even of a very weak fire *."

The anfwer to this argument is already given.
The reafoning, as in the former inftance, is conclufive only againft the action of volcanic fire,
or fire at the furface; but not againft the action
of heat deep in the bowels of the earth, and un-

S 3 der

---

* Bergman de Productis Volcaniis Opufcula, tom. iii.
p. 214, &c.

der the preffure of the fuperincumbent ocean.
In fuch a fituation, the bituminous fchiftus
might be in contact with the melted bafalt, and
yet there might be no evaporation of the volatile, nor combuftion of the inflammable parts.
It does not, however, always happen, that the
bituminous fubftances, or fubftances alterable by
fire, which are found in contact with bafaltes,
are without any mark of having endured the
operation of fire. Inftances in which fuch
operation is apparent are given above, § 30. ;
and more will be added in the conclufion of this
note.

248. The fame mineralogift founds another
argument for the aqueous formation of whin or
trap, on the exiftence of that ftone in the form
of veins, included in primeval rocks : " Inveni-
tur hoc faxum (trap) in Suecia pluribus locis,
faepeque in montibus primaevis, anguftas implens
venas, adeo fubtilis ftructurae, ut particulae fint
impalpabiles, et, dum niger eft, genuinum efficit
lapidem Lydium. In hifce montibus, nulla ad-
funt ignis fubterranei veftigia *."

The phenomenon here defcribed, namely, a
vein of compact whinftone traverfing a primary
rock, is, without doubt, as incapable of being
explained by the operation of a volcano, as it is

by

---

* Opufcula, ubi fupra.

by that of aqueous depofition. It is, however, a moft complete proof of the original foftnefs of the fubftance of which the veins confift, and affords one of the ftrongeft poffible arguments for fuch an operation of fire as is fuppofed in the prefent theory. The main arguments, therefore, which have been propofed as fubverfive of the igneous origin of bafaltes, are only fubverfive of their formation by one modification of fire, viz. of fire acting near the furface ; and thus the weapons which directly pierce the armour of the Volcanift, and inflict a mortal wound, are eafily turned afide by the fuperior temper of the *Plutonic* mail.

249. An argument founded on facts very fimilar to fome of the preceding, and leading to the fame conclufion, is employed by the mineralogift to whom the Neptunian fyftem owes its chief fupport. Werner, in his obfervations on volcanic rocks and on bafaltes, has refted his proof of the aqueous formation of the latter, on their interpofition between beds of ftone in mountains regularly ftratified, and obvioufly formed by water. He defcribes an inftance of this in the bafaltic hill of *Scheibenberg ;* and the facts, though moft of them are not uncommon, are highly deferving of attention. Near the top of this hill, and above the bafaltic rock which compofes the body of it, he tells us, that

S 4   there

there was a fand-pit; a circumftance which he appears to confider as not a little fingular. It was, however, at the bottom of the hill, that he met with the appearances which chiefly attract-ed his notice: " Firft," fays he, " or loweft, was a thick bank of quartzy fand, above that a bed of clay, then a bed of the argillaceous ftone called wacken, and upon this laft refted the ba-faltes." " When I faw," adds he, " the three firft beds running almoft horizontally under the ba-faltes, and forming its bafe; the fand becoming finer above, then argillaceous, and at laft chang-ing into real clay, as the argil was converted in-to wacken in the fuperior part; and, laftly, the wacken into bafaltes: in a word, when I found a perfect tranfition from pure fand to argilla-ceous fand, from the latter to a fandy clay, and from this fandy clay, through many gradations, to a fat clay, to wacke, and at laft bafaltes, I was irrefiftibly led to conclude, that the bafaltes, the wacke, the clay, and the fand, are all of one and the fame formation; and that they are all the effect of a chemical precipitation during one and the fame fubmerfion of this country *."

Firft,

---

* " Combien je fus furpris de voir en arrivant au fond, un épais *banc de fable quartzeux*, puis au-deffus une *couche d'argile*, enfin une couche de la pierre argileufe nommée *Wacke*, et fur celle-ci repofer le *bafalte*. Quand je

First, as to the sand on the top of this basaltic hill, it is most probably the remains of certain sandstone strata that originally covered the basaltic part, but are now worn away. We are therefore to consider this as an instance of a basaltic rock, interposed between strata that are undoubtedly of marine origin. In this, however, there is nothing inconsistent with Dr Hutton's theory of basaltes; on the contrary, it is one

---

je vis les trois premières couches s'enfoncer *presqu' horizontalement sous le basalt*, et former ainsi sa *hole*, le sable devenir plus fin au-dessus, puis argileux, et se changer enfin en vraie argile, comme l'argile se convertissoit en wacke dans sa partie supérieure; et finalement la wacke en basalte : en un mot, de trouver ici une *transition parfaite* du *sable pur* au *sable argileux*, de celui-ci a *l'argile sabloneuse*, et de *l'argile sabloneuse*, par plusieurs gradations, à l'*argile grasse*, à la *wacke*, et enfin au *basalte*.

" A cette vue, je fus sur le champ et irrésistiblement entrainé à penser, (comme l'auroit été sans doute tout connoisseur impartial frappé des conséquences de ce phénomène); je fus, dis-je, irrésistiblement entrainé aux idées suivantes : Ce *basalte*, cette *wacke*, cette *argile*, et ce *sable*, *sont d'une seule et même formation;* ils sont tous l'effet d'une *précipitation par voie humide* dans une seule et même submersion de cette contrée; les eaux qui la couvroient alors transportoient d'abord le *sable*, puis deposoient l'*argile*, et changoient peu-à-peu leur précipitation en *wacke*, et enfin en vraie *basalte.*" — Journal de Physique, tome xxxviii. (1791), partie 1. p. 415.

one of the principal facts on which that theory
is founded. It has indeed been argued by some
mineralogists, that bodies thus contiguous must
owe their origin to the same element, and that
a mineral substance cannot be of more recent
formation than that which lies above it. But
the maxim, that a fossil must have the same
origin with those that surround it, does not
hold, unless they have a certain similarity of
structure. It is, for instance, the want of this
similarity, that authorises us to assign different
periods of formation to mineral veins, and to
the rocks in which they are included.

In a succession of strata, no one can doubt,
that the lowest were the first formed, and the
others in the order in which they lie ; but, when
between two strata of sandstone or of limestone
we find an intermediate rock, so different as to
resemble lava, and to have nothing schistose or
stratified in its composition, the same instrument
cannot be supposed to have been employed in
the formation of both ; nor is there any reason
why we may not suppose, that the intermediate
body was interposed between the other two, by
some action subsequent to their formation. It
was thus that Dolomieu concluded, when he
saw a lava-like stone interposed between calcareous strata in the Val di Noto, that, though
contiguous,

contiguous, thefe two rocks could not poffibly be of the fame formation ; and thus far it is certain, that every unprejudiced obferver muft agree with him.

250. But the circumftance on which Mr Werner feems to lay the greateft ftrefs, is the gradual tranfition from the fand to the bafalt, through the intermediate fteps of clay and wacken ; this gradual tranfition he confiders as a direct proof, that they are all of the fame formation.

A gradual tranfition of one body into another, can only be faid to take place, when it is impoffible to define their common boundary, or to determine the line where the one begins and the other ends. Now, if this be the proper notion of gradual tranfition, I muft fay, that after much careful examination, I have never feen an inftance, in which fuch a tranfition takes place between whinftone and the contiguous ftrata. The *line* of feparation, though in fome places lefs evident than in others, has, on the whole, been marked out with great precifion ; and, though the ftones have been firmly united, or, as one may fay, welded one upon another, yet, when a frefh fracture was obtained, the ftratified and unftratified parts have rarely failed to be diftinguifhed. The frefh fracture is indeed often neceffary, for many fpecies of whinftone

ftone get by decompofition a granulated texture at the furface, fo as hardly to be diftinguifhed from real fandftone.

Some of the kinds of primary fchiftus alfo, particularly the argillaceous, when much indurated, have in their ftructure a confiderable refemblance to whinftone ; they are flightly granular, or laminated, and have a tendency to a fparry texture. Where it happens that this fort of fchiftus and whinftone are contiguous, it is natural to expect, that their common boundary will be traced with difficulty, and in many parts will be quite uncertain. Still, however, if a careful examination is made ; if the effects of accidental caufes are removed ; and, above all, if the more ambiguous inftances are compared with the more decifive, and interpreted by them, though fingle fpecimens may be doubtful, we will hardly ever find that any uncertainty remains with refpect to entire rocks.

251. This general fact, which I ftate on much better authority than that of my own obfervations, viz. on thofe of Dr Hutton, is not given as abfolutely without exception. The theory of whinftone which has been laid down here, leads us indeed to look for fome fuch exceptions. It is certain, that the bafis of whinftone, or the material out of which it is prepared by the action

tion of subterraneous heat, is clay in some state
or other, and probably in that of argillaceous
schistus. It follows, of consequence, that argillaceous schistus may by heat be converted into whinstone. When, therefore, melted whinstone has been poured over a rock of such schistus, it may, by its heat, have converted a part of
that rock into a stone similar to itself; and thus
may now seem to be united, by an insensible gradation, with the stratum on which it is incumbent;
and phenomena of this kind may be expected
to have really happened, though but rarely, as a
particular combination of circumstances seems
necessary to produce them. Hence it is evident,
that stones may graduate into one another, without being of the same formation; and that it is
fallacious to conclude, from the insensible transition of one kind of rock into another, without
any other circumstance of affinity, that they have
both the same origin.

I am disposed, therefore, to make some limitation to what is said in § 72, where I have expressed an absolute incredulity as to such transitions as are here referred to. The great skill
and experience of the mineralogist who has described the strata at Scheibenberg, do not allow us to doubt of his exactness, though some
of the appearances are such as decomposition
and wearing might well enough be supposed to
produce.

produce. The faireſt way is to take Mr Werner's obſervations juſt as they are given us, and to try whether they cannot be explained without the aſſiſtance of his theory. In effect, the wacken which he deſcribes, reſts, it would ſeem, on an unconſolidated bed of clay; and it may be ſuppoſed, that a part of this bed has been converted into wacken by the heat of the incumbent maſs, and has thus produced the apparent gradation from the one ſubſtance to the other. As the appearances of the rocks of Scheibenberg ſeem to be conſidered by Werner as furniſhing a very ſtrong, and even an unexpected confirmation of his ſyſtem, I cannot help thinking, that an explanation of them, on the principles of Dr Hutton, without any ſtraining or forcing of thoſe principles, contributes not a little toward extending the empire of the latter over all the phenomena of geology.

252. Another fact, which has been much inſiſted on of late, in proof of the aqueous formation of baſaltic rocks, is that ſhells are found in them. Of the reality of this fact, however, or at leaſt of the inſtances hitherto produced, great doubts I think may be reaſonably entertained. The ſpecimens of the ſuppoſed baſaltes, with ſhells included in them, that are chiefly relied on, are found at Portruſh in Ireland, a rocky promontory to the weſtward of the Giant's Cauſeway, and ſeparated from it by a
                                    conſiderable

confiderable body of calcareous ftrata. Some
of thefe fpecimens were brought to Edinburgh
about a year ago, and were fuppofed, I believe,
to contain an irrefragable proof of the Neptunian origin of the bafaltic promontory where
they were found.   I went to fee thefe fpecimens
in company with Lord Webb Seymour and Sir
James Hall; and, on examining them carefully,
we were all of opinion, that the ftones which
contained the fhells, or the impreffions of the
fhells, were no part of the real bafaltes.   They
were all very compact, and had all more or lefs of
a filiceous appearance, fuch as that of chert;
they had nothing of a fparry or cryftallized ftructure; their fracture was conchoidal, and but
flightly uneven.   In two of them, one of which
bore the impreffion of a *cornu ammonis*, the fchiftofe texture might be diftinctly perceived.   A fpecimen which accompanied them, but in which
there was no fhell, ferved very exactly to explain
the relation between thefe ftones and the true
bafaltes.   Part of this fpecimen was a true bafalt, and the reft a fort of hornftone, exactly the
fame with that in which the fhells were, and
not unlike the jafper that is under the whinftone
of Salifbury Crag, and in contact with it; fo
that on the whole it was evident, that the rock
containing the fhells is the fchiftus or ftratified ftone, which ferves as the bafe of the basaltes,

faltes, and which has acquired a high degree of
induration, by the vicinity of the great ignited
mafs of whinftone.

This folution of the difficulty has fince been
confirmed by obfervations made on the fpot by
Dr Hope, who difcovered two or three alternations of the bafaltic rock, with the beds of the
fchiftus in which the fhells are contained.

253. This alfo explains fome obfervations of
Spallanzani, made in the ifland of Cerigo, on the
coaft of Greece, the Cythæra of the ancients *.
The bafe of that ifland is limeftone; but it
abounds alfo in unftratified rocks, which the
Italian naturalift fuppofes to be of volcanic origin; but which, if I miftake not, we would regard as whinftone, or perhaps porphyry; and
they are faid to contain oyfter-fhells and pec-
tenites of a large fize, perfectly mineralized.
Thefe petrifactions, however, Spallanzani fays,
are not contained in the lava that has actually flowed, but in ftones which have only
endured a flighter action of fire. Without the
commentary afforded by the Portrufh fpecimens,
it would be difficult to make out any thing very
precife from this defcription. By help of the
information derived from thofe fpecimens, we
may conclude, that the condition of the fhells
in

---

* Journal de Phyfique, tom. xlviii. (1798), p. 278.

in them, and in the rocks of Cerigo, is perfectly alike ; and that, in both cafes, the fhells
are involved in parts of the rock which are truly
ftratified, but which have been, in fome degree,
affimilated to the bafaltes by the heat which
they have endured. Spallanzani would probably have ufed exactly the fame terms which he
employs in fpeaking of Cerigo, if he had been
required to defcribe the petrified fhells at Portrufh.

254. In the inftances juft mentioned, the petrified marine objects are not found in the real
whinftone ; but if they were found in it, when it
borders on ftratified rocks containing fuch objects, the thing would not be at all furprifing,
nor furnifh any argument againft the igneous
confolidation of the ftone. If a torrent of
melted matter was poured in among the ftrata,
by a force which at the fame time broke up and
difordered thofe ftrata, nothing could be more
natural, than that this matter fhould contain
fragments of them, and of the objects peculiar
to them.

In one inftance, mentioned by Mr Strange,
this feems actually to have taken place. In the
Veronefe, a country remarkable for a mixture
of limeftone ftrata, containing marine objects,
with volcanic or bafaltine hills, he affures us,
that he had feen a mafs of ftone, which had

T evidently

evidently concreted from fufion, in which the marine foffil bodies, originally, as he fuppo-fes, contained in the ftrata, were perfectly di-ftinguifhable, though varioufly disfigured*. It may be, that in this, as in the foregoing exam-ples, it was not real bafaltes, or real lava, which contained the fhells, but the conterminal rock; but, fuppofing it to be as Mr Strange reprefents it, there appears to be no inconfiftency between the phenomenon, and the igneous origin of the rock in which the fhells were included. Here, however, it fhould be remarked, that the pre-fence of great preffure, to prevent the conver-fion of the fhells into quicklime, feems abfolute-ly neceffary; and that the phenomenon of thefe bafaltic petrifactions, requires the application of heat to have been deep under the furface of the earth.

255. The phenomena we have been confider-ing, have been felected as the moft unfavourable to the igneous origin of bafaltic rocks; and we have feen, that when duly examined, they are not at all inconfiftent with it. We are now to take a view of fome appearances, that feem quite irreconcilable with the aqueous formation of thefe rocks.

Where

---

* Phil. Tranf. 1775, p. 25.

Where whinftone rocks are found in maffes, bounded by the ftrata, and infulated among them, they fubject the Neptunian fyftem to great difficulties. For, fuppofing it true that this ftone may be produced by the precipitation and cryftallization of mineral fubftances diffolved in water, yet it feems unaccountable, that this effect has been fo local and limited in extent, as often to be confined to an irregular figure of a few acres, while, all round, the fubftances depofited have had no tendency to cryftallization, and have been formed into the common fecondary ftrata. The rock of Salifbury *Craig*, for inftance, is a mafs of whinftone, having a perpendicular face eighty or ninety feet high toward the weft, and extending from north to fouth with a circular fweep about 900 yards. The whole of this rock refts on regular beds of fecondary fandftone, not horizontal, but confiderably depreffed toward the north-eaft : the rock is loftieft in the middle, and decreafes in thicknefs toward each end, terminating at its northern extremity in a kind of wedge. It is covered at top, toward that extremity, with regular beds of fandftone, perfectly fimilar to thofe on which it is incumbent ; and it is not improbable, that this covering formerly extended over the whole.

T 2

Now,

Now, what caufe can have determined the column of water, which refted on the bafe at prefent
occupied by this rock, to depofite nothing but
the materials of whinftone, while the water on
the fouth, weft, and north, was depofiting the
materials of arenaceous and marly ftrata?
Wherefore, within this fmall fpace, was the pre-
cipitate every where *chemical*, to ufe the language of Werner, while clofe to it, on either
fide, it was entirely *mechanical?* Why is there,
in this cafe, no gradation? and why is a mere
mathematical line the boundary between regions where fuch different laws have prevailed?·
Whence alfo, we may afk, has the bafaltic depofite been abruptly terminated toward the
weft, fo as to produce the fteep face which has
juft been mentioned? The operation of currents,
or of any motion that can take place in a fluid,
will furnifh no explanation whatever of thefe
phenomena; yet they are phenomena far from
being peculiar to a fingle hill; they are among
the moft general and charaĉteriftic appearances
in the natural hiftory of whinftone mountains;
and a geological theory which does not account
for· them, is hardly entitled to any confideration.

256. The bafaltic rock, juft defcribed, is alfo
covered, at leaft partly, with ftrata perfeĉtly fimilar

lar to thofe that lie under it. Now, it appears altogether unaccountable, that after the water had done depofiting the materials of the whin on the fpot in queftion, the former order was fo quickly refumed, and a depofition of fand, and of the other materials of the ftrata, took place juft as before. All this is quite unintelligible; and the principles of the Neptunian fyftem feem here to ftand as much in need of explanation, as any of the appearances which they are intended to account for.

257. The unequal thicknefs, and great irregularity in the furface of the whinftone mafs, here treated of, and of many rocks of the fame kind, is alfo a great objection to the notion of their aqueous formation. This feems to have been perceived by Werner, in the inftance of the rocks formerly mentioned; and he endeavours to explain it, by fuppofing, that much of thefe rocks has been deftroyed by wafte and decompofition, fo that an irregularity of their furface, and want of correfpondence has been given to them, which they did not originally poffefs. In the inftance of Salifbury *Craig*, however, we have a proof, that the great irregularity of furface, and the inequality of thicknefs, do not always arife from thefe caufes. The thinneft part of that rock, toward its northern extremity, is

ftill

ftill covered by the ftrata in their natural place,,
and has been perfectly defended by them from
every fort of wearing and decay. The cunei-
form fhape, therefore, which this rock takes at
its extremities, and the great difference of its
thicknefs at them and in the middle, is a part
of its original conftitution, and can be attributed
to nothing cafual, or fubfequent to its confolidation.

The fame may be faid of many other bafaltic
rocks, where an inequality of thicknefs, moft
unlike to what belongs to aqueous depofites, is
known to exift in beds of whinftone that are
ftill deep under the furface. Thus the toadftone
of Derbyfhire, even where it has a thick covering of ftrata over it, has been found, by the fink-
ing of perpendicular fhafts, to vary from the
thicknefs of eighteen yards to more than fixty,
within the horizontal diftance of lefs than a fur-
long. Nothing of this kind is ever found to
take place in thofe beds of rock which are certainly known to originate from aqueous depofition, and no character can more ftrongly mark an
effential difference of formation.

258. We have had frequent occafion to confider the characters of thofe maffes of whinftone
which are fo often found interpofed between
ftratified rocks. Thefe have been found in general very adverfe to the Neptunian fyftem ; and

two

two of them which yet remain to be mentioned, are even more fo than any of the reft.

Where a bed or tabular mafs of whinftone is interpofed between ftrata, and wherever an opportunity offers of feeing its termination, if the ftrata under it are not broken, it may be remarked, that they do not abut themfelves bluff and abrupt againft the whin. On the contrary, if we mark the courfe of the ftratum which covers the whinftone, and of that which is the bafe of it, we fhall find they converge toward one another, the interpofed mafs growing thinner and thinner, like a wedge. When the latter terminates, the two former come in contact, and have no ftratum interpofed between them. Thus the roof and bafe of the whinftone rock are contiguous beds, that appear as if they had been lifted up and bent, and feparated by an interpofed mafs. Had the whole been an effect of fimultaneous depofition, the regular ftrata muft have been abruptly terminated by the whin, like two courfes of different forts of mafonry where they meet with one another.

259. From this wedge-form of the whinftone maffes, and in general from the irregularity of their furfaces, another conclufion follows, fimilar to the preceding, and one which has been already mentioned. Where the furface of the interpo-

T 4 fed

fed mafs is greatly inclined to the horizon, the
ftrata which reft on this inclined plane, are neverthelefs as exactly parallel to that plane, and
to one another, as if they were really horizontal. It is certain, therefore, that they were not
depofited on the fame inclined plane on which
they now reft; for, if fo, they would have been
ftill nearly horizontal, and by no means parallel
to the inclined fide of the whinftone. This follows from the nature of aqueous depofition, as
already explained.

We have a remarkable inftance of the phenomenon here referred to, in the rock of Salifbury
Craig, of which mention has been fo often made,
and in which almoft every circumftance is united, that can ferve to elucidate the natural hiftory of bafaltic rocks. The north end of that
rock is in the figure of a wedge, with its inclined fide confiderably fteep, and covered by
ftrata of grit, perfectly regular, and parallel
to the furface on which they lie. The in-
fpection of them will convince any one, that
they were not depofited by the water, on a
bottom fo highly inclined as that on which they
now reft. They are of a ftructure very fchiftofe;
their layers very thin; fo that any inaccuracy of
their parallelifm would be readily obferved.
The appearances of the horizontal depofition of
thefe ftrata, are indeed fo clear, and fo impoffi-
bble

ble to be misunderstood, that the followers of
the Huttonian system would not risk much, if
they were to leave the whole theory of whinstone to the decision of this single fact, and
should agree to abandon that theory altogether, if
the Neptunists can shew any physical or statical
principle, on which the deposition now described
can possibly have been made ; or will point out
the rule, by which nature has given a structure
so nicely stratified to arenaceous beds deposited on a surface so highly inclined. If no
such principle can be pointed out, though we
cannot conclude that the Huttonian Theory is
true, we certainly may conclude that the Neptunian is false.

260. Proofs of the igneous formation of whinstone, still more direct, are derived from the
induration of the contiguous strata ; from their
disturbance when intersected by veins of whinstone ; and from the charring of the coal which
happens to be in contact with these veins. These
are considered above at § 66, 67, &c. ; and it
is particularly taken notice of at § 66, that pieces of sandstone are sometimes found as if floating
in the whinstone, and, at the same time, greatly
altered in their texture. One of the best and
most unequivocal instances of this sort which I
have seen, is to be found on the south side of
Arthur's Seat, near Edinburgh. The rock
which

which compofes the upper part of the hill, on
that fide, is a whinftone breccia, fuch as we
have many examples of, and, I believe, very
much refembling what is called a *lava brecciata*
by the volcanic geologifts. The ftony fragments included in this compound mafs, are for
the greater part rounded ; and fome of them
are of whinftone, others of porphyry, ftrongly
characterized by rectangular maculæ of feltfpar,
and many feem to be of fandftone, but fo confiderably altered, as to leave it at leaft difputa-
ble whether they really are fo or not. In one
part, however, where the face of the rock is
nearly perpendicular, a narrow ridge is feen
ftanding out from the reft, and of a different colour, being more entirely covered with mofs
than the rock round about it, and, as may be
prefumed from that circumftance, lefs liable
to decompofition. On examination I found,
that this ridge does not confift of whinftone, but
of a very hard and highly confolidated fandftone. It appears to be the edge of a ftratum,
of the thicknefs of about nine or ten inches, and
of the height of fifteen or fixteen feet. It is not
perfectly ftraight, but flightly waved, its general
direction being nearly vertical; and it is on
both fides firmly embraced by the whinftone.
When broken, it appears that this fandftone refembles in colour, and in every thing
but

but its greater confolidation, and more vitreous ftructure, the common grit found at the bottom of the hill, and over all the adjacent plain.

261. If all thefe circumftances are put together, there appears but one conclufion that can be drawn from them. We have here the manifeft marks of fome power which could lift up this fragment of rock from its native place, diftant at leaft feveral hundred yards from its prefent fituation, place it upright on its edge, encompafs it with a folid rock, of a nature quite heterogeneous to itfelf, and beftow on it, at the fame time, a great addition of folidity and induration. If the mafs in which this ftone is now imbedded, be fuppofed to have been once in fufion, and forcibly thrown up from below, invading the ftrata, and carrying the fragments along with it, the whole phenomena now defcribed admit of an explanation, and all the circumftances accord perfectly with one another ; but, without this fuppofition, they are fo many feparate prodigies, which have no connection with one another, nor with any thing that is known. It is indeed impoffible, that the effects of motion and heat can be more clearly expreffed than they are here, or the fubject in which thefe powers refided more diftinctly pointed out.

262. The

262. The preceding facts being fufceptible but of one interpretation, are on that account extremely valuable. The phenomena of Salifbury *Craig*, near the fame place, are almoft equally free from ambiguity. The bafaltic rock which forms that precipice, refts on arenaceous or marly ftrata; and thefe, in their immediate contact with the former, afford an inftance of what is mentioned § 67, namely, the converfion of the ftrata in fuch fituations into a kind of petrofilex, or even jafper. The line which feparates the one rock from the other, is, at the fame time, fo well defined, as, in the eyes even of the moft determined Neptunift, to exclude all idea of infenfible gradation.

263. The fame rock affords fome remarkable inftances of the difturbance of the ftrata contiguous to the whinftone. The beds of the former are bent upwards in feveral places; and, at one in particular, form an arch, with its convexity downward, fo as to make it evident, that the force which produced this bending was directed from below upwards.

264. It is, however, where whinftone takes the form of veins, interfecting the ftrata, that the induration of the latter is moft confpicuous. The coaft of Ayrfhire, and the oppofite coaft of

Arran,

Arran, exhibit thefe veins in aftonifhing variety and abundance. The ftrata are, in many inftances, fo *reticulated* by the veins, and
interfected at fuch fmall diftances, that it
feems neceffary to fuppofe, that the fiffures
in them were hardly fooner made than filled
up. This at leaft is true, if the veins are to
be accounted all of the fame formation ; and,
in the greateft number of inftances by far,
there is no mark of the one being pofterior to
the other.

265. The induration of the fides of thefe
veins, in fome cafes, has been fuch, that the fides
have become more durable than the vein itfelf ;
fo that the whinftone has been worn away by
the wafhing of the waves, and has left the fides
ftanding up, with an empty fpace, like a *ditch*,
between them. One of thefe I remarked on the
fouth fide of Brodick Bay, in Arran, which,
where it met the face of an abrupt cliff, was not
lefs than forty or fifty feet in depth.

266. I fhall pafs over whatever argument
might be drawn in favour of our fyftem, from
the flender ramifications of the veins, and the
varieties of their fizes, from a few inches to many fathoms in diameter, and alfo from the connection which they often appear to have with the
great tabular maffes of bafaltes ; and fhall only
add

add a few remarks on the charring of coal in the vicinity of veins or maſſes of whinſtone. The connection between the charring of coal and the preſence of whinſtone, was firſt obſerved by Dr Hutton; and, as far as opportunities of verifying the obſervation have yet occurred, appears to be a fact no leſs general than it is curious and intereſting. In the coal-mines of Scotland, it certainly holds remarkably, particularly in thoſe about Saltcoats in Ayrſhire, where a whinſtone dike is known to ſtretch acroſs the whole of the coal country, and to be every where accompanied with blind or uninflammable coal. At Newcaſtle, dikes of the ſame kind are met with, and one, in particular, in what is called the *Walker* Colliery, has proved the action of ſubterraneous fire, to the ſatisfaction of mineralogiſts nowiſe prejudiced in favour of the Huttonian ſyſtem.

The coal found under baſaltes, in the Iſland of Skye, has been already mentioned, § 139. To what was ſaid concerning the fibrous ſtructure of the parts of that foſſil in immediate contact with the whin, it may be added, that it is alſo charred in thoſe parts, ſo as to have hardly any flame when it is burnt, though further down it is of the nature of ordinary coal. Indeed, if there be any truth in Mr Kirwan's general remark,

mark, that it is common to find wood-coal under basaltes, it must be understood to arise from this, that the coal in contact with the basaltes is frequently charred, and its fibrous structure, by that means, rendered more visible.

267. It has been objected to the supposition of coal having its bituminous part driven off by the heat of the whinstone, that this ought not, on Dr Hutton's principles, to happen in the mineral regions. But it may be replied, as has been done above, that the local application of heat might certainly produce this effect, and might drive off the volatile parts from a hotter to a colder part of the same stratum. The bitumen has not been so volatilized and expanded as entirely to escape from the mineral regions; but it has been expelled from some parts of a mass, only to be condensed and concentrated in others. This supposition coincides exactly with the appearances.

268. The native or fossil-coke which accompanies whinstone, has been distinguished into two varieties. The first is the most common, in which, though the coal is perfectly charred, it is solid, and breaks with a smooth and shining surface. The second is also perfect charcoal, but is very porous and spungy. This substance is much rarer than the other : Dr Hutton mentions an instance

inſtance of it at the mouth of the river **Ayr,**
where there is a whinſtone dike *. I had the
ſatisfaction of viſiting it along with him. It
was in the bed of the river, below the high-water mark ; the ſpecimens had the exact appearance of a *cinder.*

In the banks of the ſame river, ſome miles
higher up, he found a piece of coal, belonging
to a regular ſtratum, involved in whinſtone, and
extremely incombuſtible. It conſumed very
ſlowly in the fire, and deflagrated with nitre like
plumbago. This he conſidered as the ſame
foſſil which has been deſcribed under the name
of *plombagine.* Near it, and connected with
the ſame vein of whinſtone, was a real and undoubted plumbago.

From theſe circumſtances he alſo concluded, that plumbago is the extreme of a gradation, of which foſſil-coal is the beginning, and
is nothing elſe than this laſt reduced to perfect charcoal. This agrees with the chemical
analyſis, which ſhows plumbago to be compoſed
of carbon, combined with iron.

In confirmation of this theory, he mentions a ſpecimen, in his poſſeſſion, of ſteati-
tical whinſtone, from Cumberland, containing
nodules of a very perfect and beautiful plumbago ; and he alſo takes notice of a mine of this
laſt,

---

* Theory of the Earth, vol. i. p, 611.

laft, in Ayrfhire, which, on the authority of Dr Kennedy, who has examined it with great care, I can ftate as being contained, or enveloped in whinftone ; and I hope the public will foon be favoured with a particular defcription of this very interefting fpot, by the fame ingenious and accurate obferver.

269. Thus the mineralogical and chemical difcoveries agree in reprefenting coal, blind-coal, plombagine, plumbago, as all modifications of the fame fubftance, and as exhibiting the fame principle, carbon, in a ftate of greater or lefs combination. As the laft and higheft term of this feries fhould be placed the *diamond ;* but we are yet unacquainted with the matrix of this curious foffil, and its geological relation to other minerals. When known, they will probably give to this fubftance the fame place in the geological, as in the chemical arrangement : in the mean time, it is hardly neceffary to remark, how well all the preceding facts agree with the hypothefis of the igneous formation of whinftone, and how anomalous and unconnected they appear, according to every other theory.

270. Notwithftanding all this accumulated and unanfwerable evidence for the igneous formation of bafaltes, a great objection would ftill remain to our theory, were it not for the very accurate and conclufive experiments concern-

U   ing

ing the fufion of this foffil, referred to above,
§ 75. A ftrong prejudice againft the production of any thing like a real ftone by means of
fufion, had arifen, even among thofe mineralogifts, who were every day witneffes of the ftony
appearance affumed by volcanic lava. They
ftill maintained, on the authority of their own
imperfect experiments, that nothing but glafs
can ever be obtained by the melting of earths or
of ftones, in whatever manner they are combined.

An ingenious naturalift, after defcribing a
block of bafaltes, in which he difcovered fuch
appearences, as inclined him to admit its igneous confolidation, rejects that hypothefis, merely from the imaginary inability of fire to give
to any fubftance a ftony character : " Quelque
mélange," fays he, " de terres que l'on fuppofe,
quelque foit le degré de feu que l'on imagine,
quelque foit le tems que l'on emploie, il eft très
certain que l'on n'obtiendra pas, par le feul fluide
igné, ni bafalte, ni rien qui lui reffemble *."

Sir James Hall's experiments have completely demonftrated the contrary of what is here
afferted ; they have added much to the evidence
of the Huttonian fyftem ; and, independently of
all

---

* Journal de Phyf. tom. xlix. (1799.) p. 36.

all theory, have narrowed the circle of prejudice
and error.

Note xv. § 83.

On Granite.

1. Granite Veins.

271. It is faid above, § 77., that granite is
found in unftratified maffes, and in veins. In the
former of thefe conditions, it conftitutes entire
mountains, and forms the central ridge of many
of the greateft chains that traverfe the furface
of the earth. It is the granite of this kind that
has been moft generally defcribed by travellers
and mineralogifts. The veins have not been
fo much attended to, though they are of peculiar importance for afcertaining the relation between granite and other foffils.

272. Though Dr Hutton was the firft geologift
who explained the nature of granite veins, and
who obferved with attention the phenomena
which accompany them, he is not the firft who
has mentioned them. M. Beffon found veins
of this kind in the Limoges, in an argillaceous
fchiftus, and unconnected, as far as appeared, with
any large mafs of granite *.

U 2   Sauffure

---

* Journal de Phyf. tom. xxix. p. 89.

Sauſſure met with granite veins in the Valor-
ſine, but did not ſee them diſtinctly.   He aſcribed them to infiltration *.   The date of this obſervation is in 1776 : He afterwards diſcovered
ſimilar appearances at Lyons †.

Werner alſo, in enumerating the ſubſtances
of which veins are formed, reckons granite as
one of them.

273. Veins of granite may be conſidered as of
two kinds, according as they are connected, or
not connected apparently with any large maſs of
granite.   It is probable, that theſe two kinds of
veins only differ in appearance, and that both
are connected with maſſes of the ſame rock,
though that connection is viſible in ſome inſtances, and inviſible in others.   The diſtinction,
however, whatever it be with reſpect to the
thing obſerved, is real with reſpect to the obſerver ; and, as it is right, in a deſcription of
facts, to avoid every thing hypothetical, I ſhall
ſpeak of theſe veins ſeparately.

274 Veins of granite, having no communication, ſo far as can be diſcovered, with any maſs of
the ſame rock, are found in the Weſtern Iſlands of Scotland, particularly in that of Coll,
                                                           where

---

* Voyages aux Alpes, tom. i. § 598, 599.

† *Ibid.* § 601.

where they traverfe the beds of gneifs and hornblend fchiftus, which compofe the main body
of the ifland.   They are fometimes feveral
fathoms in thicknefs, obliquely interfecting the
planes of the ftrata juft mentioned, which are
nearly vertical.   In thefe veins the feltfpar is
predominant ; it is very highly cryftallized, and
of a beautiful flefh colour.   Many fmaller veins
are alfo to be met with in the fame place ; but
no large mafs of granite is found, either in this
or the adjacent ifland of Tiree.

275. The Portfoy granite, of which mention
has been already made, § 80, alfo conftitutes a
vein or dike, traverfing a highly indurated micaceous fchiftus, about a mile to the eaftward of
the little town of Portfoy, and not vifibly connected with any large mafs of the fame kind.
More dikes than one of this granite have been
obferved ear the fame fpot.

A fimilar granite is likewife found inland,
in the neighbourhood of Huntly, about eighteen miles fouth of Portfoy ; but whether in the
fhape of a vein or a mafs, I have not been able
to learn.

276. Veins of granite are alfo frequent in
Cornwall, where they are known by the name
of *lodes*, the fame name which is applied in that
country to metallic veins.   The granite veins fre-

quently interfect the metallic, and are remarkable
for producing fhifts in them, or for throwing them
out of their natural direction. The mineral veins,
particularly thofe that yield copper and tin, run
nearly from eaft to weft, having the fame direction with the beds of the rock itfelf, which
is a very hard fchiftus. The granite lodes, as
alfo thofe of porphyry, called *elvan* in Cornwall,
are at right angles nearly to the former; and
it is remarked, that they generally heave the
mineral veins, but that the mineral veins feldom or never heave the crofs-veins. In this
country, therefore, the veins of granite and porphyry are pofterior in formation to the metallic
veins. Thefe veins of granite may perhaps be
connected with the great granitic mafs that runs
longitudinally through Cornwall, from Dartmoor to the Land's End. This much is certain,
that their directions in general are fuch, that,
if produced, they would interfect that mafs,
nearly at right angles.

277. The granite veins in Glentilt, where Dr
Hutton made his firft obfervations on this fubject, are not, I believe, vifibly connected with any
large mafs of the fame rock *. The bed of the river Tilt, in the diftance of little more than a mile,

is

---

* Tranf. Royal Society Edin. vol. iii. p. 77, &c.

is interfected by no lefs than fix very powerful
veins of granite, all of them accompanied with
fuch marks of diforder and confufion in the ftrata, as indicate very ftrongly the violence with
which the granite was here introduced into its
place. Thefe veins very probably belong to
the great mafs of granite which is known to
form the central ridge of the Grampians further
to the north ; but they are feveral miles diftant
from it, and the connection is perhaps invifible
in the prefent ftate of the earth's furface.

278. The fecond kind of granite vein, is one
which proceeds vifibly from a mafs of that rock,
and penetrates into the contiguous ftrata. The
importance of this clafs of veins, for afcertaining the relation between granite and other mineral bodies, has been pointed out, § 82. ; and
by means of them it has been fhewn, that the
granite, though inferior in pofition, is of more
recent formation than the fchiftus incumbent on
it ; and that the latter, inftead of having been
quietly depofited on the former, has been, long
after its depofition and confolidation, heaved up
from its horizontal pofition, by the liquid body
of granite forcibly impelled againft it from below.

It has been alleged, in order to take off the
force of the argument derived from granite
veins,

veins, that thefe veins are formed by infiltration, though, to give any probability to this
fuppofition, it would be neceffary to fhew, that
water is able to diffolve the ingredients of granite ; and even if this could be done, the direction which the veins have, in many inftances,
rifing up from the granite, is a proof, as remarked § 82., that they cannot be the effect of infiltration.

Another objection has been thrown out,
namely, that the veins here referred to are
not of true granite, according to the definition
which mineralogifts have given of that fubftance.
The force of a fact, however, is not to be leffened by a change of names, or the ufe of arbitrary
definitions. The general fact is, that the granitic mafs, and the vein proceeding from it, conftitute one continuous, and uninterrupted body,
without any line of feparation between them.
The geological argument turns on this circumftance alone ; and it is no matter whether the
rock be a fyenite, a granitelle, or a real granite.
The phenomenon fpeaks the fame language, and
leads to the fame conclufion, whatever be the
technical terms the mineralogift employs in defcribing it.

279. It muft, however, be admitted, that a
difference of character is often to be obferved
between the granite mafs and the veins proceeding

ing from it; fometimes the fubftances in the latter are more highly cryftallized than in the former; fometimes, but more rarely, they are lefs cryftallized, and, in fome inftances, an ingredient that enters into the mafs feems entirely wanting in the vein. Thefe varieties, for what we yet know, are not fubject to any general rule; but they have been held out as a proof, that the maffes and the veins are not of the fame formation. It may be anfwered, that a perfect fimilarity between fubftances that, on every hypothefis, muft have cryftallized in very different circumftances, is not always to be looked for; but the moft direct anfwer is, that this perfect fimilarity does fometimes occur, infomuch that, in certain inftances, no difference whatfoever can be difcovered between the mafs and the vein, but they confift of the fame ingredients, and have the fame degree of cryftallization. Some inftances of this are juft about to be remarked.

280. A ftrong objection to the fuppofed origin of granitic veins from infiltration, and indeed to their formation in any way but by igneous fufion, arifes from the number of fragments of fchiftus, often contained, and completely infulated in thofe veins. How thefe fragments were introduced into the fiffures of the fchiftus, and fuftained till they were furrounded

by

by the matter depofited by water, is very hard
to be conceived ; but if they were carried in
by the melted granite, nothing is more eafily
underftood.

The following are fome of the places where
the phenomena of granite veins may be diftinctly feen.

281. The ifland of Arran, remarkable for collecting into a very fmall compafs a great number
of the moft interefting facts of geology, exhibits
many inftances of the penetration of fchiftus by
veins of granite. A group of granite mountains occupies the northern extremity of the
ifland, the higheft of which, Goatfield, rifes
nearly to the height of 3000 feet, and on
the fouth fide is covered with fchiftus to the
height of 1100. From thence, the line of junction, or that at which the granite emerges from
under the fchiftus, winds, fo far as I was able
to obferve, round the whole group of monntains,
with many wavings and irregularities, rifing
fometimes to a greater, and defcending fometimes to a much lower level, than that juft
mentioned. Along this line, particularly on
the fouth, wherever the rock is laid bare,
and cut into by the torrents, innumerable veins
of granite are to be feen entering into the
fchiftus, growing narrower as they advance into
it ; and being directed, in very many cafes, from
below

below upwards, they are precifely of the kind
which the infiltration of water could not produce, even were that fluid capable of diffolving
the fubftances which the vein confifts of. From
this fouth face of the mountain, and from the
bed of a torrent that interfects it very deeply,
Dr Hutton brought a block of fchiftus, of feveral hundredweight, curioufly penetrated by granite veins, including in them many infulated
fragments of the fchiftus.

From this point, the common fection of
the granite and fchiftus defcends towards the
weft fide of the mountain, and is vifible at the
bottom of a deep glen, (Glen-Rofa), which de-
taches Goatfield from the hills farther to the
weft. The junction is laid bare at feveral places in the bed of the river which runs in the
bottom of this glen ; and in all of them exhibits, in a greater or lefs degree, the appearances of difturbance and violence which have accompanied the injection of the granite veins.
Many circumftances render this fpot interefting
to a geologift, and, among others, an interfection of the granite, a little above its junction
with the fchiftus, by a dike or vein of very compact whinftone.

The fame line of junction is found on the
oppofite, or north-eaft, fide of the mountain,
where

where it is interfected by another little river, the Sannax, which on this fide determines the bafe of the mountain. This junction is no lefs remarkable than the other two.

The ifland of Arran contains, I have no doubt, many other fpots where thefe phenomena are to be feen; but I have had no opportunity of obferving them, nor do I find that Dr Hutton met with any others in his vifit to this ifland.

282. Another feries of granite veins is found in Galloway, which was firft difcovered by Dr Hutton and his friend Mr Clerk, and afterwards more fully explored by Sir James Hall and Mr Douglas, the prefent Earl of Selkirk. The two laft traced the line of feparation between a mafs of granite and the fchiftus incumbent upon it, all round a tract of country, about eleven miles by feven, extending from the banks of Loch Ken weftward; and in all this tract they found, " that wherever the junction of the granite with the fchiftus was vifible, veins of the former, from fifty yards, to the tenth of an inch in width, were to be feen running into the latter, and pervading it in all directions, fo as to put it beyond all doubt, that the granite of thefe veins, and confequently of

the

the great body itfelf, which was obferved to
form with the veins one uninterrupted mafs,
muft have flowed in a foft or liquid ftate into
its prefent pofition *." I have only further to
add, that fome of thefe veins are remarkable
for containing granite, not fenfibly different, in
any refpect, from the mafs from which they
proceed.

283. In Invernefsfhire, between Bernera and
Fort Auguftus, the fame phenomena occur
on the north fide of Loch Chloney, where fome
granite mountains rife from under the fchiftus.
In travelling near this place, Lord Webb Seymour and myfelf were advertifed of our approach to a junction of granite and fchiftus,
by finding among the loofe ftones on the road
many pieces of fchiftus, interfected with veins
of feltfpar and granite. We walked along this
junction for more than a mile ; and toward
the eaft end, where the road leaves it, we faw,
in the bed of a ftream that runs into Loch
Chloney, many beautiful fpecimens of granitic
veins pervading the fchiftus, and branching out
into very minute ramifications.

284. The laft inftance I have to mention from my own obfervation, is at St Mi-
chael's

* Tranf. Royal Society Edin. vol. iii. p. 8.

chael's Mount in Cornwall. That mount is
entirely of granite, thruft up from under a
very hard micaceous fchiftus, which furrounds
it on all fides. At the bafe of it, on the weft
fide, a great number of veins run off from the
granite, and fpread themfelves like fo many
roots fixed in the fchiftus : they are feen at low
water. In the fmaller veins, the granite is of
very minute, though diftinct parts ; in the larger, it is more highly cryftallized, and is undi-
ftinguifhable from the mafs of the hill.

Befides the above, Cornwall probably affords
many other inftances of the fame kind, which I
have not had an opportunity to examine. Such
inftances may in particular be looked for at the
Land's End, where a promontory, confifting of
a central part of granite, and covered by micaceous fchiftus on both fides of it, is cut tranfverfely by the fea-coaft, and the contact of the
granite and fchiftus of courfe twice expofed to
view.

285. Scotland alfo affords other examples
of granite veins, and fome of them have been
actually defcribed. Mr Jamiefon has taken
notice of fome which he faw in the bottom
of the river Spey, at Glen Drummond, in
Badenach, and has reprefented them in an engraving.

graving *. They traverse the ftrata in various directions, and inclofe pieces of the micaceous fchiftus; and, from the great number of loofe blocks which he found, exhibiting portions of fuch veins, it is probable, that they are very numerous in this quarter. The fame mineralogift mentions fome inftances of fimilar veins in the Shetland Ifles †.

In Rofs-fhire, Sir George Mackenzie has obferved a great variety of granite veins, fome of them of large fize. One of them, in particular, not far from Coul, when firft difcovered, was fuppofed to be a fingle mafs, rifing from under the fchiftus; but, on a more careful examination, has been found to be a part of a great fyftem of veins, which interfects the micaceous fchiftus of this tract in various directions.

286. The granite veins are not the only proof that this ftone is more recent than fome other productions of the mineral kingdom. Specimens of granite are often found, containing round nodules of other ftones, as, for example, of gneifs or micaceous fchiftus. Such is the fpecimen of granite containing gneifs, which Werner himfelf is faid to be in poffeffion of, and

to

---

* Mineralogy of the Scottifh Ifles, vol. ii. p. 173.

† Ibid. p. 216.

to confider as a proof, that the fchiftus is of
greater antiquity than the granite.   Such alfo
feemed to me fome pieces of granite, which I
met with in Cornwall, near the Land's End ;
and others which I faw in Ayrfhire, in loofe
blocks, on the fea-coaft between Ayr and Girvan.   It is impoffible to deny that the containing ftone is more modern than the contained.
The Neptunifts indeed admit this to be true,
but allege, that all granite is not of the fame
formation ; and that, though fome granite is recent, the greater part boafts of the higheft antiquity which belongs to any thing in the foffil kingdom.   This diftinction, however, is purely hypothetical ; it is a fiction contrived on
purpofe to reconcile the fact here mentioned
with the general fyftem of aqueous depofition,
and has no fupport from any other phenomenon.

2. *Granite of Portfoy.*

287. The granite of Portfoy is one of the
moft fingular varieties of this ftone, and is remarkable for this circumftance, that the feltfpar is the fubftance which has affumed the figure of its proper cryftal, and has given its form
to

to the quartz, fo that the latter is impreffed both with the acute and obtufe angles belonging to the rhombic figure of the former. The angular pieces of quartz thus moulded on the feltfpar, and ranged by means of it in rows, give to this ftone the appearance of rude alphabetical writing.

Now, Dr Hutton argued, that fubftances precipitated from a folution, and cryftallizing at liberty, cannot be fuppofed to imprefs one another in the manner here exemplified; and that they could do fo only when the whole mafs acquired folidity at the fame time, or at the fame time nearly *. Such fimultaneous confolidation can be produced in no way that we know of, but by the cooling of a mafs that has been in fufion.

288. A granite, brought from Daouria by M. Patrin, and defcribed by him in the Journal de Phyfique for 1791, p. 295, under the name of *pierre graphique*, feemed to Dr Hutton to have fo great a refemblance to the granite of Portfoy, that he ventured to confider them both as the fame ftone, and as both containing quartz moulded on feltfpar †. It fhould feem, however,

X ever,

---

* Theory of the Earth, vol. i. p. 104.

† Tranf. Royal Society Edin. vol. iii. p. 83.

ever, from further explanations, which M. Patrin has fince given, that Dr Hutton was miftaken in his conjecture, and that, in the *pierre graphique* of the former mineralogift, the quartz gives its form to the feltfpar, preferving in its cryftals their natural angle of 120 degrees *. It is impoffible, I think, to doubt of the accuracy of this ftatement ; and the graphical ftone of Portfoy muft therefore be admitted to differ materially from that of Daouria. They are not, however, without fome confiderable affinity, befides that of their outward appearance ; for, though the quartz in the former is generally moulded on the feltfpar, the feltfpar is alfo occafionally impreffed by the quartz, and fometimes even included in it. They may be confidered as varieties of the fame fpecies of granite ; and the *pierre graphique* of Corfica is probably a third variety, different from them both.

289. It would feem, however, that all thefe ftones lead exactly to the fame conclufion. M. Patrin defcribes his fpecimen as containing quartz cryftals, that are for the moft part only *cafes*, having their interior filled with feltfpar. " Le feltfpath

---

* Journal Britannique (of Geneva), 1798, vol. viii. Sciences et Arts, p. 78.

ſpath en maſſe contient des cryſteaux quartzeux,
qui n'ont le plus ſouvent que le carcaſſe, et dont
l'interieur eſt rempli de feltſpath ; ſouvent il
manque à ces carcaſſes quelques unes de leurs
faces, et ſouvent la ſection de cette pierre dans
un ſens tranſverſal aux cryſtaux, preſente une
ſuite de figures qui ſont des portions d'hexagones,
et qui ne reſemblent pas mal à des caractères
Hebraiques *."

Theſe imperfect hexagonal caſes of quartz,
filled with feltſpar, certainly indicate the cryſtallization of ſubſtances, which all aſſumed
their ſolidity at the ſame time, and, in doing ſo,
conſtrained the figures of one another. To
uſe the words of Dr Hutton, " whether cryſtallizing quartz incloſe a body of feltſpar, or
concreting feltſpar determine the ſhape of fluid
quartz, particularly if we have, as is here the
caſe, two ſolid bodies including and included, it
amounts to a demonſtration, that thoſe bodies
have concreted from a fluid ſtate of fuſion, and
have not cryſtallized, in the manner of ſalts, from
a ſolution †."

290. The quartz in granite ſo generally receives the impreſſions of all the other ſubſtances,

X 2

particularly

---

* Journal Britannique, *ibid.*

† Tranſ. Royal Society Edin. *ubi ſupra*, p. 84.

particulary of the feltfpar and fchorl, and appears
to be fo paffive a body, that it has been doubted
by fome mineralogifts, whether in this ftone
it ever affumes its own figure, except where
cavities afford room for its cryftallization. But
it is certain that, befide the Daourian granite
juft mentioned, there are others, in which the
quartz is completely cryftallized. Of this fort
are fome fpecimens, found in a granite vein on
the weft fide of the hill of St Agnes, in Cornwall. The vein traverfes the primitive fchiftus, of which that hill confifts, from fouth to
north nearly : the ftone is much decompofed,
and the feltfpar in general is almoft reduced
to the ftate of clay. In this decompofed mafs,
quartz cryftals are found, having the fhape of
double hexagonal pyramids, perfectly regular
and complete. The fide of the hexagon,
which is the bafe of the two oppofite pyramids, varies from half a tenth to a tenth of an
inch in length, and is the fame with the altitude
of each of the pyramids. In fome few fpecimens, the two pyramids do not reft on the fame
bafe, but are feparated by a very fhort, though
regular, hexagonal prifm. The furfaces of thefe
cryftals are rough, and fomewhat opaque, with
flender fpiculæ of fhorl frequently traverfing
them. This roughnefs is occafioned by flight
furrows

furrows on the furface of the cryſtal, very regularly difpofed, and parallel to one another, being without doubt impreſſions from the thin plates of the feltfpar, which furrounded the cryſtal, and flightly indented it. They very much refemble fome impreſſions, remarked by Dr Hutton in the granite of Portfoy, and afcribed by him alfo to a fimilar caufe. He has reprefented thefe in his Theory of the Earth, vol. i. plate 2. fig. 4. The action and reaction of two cryſtallizing bodies, hardly admits of a ſtronger and more unequivocal expreſſion, than in thefe two inſtances.

Where the granite was little decompofed, the quartz was not eafily difengaged from the mafs it was imbedded in, and often broke in pieces before it could be extricated. The cryſtallization of the quartz, therefore, would not have been difcovered, but for the decompofition of the feltfpar; and it is probable, that fimilar cryſtallizations exiſt in many granites where they are not perceived.

291. Some mineralogiſts are inclined to think, that the regular cryſtallization of quartz is to be found only in what they call fecondary granites, or in thofe that are of a formation fubfequent to the great maſſes which conſtitute the granite mountains. It is indeed true, that in the in-

ſtances

ftances given here, both from Cornwall and
Daouria, the granites containing quartz-cryftals
are from veins that interfect the primary fchiftus, and are therefore, on every hypothefis, of a
formation fubfequent to that fchiftus. But it
does not follow from thence, that they are lefs
ancient than the great maffes of unftratified granite ; with thefe laft they are moft probably
coëval, nor can there be any reafon for thinking
the cryftallization of quartz a mark of more
recent formation than that of feltfpar.

3. *Stratification of Granite.*

292. What are the various modes in which
granite exifts, is a queftion not abfolutely decided among mineralogifts. 1. That it exifts as
a fchiftofe ftone of a fiffile texture, in gneifs and
veined granite, is on all hands admitted, though
in this ftate the name of granite is generally
withheld from it. 2. That it exifts often without any indication of a fiffile texture, and altogether unftratified, is likewife acknowledged.
3. That it is found in veins, interfecting the
ftrata, has been fhown above. The only mode
of its exiftence fubject to difpute, is that in
which it is faid to be ftratified in its out-
                                          ward

ward configuration, but not fchiftofe in its texture. On this point mineralogifts do not perfectly agree : Dr Hutton did not think that this was a ftate in which granite ever appears. When not fchiftofe in its ftructure, he fuppofed it to be unftratified altogether ; and he confidered it as a body which, like whinftone, was originally in a ftate of igneous fufion, and, in that condition, injected among the ftrata. The fchool of Werner, on the other hand, maintain, that granite, if not always, is generally ftratified, and difpofed in beds, fometimes horizontal, though more frequently vertical, or highly inclined.

In forming an opinion where there are great authorities on oppofite fides, a man muft truft chiefly to his own obfervations, and ought to efteem himfelf fortunate if thefe lead to any certain conclufion. Mine incline me to differ from Dr Hutton, on the one hand, and from the Neptunifts on the other, as they convince me, that granite does form ftrata where it has no character of gneifs ; and, at the fame time, induce me to fufpect, that the ftratification afcribed by the Neptunifts to the granite mountains, is, in many inftances, either an illufion, or at leaft fomething very different from what, in other ftones, is accounted ftratification.

X 4   293. The

293. The firſt example I ever ſaw of granite that was ſtratified, and yet had no character of gneiſs, was at Chorley Foreſt, in Leiceſterſhire. The greater part of that foreſt has for its baſe a horn-ſtone ſchiſtus, primary and vertical; and, on its eaſtern border, particularly near Mount Sorrel, are beds of granite, holding the ſame direction with thoſe of the ſchiſtus. The ſtone is a real gra-nite; it has nothing in its internal ſtructure of a ſchiſtoſe or fiſſile appearance; and its beds, which it is material to remark, are no thicker than thoſe of the hornſtone ſtrata in the neighbourhood. This granite is remarkable too, for being cloſe to the ſecondary ſandſtone ſtrata; I did not ſee their contact, but traced them within a ſmall diſtance of one another; ſo that I think it is not likely that any body of rock intervenes. At the ſame time that I ſtate my belief of this rock of granite being in regular ſtrata, I muſt acknow-ledge, that a very intelligent mineralogiſt, who viewed theſe rocks at the ſame time, and whoſe eye was well practiſed in geological obſervation, remained in doubt concerning them.

294. Another inſtance of a real granite, diſpo-ſed in regular beds, but without any character of gneiſs, is one which I ſaw in Berwickſhire, in Lammermuir, near the village of Prieſtlaw. The little river of Faſſnet cuts the beds acroſs,

and

and renders it eafy to obferve their ftructure. The beds are not very thick ; they run from about S. S. W. to N. N. E. like the fchiftus on either fide of them. I was in company with Sir James Hall when I faw thefe rocks ; we examined them with a good deal of attention, and traced them for more than a mile in the bed of the river; and, if I miftake not, our opinions concerning them were precifely the fame.

295. What exifts in two inftances may exift in many, and, after thefe obfervations, I fhould be guilty of great inconfiftency, in refufing to affent to the accounts of Pallas, De Luc, Sauffure, and many other mineralogifts, who fo often reprefent granite as formed into ftrata. In fome cafes, however, it is certain, that the ftratification they defcribe is extremely unlike that in the two inftances juft mentioned, and indeed very unlike any thing that is elfewhere known by the name of ftratification. For example, the ftratification muft be very ambiguous, and very obfcurely marked, that was not difcovered till after a feries of obfervations, continued for more than twenty years, by a very fkilful and diftinguifhing mineralogift. Yet fuch undoubtedly is the ftratification of Mont Blanc, and of the granite mountains in its neighbourhood, as it efcaped the eyes of Sauffure, in the repeated vifits which he made to them, during a period of

no

no lefs extent than has juft been mentioned. It was not till near the conclufion of thofe
labours, to which the geologifts of every age
will confider themfelves as highly indebted,
that, having reached the fummit of Mont
Blanc, he perceived, or thought that he perceived, the ftratification of the granite mountains. The *Aiguilles* or Needles which border
the valley of Chamouni, and even Mont Blanc
itfelf, appeared to be formed of vaft tabular
maffes of granite, in pofition nearly vertical, and
fo exactly parallel, that he did not hefitate to
call them by the name of ftrata. Till this moment, thefe fame mountains, viewed from a
lower point, had been regarded by him as compofed of great plates of rock, nearly vertical
indeed, but applied, as it were, round an axis,
and refembling the leaves of an artichoke * ;
and the fiffures by which they are feparated
from one another, had been confidered as effects
of wafte and degradation. " But now," (fays he,
fpeaking of the view from the top of Mont
Blanc), " I was fully convinced, that thefe
mountains are entirely compofed of vaft plates
of granite, perpendicular to the horizon, and
directed from N. E. to S. W. Three of thefe
plates, feparated from each other, formed the

top

---

* Voyages aux Alpes, tom. ii. § 910, &c.

top of the *Aiguille du Midi*, and other fimilar plates, decreafing gradually in height, compofe its declivity to the fouth *."

296. Sauffure was fo ftrongly impreffed with the appearances of what he accounted regular ftratification, fuch as water only can produce, and fuch as muft have been in the beginning horizontal, that, placed as he now was, on one of the higheft points of the earth's furface, he formed the bold conception, that the fummit on which he was ftanding had been once buried under the furface, to the depth at leaft of half the diameter of the mountain, and horizontally diftant from its prefent place by a line not lefs than the whole height of the mountain; the granite beds which compofe that mountain, having been raifed by fome enormous power from their horizontal pofition, and turned as on an axis, till they were brought into the vertical plane. In this notion, which fuits fo well with the nature of mountains really compofed of vertical ftrata, and which does credit to the extent of Sauffure's views, it is wonderful that he did not fee the overthrow of the geological fyftem he had adopted, which is provided with no means whatfoever of explaining thefe great effects.

Such,

---

* Voyages aux Alpes, tom. iv. § 1996.

Such, then, were the ideas fuggefted to Sauffure, by viewing the mountains of the Alps from the higheft of their fummits. His great experience, his accurate knowledge of the objects before him, and the power he had acquired of diffipating thofe illufions, to which, in viewing mountainous tracts, the eye is peculiarly fubject, all confpire to give great weight to his opinion. Yet, as this opinion is oppofed by that which he himfelf had fo long entertained, before it can be received with perfect confidence, it will require to be verified by new obfervations. It feems certain, that the beds of rock here defcribed, differ from all ordinary ftrata, both horizontal and vertical, in the circumftance of their vaft thicknefs, three of them being fo large as to form the main body of a mountain. Their parallelifm cannot eafily be afcertained; and they have at beft but a very flight refemblance to fuch beds as water is known to produce.

297. Their parallelifm is difficult to be afcertained; for, on account of the magnitude and inacceffibility of the objects, it is impoffible to place the eye in any fituation, where it fhall not be much nearer to one part of the planes whereof the parallelifm is to be eftimated, than to another. Indeed, one can perceive a caufe

which

which may have rendered the parallelism of the plates of granite which compose the *aiguilles*, more accurate in appearance than in reality, when viewed from a point so elevated as the summit of Mont Blanc. For, even on the supposition that the comparison of those plates to leaves of artichokes was just, and that the planes of their separation converged toward one another, in ascending to the top, when they were viewed from a point more elevated than that top, this convergency would be diminished, and, by the force of the perspective, might even be converted into parallelism. We cannot at present ascertain what effect this cause of deception may have actually produced.

298. The observations of Saussure concerning the stratification of granite, are not, however, in all instances, liable to these objections; and it seems to be on much less exceptionable grounds that he pronounces the granite of St Gothard to be stratified. The gneiss and micaceous schistus which constitute the lower part of that mountain, are succeeded by a granite without any schistose appearance, but divided into large plates, exactly parallel to the beds of the former gneiss. These he regards as real strata. On studying them in detail, he says, considerable irregularities were to be observed, but not greater than in the case

of

of limeftone or micaceous fchiftus *.   It may be
inferred from this, that thefe plates of granite
are not fo thick but that they admit of comparifon with beds that are known with certainty
to be of aqueous formation, and I am therefore
difpofed to believe, that the granite of St Gothard, in this part at leaft, is ftratified. The tranfition from gneifs to granite *en mafs*, is not uncommon, as Sauffure has obferved in other inftances, and as we are juft about to confider
more particularly.

299. In the mountains of our own country, fome
difficulties concerning the ftratification of granite have alfo occurred.   In Arran, for inftance,
the mountain of Goatfield, which I have mentioned above as affording an inftance of granite
fending out many veins into the fchiftus, and
rivetted, as it were, by means of them to the
fuperincumbent rock, when I vifited it, with
a view of verifying on the fpot the interefting
obfervations which Dr Hutton had there made,
appeared to me to be without any veftige of ftratification in its granitic part, as did alfo the
whole group of mountains to which it belongs.
It was, therefore, not without a good deal of fur-
prife, that I lately read, in an account of that
ifland, by a very accurate and ingenious mineralogift,

---

* Voyages aux Alpes, tom. iv. § 1830.

ralogift, that Goatfield confifts of ftratified granite *.   The impreffion which the appearance of that mountain made on my mind, is juft
the reverfe ; and though I faw large tabular maffes, fometimes nearly vertical, feparated
by fiffures, they appeared to be much too irregular, too little extended in length and height,
and vaftly too much in thicknefs, to be reckoned the effects of ftratification.   For all this, I
would by no means be underftood to fet my obfervations in oppofition to thofe of Mr Jamiefon.   In my vifit to Arran, I did not direct my
inquiries much toward this point ; the general
appearance of the rocks did not fuggeft the neceffity of doing fo, and I was not perfectly aware
how much the ftratification of granite had been
infifted on by fome mineralogifts ; fo that I
applied myfelf entirely to ftudy fome other of
the interefting phenomena which this little
ifland offers in fo great abundance.   I therefore carry my confidence in the appearances which feemed to indicate a want of ftratification in the granite of Arran no further
than to remain fceptical both as to Mr Jamiefon's conclufions and my own, till an opportunity

---

* Mineralogy of the Scottifh Ifles, vol. i. p. 35, 36.

tunity fhall occur of verifying the one or the other by actual obfervation.

300. The ftratification of granite, though it made no part of Dr Hutton's fyftem, does by no means embarrafs his theory with any new difficulty. Rocks, of which the parts are highly cryftallized, are already admitted as belonging to the ftrata, and are exemplified in marble, gneifs, and veined granite. In the two laft, we have not only ftratification, but a fchiftofe, united with a cryftallized ftructure, and the effects of depofition by water, and of fluidity by fire, are certainly nowhere more fingularly combined. The ftratification of thefe fubftances is therefore more extraordinary than even that of the moft highly cryftallized granite. Neither the one nor the other can be explained but by fuppofing, that while fuch a degree of fluidity was produced by heat, as enabled the body when it cooled to cryftallize, the whole mafs was kept in its place by great preffure acting on all fides, fo that the fhape was preferved as originally given to it by the fea. As we cannot, however, fuppofe, that the intenfity of the heat, or the fufibility of the fubftance through all the parts of a ftratum, were precifely the fame, we may expect to find in the fame ftratum, or in the fame body of ftrata, that in fome parts the marks of ftratification are

completely

completely obliterated, while in others they remain entire. It is thus that *veined granite*, or
what I think fhould be called granitic fchiftus,
often graduates into granite *in mafs*, that is, granite without any fchiftofe or fiffile texture.
Sauffure fays, that to be veined or not veined, is an affection of granite, that feems, in many cafes, accidental * ; as, in the midft of rocks
of that fubftance, moft clearly fiffile, large portions appear without any veftige of ftratification. Of this phenomenon, which is frequent
in the Alps, inftances are alfo to be met with
in the granite rocks of Scotland, and the adjacent ifles ; and I know that Dr Hope, in a mineralogical excurfion which he lately made
among the Hebrides, obferved many interefting
and curious examples of it. Indeed, when
rocks were fo much fufed as to cryftallize,
and fo compreffed, at the fame time, as to remain ftratified, they were evidently on the
verge of change ; two oppofite forces were very
nearly balanced, and each carried as far as it
could go without entirely overcoming the other ;
fo that a fmall alteration in the conditions may
have made a great alteration in the effects.
Hence a fudden tranfition from a ftratified to

Y an

---

* Voyages aux Alpes, tom. iv. § 2143.

an unftratified texture, which is only found in rocks highly cryftallized, and fuch as have endured the moft violent action of the mineralizing powers.

301. Now, though the ftratification of granite, or the mixture of the ftratified with the unftratified rocks of that genus, is not only reconcileable with the principles of the Huttonian geology, but might even have been deduced as a corollary from thofe principles, before it was actually obferved, it may be confidered as inconfiftent with the theory of granitic veins that has juft been given. A ftratum, though foft or fluid, could not invade the furrounding ftrata with violence, nor fend out veins to penetrate into them. It might, if ftrongly compreffed by another ftratum lefs fluid than itfelf, fill up any fiffures or cracks that were in that other, but this would hardly produce fuch large veins, and of fuch confiderable length, as often penetrate from the granite into the fchiftus, nor could it give rife to any appearance of difturbance. If, therefore, veins were found proceeding from fuch ftratified granite as that of Chorley Foreft or Lammermuir, I fhould think, that the explanation of them was ftill a *defideratum* in geology. The Neptunian theory of infiltration would indeed be as applicable to
them

them as to any other veins; for it is but little
affected by the condition of the phenomena to
be explained. Indeed, it is very difficult to fet
any limits to the explanations which this theory
affords; and it would certainly puzzle a Neptunift, to affign any good reafon why infiltration
has not produced veins of one fchiftus running
into another, or veins of fchiftus running into
granite, as well as of granite running into fchiftus. He will find it a hard tafk to reftrain the
activity of his theory, and to confine its explanations to thofe things that really exift.

302. As the Huttonian fyftem cannot boaft of
theories of equal verfatility, it would be not a
little embarraffed to account for veins of great
magnitude proceeding from a rock diftinctly
ftratified, and accompanied with marks of having difturbed the rocks through which they pafs.
I am, however, inclined to believe, that this embarraffment will never occur; and that the granite veins do not proceed from the rocks that are
really ftratified, but from fuch as have never been
depofited by water, and where the appearances of
ftratification, if there are any, are altogether il-
lufory. This anticipation, however, requires to be
verified by future obfervation; and it remains to
be feen, whether granitic veins ever accompany
real granitic ftrata, or are peculiar to thofe in

which

which the appearances of regular beds are either ambiguous, or are entirely wanting. The decifion of this queftion is an object highly worthy of the attention of geologifts.

303. An argument, directed at once againft the igneous origin and unftratified nature of all granite, is given in a work already mentioned : " If granite had flowed from below, how does it happen, that, after it had burft through the ftrata of micaceous fchiftus, &c. it did not overflow the neighbouring country ? If this hypothefis were true, Mont Blanc could never have exifted *."

A theory is never more unfairly dealt with, than when thofe parts are feparated which were meant to fupport one another, and each left to ftand or fall by itfelf. This, however, is precifely what is done in the prefent inftance ; for Dr Hutton's theory of granite would not deferve a moment's confideration, if it were fo inartificially conftructed, as to fuppofe that granite was originally fluid, and yet to point out no means of hindering this fluid from diffufing itfelf over the ftrata, and fettling in a horizontal plane. The truth is, that his theory, at the fame time that it conceives this ftone to have
been

---

* Mineralogy of the Scottifh Ifles, vol. ii. p. 166.

been in fufion, fuppofes it to have been, in that
ftate, injected among the ftrata already confolidated; to have heaved them up, and to have
been formed in the concavity fo produced, as in
a mould. Thus Mont Blanc, fuppofing that it
is unftratified, is underftood to confift of a mafs
that was melted by fubterraneous heat under the
ftrata, and being impelled upwards by a force,
that may ftand in fome comparifon with that
which projected the planets in their orbits,
heaved up the ftrata by which it was covered,
and in which it remained included on all fides.

304. The covering of ftrata, thus raifed up,
may have been burft afunder at the fummit,
where the curvature and elevation were the
greateft; but the melted mafs underneath may
have already acquired folidity, or may have
been fuftained by the beds of fchiftus incumbent on its fides. This fchiftus, forming the
exterior cruft, was immediately acted on by the
caufes of wafte and decompofition, which have
long fince ftripped the granite of a great part
of its covering, and are now exercifing their
power on the central mafs. That even Mont
Blanc itfelf, as well as other unftratified mountains, was once covered with fchiftus, will appear to have in it nothing incongruous, when
we confider the height to which the fchiftus ftill
rifes on its fides, or in the adjacent mountains;

Y 3   and

and when we reflect, that, from the appearances
of wafte and degradation which thefe mountains exhibit, it is certain, that the fchiftus muft
have reached much higher than it does at prefent.

It is obvious, therefore, that when the correfponding parts are brought together, and placed in their natural order, no room is left for
the reproach, that this fyftem is inconfiftent
with the *exiftence* of granite mountains. I have
no pleafure in controverfial writing ; and, notwithftanding the advantages which a weak attack always gives to a defender, I cannot but
regret, that Dr Hutton's adverfaries have been
fo much more eager to refute than to underftand his theory.

301. A remark which Dr Hutton has made
on the quantity of granite that appears at the
furface, compared with that of other mineral
bodies, has been warmly contefted. Having
affirmed, that the greater part of rocks bear
marks of being formed from the wafte and decompofition of other rocks, he alleges that granite, (a ftone which does not contain fuch
marks), does not, for as much as appears from
actual obfervation, make up a tenth, nor perhaps
even

even a hundredth part of the mineral kingdom *.
Mr Kirwan contends, that this is a very erroneous eftimate, and that the quantity of granite
vifible on the furface, far exceeds what is here
fuppofed †. The queftion is certainly of no material importance to the eftablifhment of Dr Hutton's theory : it is evident, too, that an eftimation,
which varies fo much as from a tenth to a hundredth part, cannot have been meant as any thing
precife ; yet it may not be quite fuperfluous to
fhow, that the truth probably lies nearer to the leaft
than the greateft of the limits juft mentioned.

306. Though granite forms a part, generally
the central part, of all the great chains of mountains, it ufually occupies a much lefs extent of
furface than the primary fchiftus. Thus in the
Alps, if a line be drawn from Geneva to Ivrea,
it will be about eighty-five geographical miles
in length, and will meafure the breadth of this
formidable chain of mountains, at the place of
its greateft elevation. Now, from the obfervations of Sauffure, who croffed the Alps exactly
in this direction, it may be collected, that lefs
than nine miles of this line, or not above a
tenth part of it, in the immediate vicinity of
Mont Blanc, is occupied by granite.

Y 4   307. In

---

* Theory of the Earth, vol. i. p. 211.

† Geol. Effays, p. 480.

307. In some sections of the Alps, no granite at all appears. Thus, in the rout from Chambery to Turin, acrofs Mont Cenis, which measures by the road not lefs than ninety miles, no granite is found, at leaft of that kind which is diftinctly in mafs, and different from gneifs or veined granite *.

308. In fome other places of the fame mountains, the granite is more abundant. A line from the lake of Thun, along the courfe of the Aar, and over the mountains to the upper end of Lago Maggiore, croffes a very elevated tract, and paffes by the fources of the Rhone, the Rhine, and the Teffino, which laft runs into the Po. A good deal of granite is difcovered here, in the mountains of Grimfel and St Gothard; but by far the greater part of it is the veined granite, the granite in mafs being confined chiefly to the north fide of the Grimfel. Both together do not occupy more than one-third of the line, and therefore the latter lefs than one-fixth.

309. The effay on the mineralogy of the Pyrenees, by the Abbé PALASSO, contains a mineralogical chart of thofe mountains. From this chart I have found, by computation, that the granite does not occupy one-fifth of the horizontal

* Voyages aux Alpes, tom, iii. § 1190, &c.

zontal furface on the north fide of the ridge, reckoning from one end of it to the other. Indeed, many great tracts, even of the central parts of the Pyrenees, contain no granite whatfoever ; and not a few of the higheft mountains confift entirely of calcareous fchiftus. A large deduction fhould be made from the fraction $\frac{1}{5}$, on account of the fubftances unknown, which, from the conftruction of the chart, are often confounded with the granitic tract.

310. I might add other eftimations of the fame kind, all confeffedly rude and imperfect, but ftill conveying, by means of numbers, a better idea of the limit to which our knowledge approximates, than could be done fimply by words; and, on the whole, it would appear, that if we ftate the proportion of granite to fchiftus to be that of one to four, we fhall certainly do no injuftice to the extent of the former.

It remains to form a rough eftimate from maps, and from the accounts of travellers, of what proportion of the earth's furface confifts of primary, and what of fecondary rocks. After fupplying the want of accurate meafurement by what appeared to me the moft probable fuppofitions, I have found, that about $\frac{1}{18}$ of the furface of the old continent may be conceived to be occupied by primitive mountains; of which,

if

if we take one-fifth, we have $\frac{1}{90}$ for the part of the furface occupied by granite rocks, which differs not greatly from the leaft of the two limits affigned by Dr Hutton.

311. In eftimating the granite of Scotland, Dr Hutton has certainly erred confiderably in defect *, and Mr Kirwan, who always differs from him, is here neareft the truth ; though he is right purely by accident, as the information on which he proceeds is vague and erroneous.

The places in Scotland where granite is found, are very well known ; but the extent of fome of the moft confiderable of them is not accurately afcertained.   In the fouthern parts, except the granite of Galloway, which is found in two pretty large infulated tracts, there is no other of any magnitude.   The granite of the north extends over a large diftrict.   If we fuppofe a line to be drawn, from a few miles fouth of Aberdeen to a few miles fouth

---

* Dr Hutton in this cafe no doubt made a very loofe eftimate.   He fays, the granite does not perhaps occupy more than a 500dth part of the whole furface.   The whole furface of Scotland is not much more than 23,000 geographical miles, the 500dth part of which is exactly 46 ; and this is exceeded by the granite in Kirkcudbrightfhire alone, as may be gathered from what is faid § 282.

fouth of Fort-William, it will mark out the central chain of the Grampians in its full extent, paffing over the moft elevated ground, and by the heads of the largeft rivers, in Scotland. Along this line there are many granite mountains, and large tracts in which granite is the prevailing rock. There are, however, large fpaces alfo in which no granite appears, though, if we were permitted to fpeak theoretically, and if the queftion did not entirely relate to a matter of obfervation, we might fuppofe, that, in no part of this central ridge is the granite far from the furface, notwithftanding that in fome places it may be covered by the fchiftus.

312. A great part of the Grampian mountains is on the fouth fide of the line juft mentioned, but hardly any granite is found in this divifion of them, except fuch veins as thofe of Glentilt. On the north fide of the line, the granite extends in various directions; and, if from Fort-William a line is drawn to Invernefs, the quadrilateral figure, bounded on two fides by thefe lines, and on the other two by the fea, will be found to contain much granite, and many diftricts confifting entirely of that ftone. This is in fact the great granite country of Scotland: it is a large tract, containing about 3170 fquare geographical miles, or about a feventh

part

part of the whole : but the proportion of it occupied by granite cannot at prefent be afcertained with any exactnefs, nor will, till fome mineralogift fhall find leifure to examine the courfes of the great rivers, the Dee, the Spey, &c. which traverfe this country. If we call it one-fourth of the whole furface, its extent is certainly not under-rated, and will amount to 790 fquare miles nearly ; to which adding 150, as a very full allowance for all the other granite contained in Scotland, exclufive of the ifles, we fhall have 940 fquare miles, between a twenty-fourth and twenty-fifth part of the furface of the whole.

This computation, it muft be obferved, aims at nothing precife, but I think it is fuch, that a more accurate furvey would rather diminifh than increafe the proportion affigned in it to the granite rock.

313. This refult may perhaps fall as much fhort of Mr Kirwan's notion, as it exceeds the eftimate made by Dr Hutton. If it fhall not, and if the former has, in this inftance, come neareft the truth, it cannot be afcribed to the accuracy of his information, or the foundnefs of the principles which directed his refearch. Mr WILLIAMS, whom he quotes, was a miner, of great fkill and experience in fome branches of his profeffion, to which, if he had confined himfelf, he might have written a book full of ufeful

ful information. What he fays on the fubject of granite, is, in the main I believe juft ; but it is far too general to authorife the conclufion which Mr Kirwan derives from it. Dr Ash, for whofe judgment I have great refpect, cannot, I think, have meant, when he ufed the expreffion granitic rocks, to defcribe granite ftrictly fo called. He fays, in the paffage quoted by Mr Kirwan, that " from Galloway, Dumfries, and Berwick, there is a chain of mountains, commonly fchiftofe, but often alfo granitic." Now, the fact is, that the great belt of primary rock, here alluded to, which traverfes the fouth of Scotland, confifts of vertical fchiftus of various kinds ; but except in Galloway, and again in Lammermuir, near Prieftlaw, it appears, as already mentioned, to contain no granite whatfoever. If the German mineralogift quoted by Mr Kirwan, when he fays that the Grampian mountains confift of micaceous limeftone, gneifs, porphyry, argillite, and granite, alternating with one another, means only to affirm that all thefe ftones are found in the Grampians, he is certainly in the right, and the catalogue might eafily be enlarged ; but, if he either means to fay, that thefe are nearly in equal abundance, or that the granite is commonly found in ftrata alternating with other ftrata, I muft fay, that thefe are propofitions

pofitions quite contrary to any thing I have ever
feen or heard of thofe mountains. But it is probable that this is not meant, and that the fault
lies in underftanding the expreffions much
too literally. Mr Kirwan accufes Dr Hutton
of not knowing where to look for the granite;
not aware of how much, notwithftanding any
error committed in the prefent eftimate, he
was fkilled in the art of mineralogical obfervation; an art, which thofe who have not prac-
tifed do not always know how to appreciate.
But, however imperfect Mr Kirwan's knowledge of this fubject has been, he has here had
the good fortune to correct a mineralogift of
very fuperior information. The mere difpofition to oppofe is not always without its ufe:
no man is in every thing free from error, and,
to controvert indifcriminately all the opinions
of any individual, is an infallible fecret for being
fometimes in the right.

Note XVI. § 100.

Rivers and Lakes.

314. Rivers are the caufes of wafte moft vifible to us, and moft obvioufly capable of
producing

producing great effects. It is not, however, in
the greatest rivers, that the power to change
and wear the surface of the land is most clearly
seen. It is at the heads of rivers, and in the
feeders of the larger streams, where they descend
over the most rapid slope, and are most subject
to irregular or temporary increase and diminution, that the causes which tend to preserve, and
those that tend to change the form of the earth's
surface, are farthest from balancing one another,
and where, after every season, almost after every flood, we perceive some change produced,
for which no compensation can be made, and
something removed which is never to be replaced.
When we trace up rivers and their branches
toward their source, we come at last to rivulets,
that run only in time of rain, and that are dry
at other seasons. It is there, says Dr Hutton,
that I would wish to carry my reader, that he
may be convinced, by his own observation, of
this great fact, *that the rivers have, in general,
hollowed out their valleys.* The changes of the
valley of the main river are but slow; the plain
indeed is wasted in one place, but is repaired in
another, and we do not perceive the place from
whence the repairing matter has proceeded.
That which the spectator sees here, does not
therefore immediately suggest to him what has
been the state of things before the valley was
hollowed

hollowed out.   But it is otherwife in the valley
of the rivulet ; no perfon can examine it without feeing, that the rivulet carries away matter
which cannot be repaired, except by wearing
away fome part of the furface of the place upon
which the rain that forms the ftream is gathered.
The remains of a former ftate are here vifible ;
and we can, without any long chain of reafoning, compare what has been with what is at the
prefent moment.   It requires but little ftudy to
replace the parts removed, and to fee nature at
work, refolving the moft hard and folid maffes,
by the continued influences of the fun and atmofphere *.   We fee the beginning of that long
journey, by which heavy bodies travel from the
fummit of the land to the bottom of the ocean,
and we remain convinced, that, *on our continents,
there is no fpot on which a river may not formerly
have run* †.

315. The view thus afforded of the operations, in their nafcent ftate, which have fha-
ped out and fafhioned the prefent furface of
the land, is neceffary to prepare us for following them to the utmoft extent of their
effects. From thefe effects, the truth of the
propofition, that rivers have cut and formed, not
                                        the

---

* Theory of the Earth, vol. ii. p. 294.

† *Ibid.* p. 296.

the beds only, but the whole of the valleys, or rather fyftem of valleys, through which they flow, is demonftrated on a principle which has a clofe affinity to that on which chances are ufually calculated, § 99. In order to conceive rightly the courfe of a great river, and the communication fubfifting between the main trunk and its remoteft branches, let us take the inftance of the Danube, and caft our eyes on one of the maps conftructed by MARSIGLI, for illuftrating the natural hiftory of that great river *. When it is confidered, that over all the vaft and uneven furface, which reaches from the Alps to the Euxine, and from the mountains of Crapack to thofe of Hæmus, a regular communication is kept up between every point and the line of greateft depreffion, in which the river flows, no one can hefitate to acknowledge, that it is the agency of the waters alone which has opened them a free paffage through all the intricacies of this amazing labyrinth. In effect, fuppofe this communication to be interrupted, and that fome fudden operation of nature were to erect a barrier of mountains to oppofe the Theife or the Drave, as they rolled their waters to the Danube. From this what could poffibly refult, but the damming up of thofe rivers till

Z   their

---

* Hiftoire du Danube, tom. i. tab. 34.

their waters were deep, or high enough to find
a vent, either under the bafes or over the tops of
the oppofing ridge.   Thus there would be formed immenfe lakes and immenfe cataracts, which,
by filling up what was too low, and cutting
down what was too high, would in time reftore
fuch a uniform declivity of furface as had before
prevailed.   Juft fo in the times that are paft,
whatever may have been the irregularities of the
furface at its firft emerging from the fea, or
whatever irregularities may have been produced
in it by fubfequent convulfions, the flow action of the ftreams would not fail in time to
create or renew a fyftem of valleys communicating with one another, like that which we
at prefent behold.   Water, in all circumftances, would find its way to the loweft point;
though, where the furface was quite irregular, it would not do fo till after being dammed
up in a thoufand lakes, or dafhed in cataracts
over a thoufand precipices.   Where neither of
thefe is the cafe ; and where the lake and the cataract are comparatively rare phenomena ; there
we perceive that conftitution of a furface, which
water alone, of all phyfical agents, has a tendency to produce ; and we muft conclude, that the
probability of fuch a conftitution having arifen
from another caufe, is, to the probability of its
having

having arifen from the running of water, in fuch
a proportion as unity bears to a number infinitely great.

316. The courfes of many rivers retain marks
that they once confifted of a feries of lakes,
which have been converted into dry ground, by
the twofold operation of filling up the bottoms,
and deepening the outlets. This happens, efpecially, when fucceffive terraces of gravelly and
flat land are found on the banks of a river, § 100.
Such platforms, or *haughs* as they are called in
this country, are always proofs of the wafte and
detritus produced by the river, and of the different levels on which it has run; but they
fometimes lead us farther, and make it certain, that the great mafs of gravel which forms
the fucceffive terraces on each fide of the river, was depofited in the bafon of a lake. If,
from the level of the higheft terrace, down
to the prefent bed of the river, all is alluvial,
and formed of fand and gravel, it is then evident, that the fpace as low as the river now runs
muft have been once occupied by water; at the
fame time, it is clear, that water muft have ftood,
or flowed as high at leaft, as the uppermoft furface of the meadow. It is impoffible to reconcile thefe two facts, which are both undeniable,
but by fuppofing a lake, or body of ftagnant water, to have here occupied a great hollow,
(which by us muft be held as one of the origi-

nal inequalities of the globe, becaufe we can
trace it no farther back), and that this hollow,
in the courfe of ages, has been filled up by the
gravel and alluvial earth brought down by the
river, which is now cutting its channel through
materials of its own depofiting. There is no
great river that does not afford inftances of this,
both in the hilly part of its courfe, and where
it defcends firft from thence into the plain.
Were there room here for the minuter details
of topographical defcription, this might be il-
luftrated by innumerable examples.

317. It is faid above, that the water muft
have run or ftood, in former times, as low as the
prefent bottom of the river; but there is often
clear evidence, that it has run or ftood much
lower, becaufe the alluvial land reaches far below the prefent level of the river. This is known
to hold in very many inftances, where it has
happened that pits have been funk to confiderable depths on the banks of large rivers. By
that means, the depth of the alluvial ground,
under the prefent bed of the river, has been difcovered to be great; and from this arifes the
difficulty, fo generally experienced, of finding
good foundations for bridges that are built over
rivers in large vallies, or open plains, the ground
being compofed of travelled materials to an unknown depth, without any thing like the native

or

or folid ftrata. In fuch cafes, it is evident, that formerly the water muft have been much lower, as well as much higher, than its prefent level, and this is only confiftent with the notion, that the place was once occupied by a deep lake.

318. If, following the light derived from thefe indications, we go back to the time when the river ran above the higheft of thofe levels at which it has left any traces of its operations, we fhall fee it compofed of a feries of lakes and cataracts, from which, by the filling up of the one, and the wearing down of the other, the waters have at length worked out to themfelves a quiet and uninterrupted paffage to the ocean. We may, indeed, on good evidence, go back ftill farther than the fucceffion of fuch meadows or terraces, as are above mentioned, will carry us, and may confider the whole valley, or *trough* of the river, as produced by its own operations. The original inequalities of the furface, and the difpofition of the ftrata, muft no doubt have determined the water-courfes at firft; but this does not hinder us from confidering the rivers as having modified and changed thofe inequalities, and as the *proximate* caufes of the fhape and configuration which the furface has now affumed.

319. From this gradual change of lakes into rivers, it follows, that a lake is but a temporary and accidental condition of a river, which is

Z 3 every

every day approaching to its termination; and the truth of this is attefted, not only by the lakes that have exifted, but alfo by thofe that continue to exift. Where any confiderable ftream enters a lake, a flat meadow is ufually obferved increafing from year to year. The foil of this meadow is difpofed in horizontal ftrata: the meadow is terminated by a marfh; which marfh is acquiring folidity, and is foon to be converted into a meadow, as the meadow will be into an arable field. All this while the fediment of the river makes its way flowly into the lake, forming a mound or bank under the furface of the water, with a pretty rapid flope toward the lake. This mound increafes by the addition of new earth, fand, and gravel, poured in over the flope; and thus the progrefs of filling up continually advances.

320. In fmall lakes, this progrefs may eafily be traced; and will be found fingularly confpicuous in that beautiful affemblage of lakes, which fo highly adorns the mountain fcenery of Weftmoreland and Cumberland. Among thefe a great number of inftances appear, in which lakes are either partially filled up, or have entirely difappeared. In the Lake of Kefwick, we not only difcover the marks of filling up at the upper end, which extend far into Borrowdale, from which valley a fmall river flows into the lake; but we have the cleareft proof, that this lake was once
united

united to that of Baſſenthwaite, and occupied
the whole valley from Borrowdale to Ouſe-
Bridge. Theſe two lakes are at preſent joined
only by a ſtream, which runs from the former
into the latter, and their continuity is interrupted by a conſiderable piece of alluvial land,
compoſed of beds of earth and gravel, without
rock, or any appearance of the native ſtrata.
This ſeparation, therefore, ſeems no other than
a *bar*, formed by the influx of two rivers,
that enter the valley here from oppoſite ſides,
the Greata from the eaſt, and Newland's Water from the weſt. The ſurface of this meadow is at preſent twelve or fifteen feet at leaſt
above the level of either lake ; and a quantity of
water of that depth muſt therefore have been
drawn off by the deepening of the iſſue at
Ouſe-Bridge, through which the water of both
lakes paſſes, in its way to the ocean.

Many more examples, ſimilar to this, may be
collected from the ſame lakes ; there are indeed few places from which, in this branch of
geology, more information may be collected.

321. The larger lakes exemplify the ſame progreſs. Where the Rhone enters the Lake of Geneva, the beach has been obſerved to receive an
annual increaſe ; and the Portus Valeſiæ, now Pre-
vallais, which is at preſent half a league from the
lake, was formerly cloſe upon its bank. Indeed,
the ſediments of the Rhone appear clearly to

have

have formed the valley through which it runs, to a diftance of about three leagues at leaft from the place where the river now difcharges itfelf into the lake. The ground there is perfectly ho-rizontal, compofed of fand and mud, little raifed above the level of the river, and full of marfhes. The depofition made by the Rhone after it en-ters the lake, is vifible to the eye ; and may be feen falling down in clouds to the bottom.

The great lakes of North America are under-going the fame changes, and, it would feem, even with more rapidity. As the rivers, however, which fupply thefe vaft refervoirs, are none of them very great, the filling up is much lefs re-markable than the draining off of the water, by the deepening of the outlet. An intelligent travel-ler has remarked, that in Lake Superior itfelf the diminution of the waters is apparent, and that marks can be difcovered on the rocks, of the furface having been fix feet higher than it is at prefent. In the fmaller lakes this diminution is ftill more evident *. In fome of thofe far inland, the ground all round appeared to the fame tra-veller to be the depofite from the rivers, of which the lakes themfelves may be confidered as a mere expanfion †.

322. In

---

* Mackenzie's Voyages through the Continent of North America to the Frozen and Pacific Oceans, p. xlii. and xxxvi.   † *Ibid.* p. 122.

322. In order to give uniform declivities to the rivers, the lakes muſt not only be filled up or drained, but the cataract, wherever there is one, muſt be worn away. The latter is an operation in all caſes viſible. The ſtream, as it precipitates itſelf over the rocks, hurries along with it, not only ſand and gravel, but occaſionally large ſtones, which grind and wear down the rock with a force proportioned to their magnitude and acceleration. The ſmooth ſurface of the rocks in all waterfalls, their rounded ſurface, and curious excavations, are the moſt ſatisfactory proofs of the conſtant attrition which they endure ; and, where the rocks are deeply interſected, theſe marks often reach to a great height above the level on which the water now flows. The phenomena, in ſuch inſtances, are among the arguments beſt calculated to remove all incredulity reſpecting the waſte which rivers have produced, and are continuing to produce. They ſuffer no doubt to remain, that the height and aſperity of every waterfall are continually diminiſhing ; that innumerable cataracts are entirely obliterated ; that thoſe which remain are verging toward the ſame end, and that the Falls of Montmorenci and Niagara muſt ultimately diſappear.

323. Though there can be no doubt of the juſtneſs of the preceding concluſions, when applied

to

to lakes in general, fome apparent exceptions occur, in which the progrefs of draining and filling up feems to have been fufpended, or even to have gone in a contrary direction. Thefe exceptions confift of the lakes which appear to have received a greater quantity of materials than was fufficient to have filled them up. Such, for example, is the Lake of Geneva, which receives the Rhone defcending from the Vallais, one of the deepeft and longeft vallies on the furface of the earth. Now, if this valley, or even a large proportion of it, had been excavated by the Rhone itfelf, as our theory leads us to fuppofe, the lake ought to have been entirely filled up, becaufe the materials brought down by the river feem to be much greater than the lake, on any reafonable fuppofition concerning its original magnitude, can poffibly have received. What, then, it may be faid, has become of all that the Rhone has brought down and depofited in it? The lake, at this moment retains, in fome places, the depth of more than 1000 feet; and yet, of all that the Rhone carries into it, nothing but the pure water iffues. If it has been continuing to diminifh, both in fuperficial extent and in depth, from the time when the Rhone began to run into it, what muft have been its original dimenfions?

I

I cannot pretend to remove entirely the difculty which is here ſtated ; yet I think the following remarks may go ſome length in doing ſo.

324. It is certain, that from the preſent ſtate of the lake of Geneva, and of the ground round it, we can hardly draw any inference as to its original dimenſions. Sauſſure has traced, with his uſual ſkill, the marks of the courſe of the Rhone, on a level greatly above the preſent ; and, by obſervations on the ſide of Mount Saleve, has found proofs of the running of water, at leaſt 200 toiſes above the preſent ſuperficies of the lake. But, if ever the ſuperficies of the lake ſtood at this height, or at this height nearly, though we can conjecture but little concerning the ſtate of the adjacent country, which no doubt was alſo on a higher level, the lake may very well be ſuppoſed to have been of far greater dimenſions than it is now. It may have occupied the whole ſpace from Jura to Saleve, and included the Lake of Neufchatel ; ſo that it may have been of magnitude ſufficient to receive the ſpoils of the Vallais, which, as the ſurface of its waters lowered, may have been waſhed away and carried down to the ſea. Thus it may have afforded a temporary receptacle for the *debris* of the Alps, and may have ſerved for an *entrepot*, as it were, where thoſe debris were

depoſited,

depofited, before they were carried to the place of their ultimate deftination.

325. But the great depth which the lake has at prefent, ftill remains to be explained, becaufe no mud or gravel could be carried beyond the gulf, of a thoufand feet deep, which was here ready to receive it. The reality of this difficulty muft be acknowledged ; and fome caufe feems to act, if not in the generation, yet certainly in the prefervation of lakes, with which we are but little acquainted. We can indeed imagine fome caufes of that kind to occur in the courfe of the degradation of the land, which may produce new lakes, or increafe the dimenfions of the old. The wearing away of a ftratum, or body of ftrata, may lay bare, and render acceffible to the water, fome beds of mineral fubftances foluble in that fluid. The diftrict, for inftance, in Chefhire, which contains rock-falt, extends over a tract of fourteen or fifteen miles, and is covered by a thick ftratum of clay, more or lefs indurated, which defends the falt from the water at the furface, and preferves the whole mafs in a ftate of drynefs. Should this covering be broke open by any natural convulfion, or fhould it be worn away, as it muft be in the progrefs of the general detritus, the water would gain admiffion to the faline ftrata, would

would gradually diffolve them, and form of
courfe a very deep and extenfive lake, where all
was before dry land. This event is not only
poffible, but it fhould feem, that in the courfe
of things it muft neceffarily happen.

326. Something of this kind may have taken
place in the track of the Rhone, and may have
produced the Leman Lake. It is not impoffible,
that, at a very remote period, the Rhone defcended from the Alps without forming any
lake, or at leaft any lake of which the remains
are now exifting ; and this fuppofition, which is
more probable than that of § 324, we fhall foon
find to be conformable to appearances of another
kind. The river may have wore away the fecondary limeftone ftrata over which it took its
courfe after it left the fchiftus of the mountains ;
and, in doing fo, may have reached fome ftratum of a faline nature, and this being wafhed
out, may have left behind it a lake, which is but
modern compared with many of the revolutions
that have happened on the furface of the earth *.

This explanation is no doubt hypothetical ;
but it is propofed in one of thofe cafes, in
which

* There are falt fprings at Bex, near Aigle, about
ten miles from the head of the lake : faline ftrata, therefore, are probably at no great diftance.

which hypothetical reasonings are warranted by the strictest rules of philosophical investigation. It is proposed in a case, where the causes visible to man seem inadequate to the effect, and where we must therefore have recourse to an agent that is invisible. If the operations ascribed to this agent are conformable to the analogy of nature, it is all that can in reason be required.

327. Another circumstance may also influence the generation and preservation of lakes; but it is also one with which we are but little acquainted. The strata, and indeed the whole body of mineral substances which forms the basis of our land, have been raised up from the bottom of the sea, by a progress that should seem in general to have been gradual and slow. Appearances, however, are not wanting, which shew, that this progress is not uniform; and that both rising and sinking in the surface of the land, or in the rocks which are the base of it, have happened within a period of time, which is by no means of great extent. In this progress, the elevations and depressions may not be the same for every spot. They may be partial, and one part of a stratum, or body of strata, may rise to a greater height, or be more depressed, than another. It is not impossible, that this process may affect the depth of
lakes,

lakes, and change the relative level of their
fides and bottom.

328. All lakes, however, do not involve the
difficulty which the preceding conjectures are intended to remove. The great lakes of North
America do not, for inftance, receive their fupply from very large rivers. Of courfe, it is not
from a tract great in comparifon of themfelves,
that the wafte and detritus is brought down
into them ; and it feems not at all wonderful,
that, without being filled up, they have been
able to receive it. The fame, in a degree at
leaft, is true of many other lakes.

It fhould alfo be confidered, that we may
err greatly in the eftimate we make of the materials actually carried down and depofited in
any lake. To judge of their entire amount, we
fhould know the original form of the inequalities on the earth's furface ; of the quantity of depreffion which exifted, independently of the rivers ; and though, in general, thefe original inequalities may be overlooked, and the prefent
confidered as made by the running of water,
yet, in particular inftances, this may be far from
true. The Vallais, for example, which we confider as the work of the Rhone, may, when the
Alps rofe out of the fea, have included many
depreffions of the furface, which the river joined together, and, from being a feries of lakes,
formed into one great valley.

329. The

329. The mouths by which rivers on bold rocky coasts difcharge their waters into the fea, afford a very ftriking confirmation of the conclufions concerning the general fyftem of wafte and degradation which have been drawn above. At thefe mouths we ufually fee, not only the bed of the river, but frequently a confiderable valley, cut out of the folid rock, while that rock perferves its elevation, and its precipitous afpect, wherever it is not interfected by a run of water. No convulfion that can have torn afunder the rocks ; no breach that can have been made in them, antecedent to the running of the waters, will account for the circumftance of every river finding a correfponding opening, by which it makes its way to the fea ; for that opening being fo nearly proportional to the magnitude of the river, and for fuch breaches never occurring but where ftreams of water are found.

330. The actual furvey of any bold and rocky coaft, will make this clearer than any general ftatement can poffibly do. Let us take, for an example, the coaft of the Britifh Channel, from Torbay to the Land's End, which is faced by a continued rampart of high cliffs, formed of much indurated and primeval rock. If we confider the breaches in this rampart, at the mouths of

of the Dart, of the Plym and Tamer, of the river at Fowey, of the Fal, the Hel, &c. it will appear perfectly clear, that they have been produced by their refpective ftreams. Where there
is no ftream, there is no breach in the rock, no
foftening in the bold and ftern afpect which
this fhore every where prefents to the ocean.
If we look at the fmaller ftreams, we find them
working their way through the cliffs at the prefent moment; and we fee the fteps by which
the larger valleys of the Dart and the Tamer
have been cut down to the level of the fea. If
we would have ftill clearer evidence, that no
breaches made antecedently to the running of
the rivers have opened a way for them, we need
only look to the oppofite fide, or northern fhore,
of the fame promontory, where we alfo find a
feries of outlets, all originating in the ridge of
the country, and becoming deeper as they approach the fea, but altogether unconnected with
the openings on the fouth fide; and this could
hardly have been the cafe, had they been the
effects of previous concuffions, or of any peculiarity in the original ftructure of the rocks.

331. In contemplating fuch coafts as thefe,
when we go back to the time when the rivers ran
upon a level as high as the higheft of the cliffs
on the fea-fhore, we muft fuppofe, that the land
then extended many miles farther into what is

A a   now

now occupied by the fea.   When at Plymouth,
for inftance, the Tamer and the Plym flowed on
the level of Mount Edgecombe or of Staten
Heights, if the rivers ran with a moderate
declivity into the fea, the coaft muft have
advanced many miles beyond its prefent line.
Thus the land, when higher, was alfo more extended, and the limits of our ifland in that ancient ftate, were doubtlefs very different from
thefe by which it is at prefent circumfcribed.

If with the fame views we confider any o-
ther of the bold coafts which the map of the
world prefents us with, we fhall quickly remark,
that wherever a deep interfection of the fea is
made into the land, as on the weftern fhores of
our own ifland, or on thofe of Norway, a river
runs in at the head of it, and points out by what
means fuch inlets are formed, viz. by the united
powers of the fea and of the land, the waters of
the latter having opened the way by which
thofe of the former have penetrated fo far into
the country.

332. It is not meant affuredly to deny the
irregularities of the fea-coaft, as it may have
originally exifted ; thefe irregularities no doubt
determined the initial operations of that wafte
and decay, by which, in procefs of time, they
were themfelves entirely effaced.   The line of
our

our coafts may be compared to one of thofe curves, which are fometimes treated of in the higher geometry, where the ordinates are functions, not only of their abfciffæ, but alfo of the time elapfed fince a certain epocha. The form of the curve at that epocha, or when the time began to flow, correfponds to the original form of the fea-çoaft, on its emerging from the ocean, and before the powers of wafting and decay had begun to act upon it. To fpeak ftrictly, the original figure, in both cafes, influences all the fubfequent; but the farther removed from it in point of time, the lefs is that influence; fo that, in phyfical queftions, and for the purpofe of fuch approximations as fuit the imperfection of our knowledge, the confideration of the original figure may be wholly left out.

Note XVII. § 105.

Remains of Decompofed Rocks.

333. The plain of Crau was the *Campus Lapideus* of the ancients; and, as mythology always feeks to connect itfelf with the extraordinary facts in natural hiftory, it was faid to be the fpot where Hercules, fighting with the fons

of

of Neptune, and being in want of weapons, was supplied from heaven by a shower of stones: hence it was called *Campus Herculeus.*

This plain is on the east side of the Rhone, between Salon and Arles: it is of a triangular form, about twenty square leagues in extent, and is covered almost entirely with quartzy gravel. This immense collection of gravel has been supposed by some to have been brought down by the Durance from the Alps of Dauphiny; by others it has been ascribed to the Rhone; and by many to the sea, as being a work too great for any river. The explanation mentioned above, § 105, namely, that the loose gravel on the plain arises from the decomposition of a great stratum of pudding-stone, which is the basis of the whole, is the opinion of Saussure, and is founded on his own observations *.

334. The theories that have been contrived for explaining the phenomena of the plain of Crau, afford an instance of the necessity of generalizing our observations before we can explain a particular appearance: in other words, they prove

the

---

* See Voyages aux Alpes, tom. iii. § 1592, et 1597. See also on this subject a Memoir by Lamanon, Journal de Physique, tom. xxii. p. 477; and another by M. De Servieres, *ibid.* p. 270.

the truth of Lord Bacon's maxim, That the explanation of a phenomenon fhould not be fought for from the ftudy of that phenomenon alone, but from the comparifon of it with others. One of the theories of this plain is, that the breccia, which is the bafe of it, is formed from the confolidation of the loofe gravel of the plain, by water percolating through it, and carrying fome cementing fubftance along with it, or fome *lapidific juice*, as it is called. And indeed, whether the gravel is formed from the breccia, or the breccia from the gravel, is a queftion which probably could never be refolved by the mere examination of the plain itfelf. But the queftion is very foon decided, when we compare what is obferved here with other appearances in the natural hiftory of the earth's furface, and confider how much more frequent the decompofition of folids is, than their reconfolidation, in any place above the level of the fea.

335. The argument for the decompofition of ftony fubftances which is afforded by the ftate of this fingular plain, may be confirmed by the appearances obferved in many extenfive tracts of land all over the world, and efpecially in fome parts of Great Britain. The road to Exeter from Taunton Dean, between the latter and Honiton, paffes over a large heath or down, confiderably elevated above the plain of Taunton. The rock

A a 3   which

which is the bafe of this heath, as far as can be
difcovered, is limeftone, and over the furface
of it large flints, in the form of gravel, are
very thickly fpread. There is no higher ground
in the neighbourhood from which this gravel
can be fuppofed to have come, nor any ftream
that can have carried it, fo that no explanation
of it remains, but that it is formed of the flints
contained in beds of limeftone, which are now
worn away. The flints on the heath are precifely of the kind found in limeftone ; many of them are not much worn, and cannot
have travelled far from the rock in which
they were originally contained. It feems certain, therefore, that they are the *debris* of limeftone ftrata, now entirely decompofed, that once
lay above the ftrata which at prefent form
the bafe of this elevated plain, and probably covered them to a confiderable height.
This explanation carries the greater probability
with it, that any other way of accounting for
the fact in queftion, as the travelling of the gravel from higher grounds, or the immerfion of
the furface under the fea, will imply changes
in the face of the country, incomparably greater
than are here fuppofed. Our hypothefis feems
to give the *minimum* of all the kinds of change
that can poffibly account for the phenomenon.

336. The

336. The fame remarks may be made on the high plain of Blackdown, which the road paffes over in going from Exeter to the weftward. The flints there are diffeminated over the furface as thickly as in the other inftance, and can be explained only on the fame fuppofition.

Again, in the interior of England, beginning from about Worcefter and Birmingham, and proceeding north-eaft through Warwickfhire, Leicefterfhire, Nottinghamfhire, as far as the fouth of Yorkfhire, a particular fpecies of highly indurated gravel, formed of granulated quartz, is found every where in great abundance. This fame gravel extends to the weft and north-weft, as far as Afhburn in Derbyfhire, and perhaps ftill farther to the north. The quantity of it about Birmingham is very remarkable, as well as in many other places; and the phenomenon is the more furprifing, that no rock of the fame fort is feen in its native place. It is fuch gravel as might be expected in a mountainous country, in Scotland, for inftance, or in Switzerland, but not at all in the fertile and fecondary plains of England.

This enigma is explained, however, when it is obferved, that the bafis of the whole tract juft defcribed is a red fandftone, often containing in it a hard quartzy gravel, perfectly fimilar to that which has juft been mentioned. From

the

the diffolution of beds of this fandftone, which formerly covered the prefent, there can be no doubt that this gravel is derived. But, as the gravel is in general thinly difperfed through the fandftone, and abounds only in fome of its layers, it fhould therefore feem, that a vaft body of ftrata muft have been worn away and decompofed, before fuch quantities of gravel as now exift in the foil could have been let loofe.

337. I have faid, that a rock capable of affording fuch gravel as this, is not to be found in the tract of country juft mentioned. This, however, is not ftrictly true; for in Worcefterfhire, between Bromefgrove and Birmingham, about feven miles from the latter, a rock is found confifting of indurated ftrata, greatly elevated, and without doubt primitive, from the detritus of which fuch gravel as we are now fpeaking of might be produced. Thefe ftrata feem to rife up from under the fecondary, where they are interfected by the road; and, for as much as appears, are not of great thicknefs, fo that they cannot have afforded the materials of this gravel directly, though they may have done fo indirectly, or through the medium of the red fandftone; that is to fay, a primary rock of which they are the remains, may have afforded materials for the gravel in the fandftone; and this fandftone may in its turn have afforded the materials

terials of the prefent foil, and particularly the gravel contained in it.

338. Pudding-ftones being very liable to decompofition, have probably, in moft countries, afforded a large proportion of the loofe gravel now found in the foil. The mountains, or at leaft hills, of this rock, which are found in many places, prove the great extent of fuch decompofition. Mount Rigi, for inftance, on the fide of the Lake of Lucerne, is entirely of pudding-ftone, and is 742 toifes in height, meafured from the level of the lake. By the defcriptions given of it, as well as of other hills of the fame kind in Switzerland, we may, without due attention, be led to fuppofe that they are entirely formed of loofe gravel. Even M. Sauffure's defcription is chargeable with this fault, though, when attended to, it will be found to contain a fufficient proof, that this hill is compofed of real pudding-ftone *. The nature of the thing alfo, would be fufficient to convince us, that a hill, more than 4000 feet in height, could not confift of loofe and unconfolidated materials.

If, then, we regard Mount Rigi as the remains of a body of pudding-ftone ftrata, we muft conclude, that thefe ftrata were originally more extenfive, and the adjacent valleys and plains will ferve,

* Voyages aux Alpes, tom. iv. § 1941,

ferve, in fome degree, to meafure the quantity of them which time has deftroyed.

339. If the theory of unftratified mountains, namely thofe of whinftone, porphyry, and granite, be admitted as laid down above, it will furnifh a meafure of the deftruction which has taken place in the ftratified rocks, and of the vaft depredations which have been made upon them fince they were raifed up from the bottom of the fea. Like every other meafure, however, of wafting, by a thing that is itfelf fubject to wafte, it can only give a *minimum*, or a limit which the quantity wafted muft neceffarily exceed.

The abrupt face of a whinftone rock muft be underftood as an evidence, that fome body of ftrata which fupported it when fluid, remained in contact with it, when it was become folid ; and if this part of the mould in which the whinftone was caft, has difappeared, it muft generally be afcribed to the operation of wafte and decompofition. Such a face, for inftance, as that which Salifbury *Craig* prefents to the weft, viz. a perpendicular wall of whinftone, about ninety feet high, raifed on a body of fandftone ftrata of the height of about 300 feet, can have been produced only by having been abutted againft fome ftratified rock, equally abrupt,

and

and of the fame elevation with itfelf. Of this rock no part remains.

The bafaltic rock of Edinburgh Caftle is near-ly in the fame ftate. Its perpendicular fides on the fouth, weft, and north, are now difengaged from the ftrata by which they were once en-compaffed.

340. The granite mountains alfo, where they are quite unftratified, give rife to the fame con-clufion. Thofe central chains which we find in fo many inftances towering above the fchiftus which cover their fides, have probably been once completely enveloped by the latter ; and, on this fuppofition, an eftimate may fometimes be formed of the original height of fuch mountains.

In thefe eftimations, however, fome uncer-tainty muft arife, from our being unable to di-ftinguifh between the effects which are to be afcribed to the fracture and diflocation that took place when the compound body of ftrati-fied and unftratified rocks was raifed up from the bottom of the fea, and the effects produced by the fubfequent wafte and decompofition at the furface. In this, as in many other inftances, we are not always able to feparate between the original inequalities of the furface, and thofe which wearing has produced.

341. It would be important to afcertain the rate at which the elevation of mountains decreafes, and

this

this is what we may perhaps expect to be accomplished, by the progress of geological science, and the multiplying of accurate observations. It has been supposed, that the Pyrenees diminish about ten inches in a century ; but what confidence is to be put in this estimate, I am unable to determine *.

A very unequivocal mark of the degradation of mountains is often to be met with in the heaps of loose stones found on their tops. These stones, it is obvious, cannot have come from any other place by natural means, and they are accordingly always sharp and angular, and have none of the characters of transported rocks. They are said sometimes to have been brought by men's hands ; but this is highly improbable, their quantity is often so considerable, and the difficulty of transportation so great. Where any purpose was to be served by heaping them together, men have availed themselves of the stones that they found ready prepared on the summit, and have constructed from them cairns, which have served as signals, useful in their pastoral, and sometimes in their military occupations.

Note

---

* Essai sur le Mineralogie des Pyrenées, p. 87.

Note XVIII. § 112.

Transportation of Stones, &c.

342. NATURE supplies the means of tracing with considerable certainty the migration of fossil bodies on the surface of the earth, as only the more indurated stones, and those most strongly characterised, can endure the accidents that must befal them in travelling to a distance from their native place.

It is a fact very generally observed, that where the valleys among primitive mountains open into large plains, the gravel of those plains consists of stones, evidently derived from the mountains. The nearer that any spot is to the mountains, the larger are the gravel stones, and the less rounded is their figure ; and, as the distance increases, this gravel, which often forms a stratum nearly level, is covered with a thicker bed of earth or vegetable soil. This progression has particularly been observed in the valleys of Piedmont and the plains of Lombardy, where a bed of gravel forms the basis of the soil, from the foot of the Alps to the shores of the Hadriatic.

Hadriatic *. We may collect from GUETTARD,
that a fimilar gradation is found in the gravel
and earth which cover the great plain of Poland,
from Mount Krapack to the Baltic †. The reafon of this gradation is evident ; the farther the
ftones have travelled, and the more rubbing
they have endured, the fmaller they grow, the
more regular is the figure they affume, and the
greater the quantity of that finer detritus which
conftitutes the foil. The wafhing of the rains
and rivers is here obvious ; and each of the
three quantities juft mentioned, if not directly
proportional to the diftance which the ftones
have migrated from their native plaçe, may be
faid, in the language of geometry, to be at leaft
proportional to a certain function of that diftance.

343. The immenfe quantity of *cailloux roulés*,
or rounded gravel, collected in the immediate vicinity of mountainous tracts, has led fome geologifts to fuppofe the exiftence of ancient currents, which defcended from the mountains, in
a quantity, and with a *momentum*, of which there
is no example in the prefent ftate of the world.
Thus Sauffure imagines, that the hill of Supergue, near Turin, which is formed of gravel,
can only be explained by fuppofing fuch currents

* Voyages aux Alpes, tom. iii. § 1315.

† Mém. Acad. des Sciences, 1762, p. 234 ; 293, &c.

rents as are juft mentioned, or what he terms a
debacle, to have taken place at fome former period *. If, however, we afcribe to the mountains a magnitude and elevation vaftly greater
than that which they now poffefs ; if we regard
the vallies between them as cut out by the rivers and torrents from an immenfe rampart of
folid rock, neither materials fufficiently great,
nor agents fufficiently powerful, will appear to
be wanting, for collecting bodies of gravel and
other loofe materials, equal to any that are found
on the furface of the earth. The neceffity of
introducing a *debacle*, or any other unknown
agent, to account for the tranfportation of foffils,
feems to arife from under-rating the effects of
action long continued, and not limited by fuch
fhort periods as circumfcribe the works, and
even the obfervations, of men.

344. The fupply of gravel and *cailloux roulés*,
for the plains extended at the feet of primitive
mountains, is doubtlefs in many cafes much increafed by the pudding-ftone, interpofed between
the fecondary and the primary ftrata. The beds of
pudding-ftone contain gravel already formed on
the fhores of continents, that ceafed to exift before
the prefent were produced ; and the cement of
.   this

---

* Voyages aux Alpes, tom. iii, § 1303.

this gravel, yielding eafily to the weather, al-
lows the ftones included in it to be wafhed down
by the torrents, and fcattered over the plains,
I know not if the hill of Supergue, above mentioned, is not in reality a mafs of the pudding-
ftone which forms the border of the Alps, and
of which the materials have fuffered no tranfportation fince the time of their laft confolidation. This at leaft is certain, that Sauffure, notwithftanding his accuracy, has fometimes confounded the loofe gravel on the furface with
that which is confolidated into rock ; an inaccuracy which is to be charged, as I have elfewhere obferved, rather againft his fyftem than
himfelf.

345. The loofe ftones found on the fides of
hills, and the bottoms of valleys, when traced back to their original place, point out
with demonftrative evidence the great changes which have happened fince the commencement of their journey ; and in particular
ferve to fhow, that many valleys which now
deeply interfect the furface, had not begun to
be cut out when thefe ftones were firft detached
from their native rocks. We know, for inftance,
that ftones under the influence of fuch forces
as we are now confidering, cannot have firft defcended from one ridge, and then afcended on
the fide of an oppofite ridge. But the granite
of

of Mont Blanc has been found, as mentioned above, on the fides of Jura, and even on the fide of it fartheft from the Alps. Now, in the prefent ftate of the earth's furface, between the central chain of the Alps, from which thefe pieces of granite muft have come, and the ridge of Mont Jura, befides many fmaller valleys, there is the great valley of the Rhone, from the bottom of which, to the place where they now lie, is a height of not lefs than 3000 feet. Stones could not, by any force that we know of, be made to afcend over this height. We muft therefore fuppofe, that when they travelled from Mont Blanc to Jura, this deep valley did not exift, but that fuch a uniform declivity, as water can run on with rapidity, extended from the one fummit to the other. This fuppofition accords well with what has been already faid concerning the recent formation of the Leman Lake, and of the prefent valley of the Rhone.

346. We can derive, in a matter of this fort, but little aid from calculation; yet we may difcover by it, whether our hypothefis tranfgreffes materially againft the laws of probability, and is inconfiftent with phyfical principles already eftablifhed. The horizontal diftance from Mont Jura to the granite mountains, at the head of the Arve, may be accounted fifty geo-

B b   graphic

graphic miles. Though we fuppofe Mont Blanc, and the reft of thofe mountains, to have been originally much higher than they are at prefent, the ridge of Jura muft have been fo likewife; and though probably not by an equal quantity, yet it is the faireft way to fuppofe the difference of their height to have been nearly the fame in former ages that it is at prefent, and it may therefore be taken at 10,000 feet. The declivity of a plane from the top of Mont Jura to the top of Mont Blanc, would therefore be about one mile and three quarters in fifty, or one foot in thirty; an inclination much greater than is neceffary for water to run on, even with extreme rapidity, and more than fufficient to enable a river or a torrent to carry with it ftones or fragments of rock, almoft to any diftance.

Sauffure, in relating the fact that pieces of granite are found among the high paffes near the fummits of Mont Jura, alleges, that they are only found in fpots from which the central chain of the Alps may be feen. But it fhould feem that this coincidence is accidental, becaufe, from whatever caufe the tranfportation of thefe blocks has proceeded, the form of the mountains, efpecially of Mont Jura, muft be too much changed to admit of the fuppofition, that the places of it from which Mont Blanc is now vifible, viſible, are the ſame from which that mountain was viſible when theſe ſtones were tranſported hither. It may be, however, that the paſſes which now exiſt in Mont Jura are the remains of valleys or beds of torrents, which once flowed weſtward from the Alps; and it is natural, that the fragments from the latter mountains ſhould be found in the neighbourhood of thoſe ancient water-tracks.

347. Sauſſure obſerved in another part of the Alps, that where the Drance deſcends from the ſides of Mont Velan and the Great St Bernard, to join the Rhone in the Vallais, the valley it runs in lies between mountains of primary ſchiſtus, in which no granite appears, and yet that the bottom of this valley, toward its lower extremity, is for a conſiderable way covered with looſe blocks of granite *. His familiar acquaintance with all the rocks of thoſe mountains, led him immediately to ſuſpect, that theſe ſtones came from the granite chain of Mont Blanc, which is weſtward of the Drance, and conſiderably higher than the intervening mountains. This conjecture was verified by the obſervations of one of his friends, who found the ſtones in queſtion to agree exactly with a

B b 2   rock

---

* Voyages aux Alpes, tom. ii. § 1022.

rock at the point of Ornex, the neareſt part of the granite chain.

In the preſent ſtate of the ſurface, however, the valley of Orſiere lies between the rocks of Ornex and the valley of the Drance, and would certainly have intercepted the granite blocks in their way from the one of theſe points to the other, if it had exiſted at the time when they were paſſing over that tract. The valley of Or-ſiere, therefore, was not formed, when the tor-rents, or the glaciers tranſported theſe fragments from their native place.

Mountainous countries, when carefully ex-amined, afford ſo many facts ſimilar to the pre-ceding, that we ſhould never have done were we to enumerate all the inſtances in which they occur. They lead to concluſions of great uſe, if we would compare the machinery which na-ture actually employs in the tranſportation of rocks, with the largeſt fragments of rock which appear to have been removed, at ſome former period, from their native place.

348. For the moving of large maſſes of rock, the moſt powerful engines without doubt which nature employs are the glaciers, thoſe lakes or rivers of ice which are formed in the higheſt valleys of the Alps, and other mountains of the firſt order. Theſe great maſſes are in perpetual motion,

motion, undermined by the influx of heat from
the earth, and impelled down the declivities on
which they reſt by their own enormous weight,
together with that of the innumerable fragments
of rock with which they are loaded. Theſe
fragments they gradually tranſport to their utmoſt boundaries, where a formidable wall aſcer-
tains the magnitude, and atteſts the force, of the
great engine by which it was erected. The im-
menſe quantity and ſize of the rocks thus tranſported, have been remarked with aſtoniſhment
by every obſerver *, and explain ſufficiently how
fragments of rock may be put in motion, even
where there is but little declivity, and where the
actual ſurface of the ground is conſiderably uneven. In this manner, before the valleys were cut
out in the form they now are, and when the mountains were ſtill more elevated, huge fragments of
rock may have been carried to a great diſtance; and
it is not wonderful, if theſe ſame maſſes, greatly
diminiſhed in ſize, and reduced to gravel or ſand,
have reached the ſhores, or even the bottom, of
the ocean.

349. Next in force to the glaciers, the torrents
are the moſt powerful inſtruments employed in

the

* The ſtones collected on the *Glacier de Miage*, when
Sauſſure viſited it, were in ſuch quantity as to conceal
the ice entirely. Voyages aux Alpes, tom. ii. § 854.

the tranfportation of ftones.   Thefe, when they
defcend from the fides of mountains, and even
where the declivity of their courfe is not very
great, produce effects which nothing but direct
experience could render credible.   The fragments of rock which oppofe the torrent, are rendered fpecifically lighter by the fluid in which
they are immerfed, and lofe by that means at
leaft a third part of their weight : they are, at
the fame time, impelled by a force proportional
to the fquare of the velocity with which the
water rufhes againft them, and proportional alfo
to the quantity of gravel and ftones which it
has already put in motion.   Perhaps, after taking all thefe circumftances into computation,
in the midft of a fcene perfectly quiet and undifturbed, a philofopher might remain in doubt as
to the power of torrents to move the enormous
bodies of rock which are feen in the bottom of
the narrow valleys or deep glens of a mountainous country ; but his incredulity, fays an experienced traveller, will ceafe altogether, if he has
been furprifed by a ftorm in the midft of fome
Alpine region ; if he has feen the number and
impetuofity of the cataracts which rufhed down
the fides of the mountains, and beheld the ruin
which accompanied them ; and if, when the tem-
peft was paffed, he has viewed thofe meadows,
which

which a few hours before were covered with verdure, now buried under heaps of ftones, or overwhelmed by maffes of liquid mud, and the fides of the mountains cut by deep ravines, where the track of the fmalleft rivulet was not before to be difcovered *.

It is but rarely, however, even on occafions like thefe, that fuch vaft maffes of rock can be feen actually in motion, as are often found on the furface, apparently removed to a great diftance from their native place. The magnitude of thefe is fo great, in many inftances, that their tranfportation cannot be explained without fuppofing, that the furface was very different when thefe tranfportations took place from what it is at prefent ; that the elevation of the mountains was greater, and the ground fmoother and more uniform, at leaft in fome directions. If thefe fuppofitions are admitted, and they are countenanced, as we have already feen, by almoft every phenomenon in geology, the difficulties which prefent themfelves here will not appear infurmountable.

350. One of the largeft blocks of granite that we know of, is on the eaft fide of the lake of

B b 4   Geneva,

---

* See an account of a thunder ftorm near Bareges, in the Effai fur la Mineralogie des Pyrenees, p. 134.

Geneva, called *Pierre de Gouté*, about ten feet
in height, with a horizontal fection of fifteen by
twenty *. Another block not far from it, and
nearly of the fame fize, has fome remains of
fchiftus attached to it. Thefe ftones very much
refemble thofe which have fallen from the
Aiguilles, in the valley of Chamouny. The diftance from their prefent fituation to thofe *Aiguilles* is about thirty Englifh miles, with many
mountains and valleys at prefent interpofed.
By whatever means, therefore, thefe blocks were
tranfported, their motion muft have been over a
furface of much more uniform declivity than the
prefent. If the furface was without great inequalities, and its general declivity about one
foot in thirty, as already computed, the glaciers, in the firft place, and the torrents afterwards, may have ferved for the tranfportation
even of thefe rocks.

351. Again, in the narrow vale or glen which
feparates the Great from the Little Saleve, the ftrata are all calcareous, but a great number of loofe
blocks of granite and primary fchiftus are fcattered over the furface. A block of the former, near
the lower end of the valley, is about the fize of
1200 cubic feet. Two other large blocks of the
fame kind of ftone reft on a bafe of horizontal
limeftone,

---

* Voyages aux Alpes, tom. i. § 308.

limeftone, elevated two or three feet above the
reft of the furface. This elevation arifes no
doubt from the protection which the ftones have
afforded to the calcareous beds on which they
lie, fo that thefe beds do not wear away fo
faft as thofe which are fully expofed to the
weather. But it is furely to take a very limited
view of the operations on the furface, to fuppofe, with Sauffure, that the parts of the calcareous rock under thefe ftones has fuffered
no wafte whatfoever, fo that the ftones remain
now in the identical fpot where they were placed by the great *debacle* which brought them
down from the high Alps *. For my part, I have
no doubt that the Arve, which is ftill at no great
diftance, when it ran on a higher level, and in
a line different from the prefent, aided by the
glaciers and fuperior elevation of the mountains,
was an engine fufficiently powerful for effecting
the tranfportation of thefe ftones.

352. Thefe phenomena are not peculiar to the
Alps, but prevail, in a greater or lefs degree, in
the vicinity of all primary or granite mountains.
In the ifland of Arran, a fragment of the fame
kind with that which conftitutes the upper part
of Goatfield, is found on the fea-fhore, at leaft
three miles from the neareft granite rock, and
with

* *Ibid.* § 227.

with a bay of the fea intervening. Its dimenfions are not far from thofe of the *pierre de
gouté*. In fome former ftate of the granitic
mountains in that ifland, the declivity from the
top of Goatfield may have been very uniform,
and more rapid than it is at prefent.

353. Befides glaciers and torrents, which have
no doubt been the principal inftruments in producing thefe changes, other caufes may have occafionally operated. Large ftones, when once
detached, and refting on an inclined plane, from
the effects of wafte and decompofition, may advance horizontally, at the fame time that they
defcend perpendicularly, and this will happen
though they be not urged by any torrent, or any
thing but their own weight; for the furface of
the ground, as it waftes, remains higher under the ftone, and for a little way round it,
than at a greater diftance, on account of the
protection which it receives from the ftone,
as in the inftances at Saleve, juft mentioned. The ftone itfelf alfo becomes rounded at
the bottom; and thus the furface in contact
with the ground is diminifhed in extent, and
the two furfaces rendered convex towards
one another. It muft therefore happen, that
the fupport, continually weakening, will at
length give way, and the ftone incline or roll
toward the lower fide, and may even roll confiderably,

fiderably, if its centre of gravity has been high above its point of support, and if its furface has had much convexity : Thus the horizontal may very far exceed the perpendicular motion ; and, in the courfe of ages, the ftone may travel to a great diftance. A ftone, however, which travels in this manner, muft diminifh as it proceeds, and muft have been much greater in the beginning than it is at prefent.

354. This kind of motion may be aided by particular circumftances. When a ftone refts on an inclined plane, fo as to be in a ftate not very remote from equilibrium, if a part be taken away from the upper fide, the equilibrium will be loft, and the ftone will thereby be put in motion. That ftones which lie on other ftones, may, by wearing, be brought very near an equilibrium, is proved by what are called *rocking-ftones*, or in Cornwall *Logan ftones*, which have fometimes been miftaken for works of art ; but that are certainly nothing elfe than ftones, which have been fubjected to the univerfal law of wafting and decay, in fuch peculiar circumftances, as nearly to bring about an equilibrium of that ftable kind, which, when flightly difturbed, re-eftablifhes itfelf*. The logan ftone at the

---

* I do not prefume fo far as to fay, that all rocking-ftones are produced by natural means: I have not fufficient

the Land's End, is a mass of granite, weighing more than sixty tons, resting on a rock of granite, of considerable height, and close on the sea-shore. The two stones touch but in a small spot, their surfaces being considerably convex towards one another. The uppermost is so nearly in an equilibrium, that it can be made to vibrate by the strength of a man, though to overset it entirely would require a vast force. This arises from the centre of gravity of the stone being somewhat lower than the centre of curvature of that part of it on which it has a tendency to roll; the consequence of which is, that any motion impressed on the stone, forces its centre of gravity to rise, (though not very considerably), by which means it returns whenever the force is removed, and vibrates backward and forward, till it is reduced to rest. Were it required to remove the stone from its place, it might

---

cient information to justify that assertion; but the great size of that at the Land's End, its elevated position, and the approaches toward something of the same kind which are to be seen in other parts of that shore, prove that it is no work of art. They who ascribe it to the Druids, do not consider the rapidity with which the Cornish granite wastes, nor think how improbable it is, that the conditions necessary to a rocking-stone, whether produced by nature or art, should have remained the same for sixteen or seventeen hundred years.

might be moft eafily done, by cutting off a part
from one fide, or blowing it away by gunpowder ; the ftone would then lofe its balance,
would tumble from its pedeftal, and might roll
to a confiderable diftance. Now, what art is
here fuppofed to perform, nature herfelf in time
will probably effect. If the wafte on one fide
of this great mafs fhall exceed that on the oppofite in more than a certain proportion, and it
is not likely that that proportion will be always
maintained, the equilibrium of the Logan ftone
will be fubverted, never to return. Thus we
perceive how motion may be produced by the
combined action of the decompofition and gravitation of large maffes of rock.

355. Befides the gradual wafte to which ftones
expofed to the atmofphere are neceffarily fubject,
thofe of a great fize appear to be liable to fplit-
ting, and dividing into large portions, no doubt
from their weight. This may be obferved in
almoft all ftones that happen to be in fuch circumftances as we are now confidering ; and from
this caufe the fubverfion of their balance may
be more fudden, and of greater amount, than
could be expected from their gradual decay.

Thus, if to the wafting of a ftone at the bottom, we add the accidents that may befal it in
the wafting of its fides, we fee at leaft the phyfical poffibility of detached ftones being put in
motion,

motion, merely by their own weight. It is indeed remarkable, that fome of the largeft of thefe ftones reft on very narrow bafes. Thofe at the foot of Saleve touch the ground only in a few points: The Boulder-ftone of Borrowdale is fupported on a narrow ridge like the keel of a fhip, and is prevented from tumbling by a ftone or two, that ferve as a kind of fhores to prop it up. Very unexpected accidents fometimes happen to difturb the reft of fuch fragments of rock as have once migrated from their own place. Sauffure mentions a great mafs of *lapis ollaris* *, that lies detached on the fide of a declivity in the valley of Urferen, in the canton of Uri. The people ufe this ftone as a quarry, and are working it away on the upper fide, in confequence of which it will probably be foon overfet, and will roll to the bottom of the valley.

356. In many inftances it cannot be doubted, that ftones of the kind here referred to are the remains of maffes or veins of whinftone or granite, now worn away, and that they have travelled but a very fhort way, or perhaps not at all, from their original place. Many of the large blocks of whinftone which we find in this country, fometimes fingle, and fometimes fcattered

tered

* Voyages aux Alpes, tom. iv. § 1851.

tered in confiderable abundance over a particular fpot, are certainly to be referred to this
caufe.   But the moft remarkable examples of
this fort are the ftones found at the Cape of
Good Hope, on the hill called *Paarlberg*, which
takes its name from a chain of large round ftones,
like the pearls of a necklace, that paffes over the
fummit.   Two of thefe, placed near the higheft
point, are called the Pearl and the Diamond,
and were mentioned feveral years ago in the Philofophical Tranfactions *.   From a more recent
account, thefe ftones appear to be a fpecies of
granite, though the hill on which they lie is
compofed of fandftone ftrata †.   The Pearl is a
naked rock, that rifes to the height of 400 feet
above the fummit of the hill; the Diamond is
higher, but its bafe is lefs, and it is more inac-
ceffible.

From the above ftones forming a regular
chain, as well as from the immenfe fize of the
two largeft, it is impoffible to fuppofe that they
have been moved ; and it is infinitely more probable, that they are parts of a granite vein,
which runs acrofs the fandftone ftrata, and of
which fome parts have refifted the action of the
weather, while the reft have yielded to it.   The
whole

---

* Vol. lxviii. p. 102.

† Barrow's Travels into Southern Africa, p. 60.

whole geological hiſtory of this part of Africa
ſeems highly intereſting, ſince, as far as can be
collected from the accounts of the ingenious
traveller juſt mentioned, it conſiſts of horizontal
beds of ſandſtone or limeſtone, reſting immediately on granite, or on primary ſchiſtus. Looſe
blocks of granite are ſeen in great abundance at
the foot of the Table Mountain, and along the
ſea-ſhore.

———

357. The ſyſtem which accounts for ſuch
phenomena as have been conſidered in this and
ſome of the preceding notes, by the operation of
a great deluge, or *debacle* as it is called, has
been already mentioned.   In Dr Hutton's theory, nothing whatever is aſcribed to ſuch accidental and unknown cauſes ; and, though their
exiſtence is not abſolutely denied, their effects,
whatever they may have been, are alleged to
be entirely obliterated, ſo that they can be referred to no other claſs but that of mere poſſi-
bilities.   A minute diſcuſſion, however, of the
queſtion, Whether there are, on the ſurface of
the earth, any effects that require the interpo-
ſition of an extraordinary cauſe, would lead into a longer digreſſion than is ſuited to this place.
I ſhall briefly ſtate what appear to be the principal

cipal objections to all such explanations of the phenomena of geology.

358. The general structure of valleys among mountains, is highly unfavourable to the notion that they were produced by any single great torrent, which swept over the surface of the earth. In some instances, valleys diverge, as it were from a centre, in all directions. In others, they originate from a ridge, and proceed with equal depth and extent on both sides of it, plainly indicating, that the force which produced them was *nothing*, or evanescent at the summit of that ridge, and increased on both sides, as the distance from the ridge increased. The working of water collected from the rains and the snows, and seeking its way from a higher to a lower level, is the only cause we know of, which is subject to this law.

359. Again, if we consider a valley as a space, which perhaps with many windings and irregularities, has been hollowed out of the solid rock, it is plain, that no force of water, suddenly applied, could loosen and remove the great mass of stone which has actually disappeared. The greatest column of water that could be brought to act against such a mass, whatever be the velocity we ascribe to it, could not break asunder and displace beds of rock many leagues in length, and in continuity with

C c   the

the rock on either fide of them. The flow working of water, on the other hand, or the powers
that we fee every day in action, are quite sufficient for this effect, if time only is allowed them.

360. Some valleys are fo particularly conftructed, as to carry with them a ftill ftronger
refutation of the exiftence of a *debacle*. Thefe
are the longitudinal valleys, which have the
openings by which the water is difcharged,
not at one extremity, but at the broadfide.
Such is that on the eaft fide of Mont Blanc,
deeply excavated on the confines of the granite
and fchiftus rock, and extending parallel to the
beds of the latter, from the Col de la Segne to
the Col de Ferret ; its opening is nearly in the
middle, from which the Dorea iffues, and takes
its courfe through a great valley, nearly at right
angles to the chain of the Alps, and to the
valley juft mentioned. From the ftructure of
thefe valleys, Sauffure has argued very juftly
againft Buffon's hypothefis, concerning the formation of valleys by currents at the bottom of the
fea *. It affords indeed a complete refutation of
that hypothefis ; and it affords one no lefs complete of the fyftem which Sauffure himfelf feems
on fome occafions fo much inclined to fupport.
For if it be faid, that this valley was cut out by the
current

---

* Voyages aux Alpes, tom. ii. § 920.

current of a *debacle*, that current muſt either have run in the direction of the valley of Ferret, or in that of the Dorea, which iſſues from it. If it had the direction of the firſt, it could not cut out the ſecond ; and if it had the direction of the ſecond, it could not cut out the firſt. Beſides, the force which excavated this valley muſt have been *nothing* at the two extreme points, viz. at the Col de Segne and the Col de Ferret, and muſt have increaſed with the diſtance from each. It can have been produced, therefore, only by the running of two ſtreams in oppoſite directions, on a ſurface that was but ſlightly uneven, theſe ſtreams at meeting taking a new direction, nearly at right angles to the former. A clearer proof could hardly be required than is afforded in this caſe, that what is now a deep valley was formerly ſolid rock, which the running of the waters has gradually worn away ; and that the waters, when they began to run, were on a level as high, at leaſt, as the tops of thoſe mountains by which the valley is bounded toward the lower ſide.

361. Longitudinal valleys, with the water burſting out tranſverſely from their ſides, like the preceding, are by no means confined to mountains of the firſt order. We have a very good example, though on a ſmall ſcale, of a valley of this ſort, within a few miles of Edin-

C c 2 burgh.

burgh. The Pentland Hills form a double ridge, feparated by a fmall longitudinal valley, that runs from N. E. to S. W., the water of which iffues from an opening almoft in the middle, and directed towards the fouth. This, therefore, is not the work of any great torrent, which overwhelmed the country; for no one direction, which it is poffible to affign to fuch a torrent, will afford an explanation, both of the valley and its outlet *.

362. They

---

* In Scotland there is one valley, of a kind that I believe is extremely rare in any part of the world, in accounting for which, the hypothefis of a torrent or *debacle* might, if any where, be employed to advantage. This is the valley which extends acrofs the ifland, from Invernefs to Fort-William, or from fea to fea, being open at both ends, and very little elevated in the middle. It is nearly ftraight, and of a very uniform breadth, except that towards each end it widens confiderably. The bottom, reckoning tranfverfely, is flat, without any gradual flope from the fides towards the middle. From the fides the mountains rife immediately, and form two continued ridges of great height, like ramparts or embankments on each fide of a large foffé. A great part of the bottom of this fingular valley is occupied by lakes, namely, Loch Nefs, Loch Oich, and Loch Lochy. Its length is about fixty-two miles, and the point of partition from which the waters run different ways, viz. north-eaft to the

German

362. They who maintain the exiſtence of the *debacle*, will no doubt allege, that though theſe

valleys

German Ocean, and ſouth-weſt to the Atlantic, is between Loch Oich and Loch Lochy; and, by the eſtimation of the eye, I ſhould hardly think that it is elevated more than ten or fifteen feet above the ſurface of either lake. The country on both ſides is rugged and mountainous, and the ſtreams which deſcend from thence into the valley, either fall directly into the lakes, or turn off almoſt at right angles when they enter the valley. Though the bottom of this valley, therefore, is every where alluvial, with the exception, perhaps, of a few rocks which appear at the ſurface, it is certainly not excavated by the rivers which now flow in it. The direction of the valley, it is to be obſerved, is the ſame with that of the vertical ſtrata which compoſe the mountains on either ſide.

Here, then, we have a valley, not cut out by the working of any ſtreams which now appear; and we may therefore make trial of the hypotheſis of a *debacle*. This, however, will afford us no aſſiſtance; becauſe, if we ſuppoſe what is now hollow to have been once occupied by the ſame kind of rock which is on either ſide, no force of torrents can have ſuddenly looſened and removed from its place a body of ſuch vaſt magnitude. A greater column of water, than one having for its baſe a tranſverſe ſection of the valley, could not act againſt it, and this would have to overcome

the

valleys were not cut out by means of it, yet others may. But it muſt be recollected, that if

ſome

---

the coheſion and inertia of a column of rock of the ſame ſection, and of the length of ſixty-two miles. It is not hazarding much to affirm, that no velocity which could be communicated to water, not even that which it could acquire by falling from an infinite height, could give to it a force in any degree adequate to this great effect.

The explanation of this valley, which appears to me the moſt probable, is the following. It will be ſhewn hereafter, that there is good reaſon to ſuppoſe, that, in moſt parts of our iſland, the relative level of the ſea and land has been in paſt ages confiderably higher than it is at preſent. In ſuch circumſtances, this valley may have been under the ſurface of the ſea, the higheſt part of it being ſcarcely 100 feet above that level at preſent. It may have been a kind of ſound, therefore, or ſtrait, which connected the German Sea with the Atlantic; and the ſtrong currents, which, on account of the different times of high water in theſe two ſeas, muſt have run alternately up and down this ſtrait, may have produced that flatneſs of the bottom, and ſtraightneſs of the ſides, and that widening at the extremities, which are mentioned above. In this way, too, ſome difficulties are removed relative to Loch Neſs, which is ſo deep as hardly to be confiſtent with the indefinite length of the period of waſte that muſt be aſcribed to the mountains on each ſide of it. Its depth is ſaid, where greateſt, not

to

some of the greatest and deepest valleys on the face of the earth, such as that just mentioned, on the east side of Mont Blanc, are thus shewn to be the work of the daily wasting of the surface, what other inequalities can be great enough to require the interposition of a more powerful cause? If a *dignus vindice nodus* does not exist here, in what part of the natural history of the earth is it likely to be found?

363. The large masses of rock so often met with at a distance from their original place, are one of the arguments used for the *debacle*. It has, however, been shewn, that, supposing a form of the earth's surface considerably different from the present, especially, supposing the absence of the valleys which the rivers have gradually cut out, the transportation of such stones is not impossible, even by such powers as nature employs at present. Now, without the supposition that the surface was more continuous, and that its present inequalities did not exist, no force of torrents, whatever their velocity and magnitude may have been, could have produced this transportation. No force of water could raise a stone like the *pierre de goutté* from the bottom of a

C c 4   valley,

---

to be less than 180 fathoms. According to this hypothesis, it may, at no very distant period, have been a part of the bottom of the sea.

valley, to the top of a steep hill. Indeed, if we suppose a great fragment of rock to be hurried along on a horizontal or an inclined plane, by the force of water, the moment it comes to a deep valley, and has to rise up over an ascent of a certain steepness, it will remain at rest; the water itself will lose its velocity, and the heavy bodies which it carried with it will proceed no farther. Thus, therefore, we have the following dilemma. If the surface is not supposed to have had a certain degree of uniformity in past times, a *debacle* is insufficient for the transportation of stones : If it is supposed to have had that uniformity, a *debacle* is unnecessary.

364. Another fact, which has been supposed favourable to the opinion of the action of great torrents at some former period, is, that in countries like that round Edinburgh, where whinstone hills rise up from among secondary strata, a remarkable uniformity is observed in the direction of their abrupt faces. Thus, in the country just mentioned, the steep faces generally front the west, while, in the opposite direction, the slope is gentle, and the hills decline gradually into the plain. Hence it is supposed, that a torrent, sweeping from west to east, has carried off the strata from the west side of these hills, but, being obstructed by the whinstone rock,

has

has left the ftrata on the eaft fide in their natural place.

But, befides that no force which can ever be
afcribed to a torrent could have removed at
once bodies of ftrata 300 or 400 feet, nay even
800 or 1000 in thicknefs, which muft have been
the cafe if this were the true explanation of the
fact, there is a circumftance which may perhaps
enable us to explain thefe phenomena without
the affiftance of any extraordinary caufe.   The
fecondary-ftrata in which the whinftone hills
are found in this part of Scotland, are not horizontal, but rife or *head* towards the weft, dipping towards the eaft.   The fide, therefore, of
the whinftone hills which is precipitous, is the
fame with that towards which the ftrata rife.
Now, from the manner in which thefe hills are
fuppofed to have been elevated, the ftrata are
likely to have been moft broken and fhattered
towards that fide, while, on the oppofite, they
had the fupport of the whinftone rock.   They
would become a prey, therefore, more eafily to
the common caufes of erofion and wafte on the
upper fide than on the lower.   The ftreams that
flowed from the higher grounds would wear
them on the former moft readily ; and the action
of thefe ftreams would be refifted by the fuperior hardnefs of the whinftone, juft as the great
torrent of the debacle is fuppofed to have been.

It

It fhould alfo be obferved, that this fact of the uniform direction of the abrupt faces of mountains, is often too haftily generalized. In primitive countries, it is no farther obferved than by the fteep faces of the mountains being moft frequently turned toward the central chain. In Scotland, as foon as you leave the flat country, and enter the Highlands, the fcarps of the hills face indifcriminately all the points of the compafs, and are directed as often to the eaft as to the weft.

365. Where the ftrata are nearly horizontal, they afford the moft diftinct information concerning the direction and progrefs of the wafting of the land. The inclined pofition of the ftrata, which in all other cafes muft enter for fo much into our eftimate of the caufes which have produced the prefent inequality of the earth's furface, difappears there entirely ; and the whole of that inequality is to be afcribed to the operations at the furface, whether they have been fudden or gradual. A very important fact from a country of this fort, is related by BARROW, in his Travels into Southern Africa. The mountains about the Cape of Good Hope, and as far to the north as that ingenious traveller profecuted his journey, are chiefly of horizontal ftrata of fandftone and limeftone, exhibiting the appearance, on their abrupt fides, of regular layers of mafonry, of towers, fortifications, &c. Now, among

among all thefe mountains, he obferved, that
the high or fteep fides look conftantly down
the rivers, while the floping or inclined fides
have juft the oppofite direction. When, in travelling northward, he paffed the line of partition, where the waters from running fouth take
their direction to the north, he found, that the
gradual flope, which had hitherto been turned
to the north, was now turned to the fouth : The
abrupt afpect of the mountains, in like manner,
from facing the fouth, was directed to the north ;
fo that, in both cafes, the hills turned their backs
on the line of greateft elevation *.

It is evident, therefore, that the form of this
land has been determined by the flow working
of the ftreams. The caufes which produced the
effects here defcribed, began their action from
the line of greateft elevation, and extended it
from thence on both fides, in oppofite directions.
This is the moft precife character that can mark
the alluvial operations, and diftinguifh them from
the overwhelming power of a great *debacle*.

366. Laftly, If there were any where a hill, or
any large mafs compofed of broken and fhapelefs
ftones, thrown together like rubbifh, and neither
worked into gravel nor d fpofed with any regularity, we muft afcribe it to fome other caufe
than

---

* Barrow's Travels into Southern Africa, p. 245.

than the ordinary *detritus* and wafting of the land. This, however, has never yet occurred; and it feems beft to wait till the phenomenon is obferved, before we feek for the explanation of it.

367. Thefe arguments appear to me conclufive againft the neceffity of fuppofing the action of fudden and irregular caufes on the furface of the earth. In this, however, I am perhaps deceived: neither Pallas, nor Sauffure, nor Dolomieu, nor any other author who has efpoufed the hypothefis of fuch caufes, has explained his notions with any precifion; on the contrary, they have all fpoken with fuch referve and myftery, as feemed to betray the weaknefs, but may have concealed the ftrength of their caufe. I have therefore been combating an enemy, that was in fome refpects unknown; and I may have fuppofed him diflodged, only becaufe I could not penetrate to his ftrong-holds. The queftion, however, is likely foon to affume a more determinate form. A zealous friend of Dr Hutton's theory, has lately * declared his approbation of the hypothefis which has here been reprefented as fo adverfe to that theory; and, from his ability and vigour of refearch, it is likely to receive every improvement of which it is fufceptible.

NOTE

---

* Tranf. Royal Society Edin. vol. v. p. 68.

Note XIX. § 117.

Transportation of Materials by the Sea.

368. The exiftence of the great and extenfive operations, by which the fpoils of the land
are carried all over the ocean, and fpread out
on the bottom of it, may be fuppofed to require
fome further elucidation. We muft attend,
therefore, to the following circumftances.

When the detritus of the land is delivered
by the rivers into the fea, the heavieft parts are
depofited firft, and the lighter are carried to a
greater diftance from the fhore. The accumulation of matter which would be made in this
manner on the coaft, is prevented by the farther
operation of the tides and currents, in confequence of which the fubftances depofited continue to be worn away, and are gradually removed further from the land. The reality of
this operation is certain; for otherwife we fhould
have on the fea-fhore a conftant and unlimited
accumulation of fand and gravel, which, being
perpetually brought down from the land, would
continually increafe on the fhore, if nature did
not employ fome machinery for removing the
advanced

advanced part into the fea, in proportion to the fupply from behind.

The conftant agitation of the waters, and the declivity of the bottom, are no doubt the caufes of this gradual and widely-extended depofition. A foft mafs of alluvial depofite, having its pores filled with water, and being fubject to the vibrations of a fuperincumbent fluid, will yield to the preffure of that fluid on the fide of the leaft refiftance, that is, on the fide toward the fea, and thus will be gradually extended more and more over the bottom. This will happen not only to the finer parts of the detritus, but even to the groffer, fuch as fand and gravel. For fuppofe that a body of gravel refts on a plane fomewhat inclined, at the fame time that it is covered with water to a confiderable depth, that water being fubject not only to moderate reciprocations, but alfo to fuch violent agitation as we fee occafionally communicated to the waters of the ocean ; the gravel, being rendered lighter by its immerfion in the water, and on that account more moveable, will, when the undulations are confiderable, be alternately heaved up and let down again. Now, at each time that it is heaved up, however fmall the fpace may be, it muft be fomewhat accelerated in its defcent, and will hardly fettle on the fame point where it refted before. Thus it will gain a little

tle ground at each undulation, and will flowly
make its way towards the depths of the ocean,
or to the loweſt ſituation it can reach. This, as
far as we may preſume to follow a progreſs which
is not the ſubject of immediate obſervation, is
one of the great means by which looſe materials
of every kind are tranſported to a great diſtance,
and ſpread out in beds at the bottom of the
ocean.

369. The lighter parts are more eaſily carried
to great diſtances, being actually ſuſpended in the
water, by which they are very gradually and
flowly depoſited. A remarkable proof of this is
furniſhed from an obſervation made by Lord
Mulgrave, in his voyage to the North Pole. In
the latitude of 65° nearly, and about 250 miles
diſtant from the neareſt land, which was the
coaſt of Norway, he ſounded with a line of 683
fathoms, or 4098 feet; and the lead, when it
ſtruck the ground, ſunk in a ſoft blue clay to the
depth of 10 feet*. The tenuity and fineneſs
of the mud, which allowed the lead to ſink ſo
deep into it, muſt have reſulted from a depoſition of the lighter kinds of earth, which being
ſuſpended in the water, had been carried to a
great diſtance, and were now without doubt
forming

---

* Phipps's Voyage, p. 74, 141.

forming a regular ftratum at the bottom of the fea.

370. The quantity of detritus brought down by the rivers, and diftributed in this manner over the bottom of the fea, is fo great, that feveral narrow feas have been thereby rendered fenfibly fhallower. The Baltic has been computed to decreafe in depth at the rate of forty inches in a hundred years. The Yellow Sea, which is a large gulf contained between the coaft of China and the peninfula of Corea, receives fo much mud from the great rivers that run into it, that it takes its colour, as well as its name, from that circumftance; and the European mariners, who have lately navigated it, obferved, that the mud was drawn up by the fhips, fo as to be vifible in their wake to a confiderable diftance *. Computations have been made of the time that it will require to fill up this gulf, and to withdraw it entirely from the dominion of the ocean : but the data are not fufficiently exact to afford any precife refult, and are no doubt particularly defective from this caufe, that much of the earth carried into the gulf by the rivers, muft be carried out of it by the currents and tides, and the finer parts wafted probably to great diftances

* Staunton's Account of the Embaffy to China, vol. i. p. 448.

ftances in the Pacific Ocean *. The mere attempt, however, towards fuch a computation,
fhews how evident the progrefs of filling up is
to every attentive obferver ; and, though it may
not afcertain the meafure, it fufficiently declares
the reality of the operations, by which the wafte
of the prefent continents is made fubfervient to
the formation of new land.

371. Sand-banks, fuch as abound in the German Ocean, to whatever they owe their origin,
are certainly modified, and their form determined, by the tides and currents. Without the operation of thefe laft, banks of loofe fand and mud
could hardly preferve their form, and remain
interfected by many narrow channels. The formation of the banks on the coaft of Holland,
and even of the Dogger Bank itfelf, has been
afcribed to the meeting of tides, by which a ftate
of tranquillity is produced in the waters, and of
confequence a more copious depofition of their
mud. Even the great bank of Newfoundland
feems to be determined in its extent by the

D d action

---

* Peroufe, in failing along the coaft of China, from
Formofa to the ftrait between Corea and Japan, though
generally fifty or fixty leagues from the land, had foundings at the depth of forty five fathoms, and fometimes
at that of twenty-two. Atlas du Voyage de la Peroufe,
No. 43.

action of the gulf-stream. In the North Sea,
the current which sets out of the Baltic, has evidently determined the shape of the sand-banks
opposite to the coast of Norway, and produced
a circular sweep in them, of which it is impossible to mistake the cause.

In proof of the action here ascribed to the
waters of the sea, in transporting materials to an
unlimited extent, we may add the well-known
observation, that the stones brought up by the
lead from the bottom of the sea, are generally
round and polished, hardly ever sharp and angular. This could never happen to stones that
were not subject to perpetual attrition.

372. Currents are no doubt the great agents in
diffusing the detritus of the land over the bottom
of the sea. These have been long known to exist; but it is only since the later improvements
in navigation, that they have been understood to
constitute a system of great permanence, regularity and extent, connected with the trade-
winds, and other circumstances in the natural
history of the globe. The gulf-stream was many years since observed to transport the water,
and the temperature of the tropical regions into
the climates of the north; and we are indebted to
the researches of Major RENNEL, for the knowledge of a great system of currents, of which it is
only a part. That geographer, who is so eminent
for

for enriching the details of his fcience with the moft interefting facts in hiftory or in phyfics, has fhewn, that along the eaftern coaft of Africa, from about the mouth of the Red Sea, a current fifty leagues in breadth fets continually towards the fouth-weft *. It doubles the Cape of Good Hope, runs from thence north-weft, preferving on the whole the direction of the coaft, but reaching fo far into the ocean, that, about the parallel of St Helena, its breadth exceeds 1000 miles. From thence, as it approaches the line, its direction is more nearly eaft; and meeting in the parallel of 3° north, with a current which has come along the weftern coaft of Africa from the north, the two united ftretch acrofs the Atlantic, in a line fomewhat fouth of weft, and in a very wide and rapid ftream. This ftream meets the American land at Cape St Roque, where it is joined by another coming up along the eaftern fhore of that continent, and directed towards the north. They proceed northward together till they enter the Gulf of Florida, from which being as it were reflected, they form the Gulf-ftream, paffing along the coaft of North America, and ftretching acrofs the Atlantic to the Britifh Ifles. From thence the current turns to the fouth, and, proceeding down

D d 2   the

* Geography of Herodotus, p. 672.

the coaſt of Spain and Africa, meets the ſtream
aſcending from the ſouth, as already deſcribed,
and thus continues in perpetual circulation.
The velocity of theſe currents is not leſs remarkable than their extent. At the Cape of Good
Hope, the rate is thirty nautical miles in twenty-
four hours ; in ſome places forty-five ; and under the line ſeventy-ſeven. When the Gulf-ſtream
iſſues from the Straits of Bahama, it runs at the
rate of four miles an hour, and proceeds to the
diſtance of 1800 miles, before its velocity is reduced to half that quantity. In the parallel of
38°, near 1000 miles from the above ſtrait, the
water of the ſtream has been found ten degrees
warmer than the air.

373. The courſe of the Gulf-ſtream is ſo fixed
and regular, that nuts and plants from the Weſt
Indies are annually thrown aſhore on the Weſtern Iſlands of Scotland. The maſt of a man
of war, burnt at Jamaica, was driven ſeveral
months afterwards on the Hebrides *, after performing a voyage of more than 4000 miles, under the direction of a current, which, in the
midſt of the ocean, maintains its courſe as ſtea-
dily as a river does upon the land.

The great ſyſtem of currents thus traced
through the Atlantic, has no doubt phenomena
corresponding

---

* Pennant's Arctic Zoology, Introd. p. 70.

correfponding to it in the Indian and Pacific Oceans, which the induftry of future navigators may difcover. The whole appears to be connected with the trade-winds, the figure of our continents, the temperature of the feas themfelves, and perhaps with fome inequalities in the ftructure of the globe. The difturbance produced by thefe caufes in the equilibrium of the fea, probably reaches to the very bottom of it, and gives rife to thofe counter currents, which have fometimes been difcovered at great depths under the furface *.

The great tranfportation of materials that muft refult from the action of thefe combined currents is obvious, and ferves not a little to diminifh our wonder, at finding the productions of one climate fo frequently included among the foffils of another. Amid all the revolutions of the globe, the economy of nature has been uniform, in this refpect, as well as in fo many others, and her laws are the only thing that have refifted the general movement. The rivers and the rocks, the feas and the continents, have been changed in all their parts; but the laws which direct thofe changes, and the rules

D d 3   to

---

* Hiftoire Naturelle de Buffon, fupplément, tom. ix. p. 479. 8vo.

to which they are fubject, have remained invariably the fame.

374. Objections have been made to that tranflation of materials by the waters of the ocean
which is fuppofed in this theory, particularly by
Mr Kirwan, in his Geological Effays; and, though
I might perhaps content myfelf with the remark
already made, that the Neptunian fyftem involves fuppofitions concerning the tranfportation
of folid bodies by the fea, in the early ages of
the world, as wonderful as thofe which, according to our theory, are common to all ages, I am
unwilling to remain fatisfied with a mere *ar-
gumentum ad hominem*, where the fallacy of the
reafoning is fo eafily detected.

375. One of Mr Kirwan's objections to the depofition of materials at the bottom of the fea, is
thus ftated : " FRISI has remarked, in his mathematical difcourfes, that if any confiderable
mafs of matter were accumulated in the interior
of the ocean, the diurnal motion of the globe
would be difturbed, and confequently it would
be perceptible ; a phenomenon, however, of
which no hiftory or tradition gives any account *."

The appeal made here to Frifi is fingularly
unfortunate, as that philofopher has demonftrated

---

* Geol. Effays, p. 441.

ted the very contrary of Mr Kirwan's poſition, and has proved, that the diſturbance given to the diurnal motion by the cauſes here
referred to may be real, but cannot be perceptible. Having inveſtigated a formula expreſſing
the law which all ſuch diſturbances muſt neceſſarily obſerve, he concludes, " Hâc autem
formulâ manifeſtum fiet, ex iis omnibus varia-
tionibus quæ in terreſtri ſuperficie obſervari ſo-
lent, montium et collium abraſione, dilapſu cor-
porum ponderoſiorum in inferiores telluris ſinus,
nullam oriri poſſe variationem *ſenſibilem* diurni
motûs. Nam ſi ſtatuamus data aliqua annorum
periodo terreſtrem ſuperficiem ad duos uſque
pedes abradi undique, eam vero materiæ quan-
titatem ad profunditatem pedum 1000 dilabi ;
erit omne quod inde orietur incrementum velo-
citatis diurni motûs $\frac{30000}{(19638051)^2} = \frac{1}{12855068184}$ *."

Here, it is evident, that Friſi admits thoſe
very changes on the ſurface which we are contending for, and ſhews, that their tendency is to
accelerate the earth's diurnal motion, but, by a
quantity ſo ſmall, that, in a ſpace of time amounting at leaſt to 200 years, the increaſe of the diurnal motion would only be ſuch a part of the

---

* Friſii Opera, tom. iii. p. 269.

whole as the preceding fraction is of unity *.

376. The

---

* The time requisite for taking away by waste and
erosion two feet from the surface of all our continents,
and depositing it at the bottom of the sea, cannot be reckoned less than 200 years. The fraction $\frac{1}{128550068184}$,
reduced to parts of a day, is $\frac{1}{148554}$ of a second; so
that it would require 200 years to shorten the length of
the day, by the above fraction of a second; and therefore it would require 148554 times 200 years, or
29710800 years, to diminish it an entire second. The
accumulated effect, however, of all the diminutions during that period, would amount to much more: and if
we had any perfectly uniform standard to compare the
motion of the earth with, its difference from that standard would increase as the squares of the time, and the
total acceleration would amount to one second in
77080 years. Whatever relation this bears to the
age of the globe itself, it exceeds more than ten times
the age of any historical record.

Though Frisius concludes, as is stated here, that the
acceleration produced in the diurnal motion of the
earth, is far too inconsiderable to become the object of
astronomical observation, he makes a supposition difficult to be reconciled with this conclusion, namely, that
the acceleration has had a sensible effect on the figure of
the earth, or rather of the sea, having increased the centrifugal force, and thereby accumulated the waters under the equator, in the present, more than in former
ages. Such an accumulation, he thinks agreeable to
certain

376. The inftance juft given may ferve as one of many, to fhew what confidence is to be placed in that indigefted mafs of facts and quotations which Mr Kirwan, without difcrimination, and without difcuffion, has brought together from all quarters. He has no intention, I believe, to deceive his readers; but we may judge, from this fpecimen, of the precautions he has taken againft being deceived himfelf.

In fome refpects, the refult of Frifi's invefti-gation muft be confidered as imperfect. If there were no relative motion in the parts of our globe, but that by which things defcend from a high-er to a lower level, a continual acceleration of its rotation, though extremely flow, would take place, as above computed. But as, in the in-terior of the earth, there are undoubtedly mo-tions of a tendency oppofite to thofe on the fur-face, and directed from the centre towards the circumference,

---

certain appearances that have been obferved refpecting the ancient level of the fea. Thefe appearances will be afterwards confidered: it is fufficient to remark here, that though the fraction, expreffing the increment of the centrifugal force, muft be double that which expreffes the acceleration, it muft be too fmall to have any per-ceptible effect in elevating the fea, except after an im-menfe interval of time; and the compenfations which arife from other caufes, probably muft prevent it from becoming fenfible in any length of time whatfoever.

circumference, they muſt produce a retardation in the diurnal revolution ; and from this muſt ariſe an inequality, not uniformly progreſſive in the ſame direction, but periodical, and confined within certain limits, as the cauſes are by which it is produced *.

377. Mr

---

* Even in the deſcent of bodies from a higher to a lower level at the ſurface of the earth, the whole tendency is not to increaſe the velocity of the earth's rotation, and many compenſations take place, which, when the matter is conſidered only in general, are neceſſarily overlooked. This will appear evident, if we reflect, that it is not ſimply the approach of a body towards the centre of the earth, or its removal from that centre, which tends to diſturb the rotation of the earth ; but its approach to the axis of the earth, or its removal from that axis. The velocity with which a particle of matter revolves, whether on the ſurface, or in the interior of the globe, is proportional to its diſtance from the axis of rotation ; and therefore, when a body comes nearer to the axis, it loſes a part of the motion which it had before ; which part, of conſequence, is communicated to the whole maſs of the earth, and therefore tends to increaſe the velocity with which it revolves. The contrary happens when a body recedes from the axis ; for it then receives an addition to its velocity, which, of courſe, is taken away from the rotatory motion of the earth.

Hence, bodies moving in a horizontal plane, may increaſe or diminiſh the ſwiftneſs of the diurnal motion, according

377. Mr Kirwan's fecond objection is founded on the mifapprehenfion of a well-known fact in the

according as they move towards the poles or towards the equator; and thofe which defcend from a higher to a lower level, difturb the earth's rotation, much more in confequence of their horizontal, than of their perpendicular motion. The Ganges, for inftance, though its fource is probably elevated no lefs than 7000 feet above the level of the fea, tends to retard the earth's rotation, by bringing its waters, and the mud contained in them, from the parallel of 31° to that of 22°, and fo increafing their diftance from the earth's axis by more than $\frac{1}{12}$th part. Had the Ganges flowed towards the north, as the Nile does, its effect would have been juft the contrary.

In the fame manner, a ftone defcending from the top of a mountain, may accelerate or retard the earth's rotation, according to the direction in which it defcends. If it defcend on the fide of the elevated pole, it will then produce acceleration, becaufe its diftance from the axis will be diminifhed; but if it defcend on the fide of the deprefled pole, and if the direction in which it is moved, be over a line lefs inclined, than a line drawn from the fame point to the deprefled pole, it will then produce a retardation, becaufe its diftance from the axis will be increafed.

Let us fuppofe, for example, that the top of Mount Blanc is in latitude 45° 49′, and that its height is 2450 toifes above the level of the fea. The point at which a line drawn from the top of this mountain, parallel to the

the natural hiſtory of the earth. " Rivers," ſays this author, " do not carry into the ſea the ſpoils which they bring from the land, but employ them in the formation of deltas of low alluvial land at their mouths, according to what Major Rennell has proved." The faƈt of the formation of *del-tas* from the ſpoils which the rivers carry from the

---

the earth's axis, will meet the ſuperficies of the ſea, (ſuppoſing that ſuperficies continued inland from the Mediterranean), muſt be about 2382 toiſes in horizontal diſtance, or about $2\frac{1}{2}$ minutes ſouth of the ſummit, that is, in the parallel of 45° $46\frac{1}{2}'$; and if this parallel be continued all round the globe, the points of the earth's ſurface between it and the equator, are all more diſtant from the earth's axis than the top of Mount Blanc is; whereas all the points to the north of it are nearer to that axis. A ſtone, therefore, from the top of Mount Blanc, if carried any where to the ſouth of the above parallel, will retard the earth's diurnal motion; but if carried any where to the north of the ſame line, will ac-celerate that motion.

The ſame quantity of matter, however, carried an equal diſtance toward the pole, and toward the equator, from any point, will Ioſe more velocity in the former caſe than it will gain in the latter, as eaſily follows from the nature of circle. Therefore, ſuppoſing an equal diſperſion of the detritus of a mountain in all di-reƈtions, the parts that go toward the pole will moſt di-ſturb the diurnal motion; and hence a balance on their ſide, or in favour of acceleration, as already obſerved,

the higher grounds, is perfectly ascertained; and the detail into which Major Rennel has entered in the passage referred to by Mr Kirwan, does credit to the acuteness and accuracy of that excellent geographer. But it is not there asserted, that rivers employ *all* the materials which they carry with them, in the formation of those deltas, and deliver none of them into the sea. On the contrary, they carry from the *delta* itself mud and earth, which they can deposite nowhere but in the sea; and it is this circumstance chiefly that limits the increase of those alluvial lands, and makes them either cease to increase, or makes them increase very slowly after a certain period, though the supply of earth from the higher grounds remains nearly the same. To make Mr Kirwan's argument conclusive, it would be necessary to prove, that *all* the mud carried down by the Nile or the Ganges, was deposited on the low lands before these rivers enter the sea; a thing so obviously absurd, that nothing but his haste to obtain a conclusion unfavourable to the Plutonic system, could have prevented him from perceiving it *.

378. A

---

* The instance mentioned in the Geological Essays, from the travels of the Abbé Fortis, concerning urns thrown into the Adriatic, upwards of 1400 years ago,
and

378. A remark which Major Rennell has made concerning the mouths of rivers, in his Geography of Herodotus, deferves Mr Kirwan's attention, though perhaps he may not be able to put on it an interpretation quite fo favourable to his fyftem. The remark is, that the mouths of great rivers are often formed on principles quite oppofite to one another, fo that fome of them have a real delta or triangle of flat land at their mouths, while others have an eftuary, or what may not improperly be called a *negative* delta. Of the latter kind are fome of the greateft rivers in the world, the Plata, the Oroonoko and the Maranon, and by far the greateft number of our European rivers. Nobody can doubt, that the three rivers juft named carry with them as much earth as the Nile, or the Euphrates, or any other river in the world. All this they have depofited in the fea, and committed to the currents, which fweep along the fhore of the American continent, and by thefe they have been fpread out over the unlimited tracts of the ocean.

Indeed,

and not yet covered with mud, muft be explained from peculiar circumftances, or local caufes, with which we are unacquainted, as it makes againft the depofition of earth near the fhore, and in narrow feas; a general fact, which, I think, every body admits.

Indeed, nothing can be more juft than Dr Hutton's obfervation, that where low land is formed at the mouths of rivers, there the rivers bring down more than the fea is able to carry away; but that where fuch land is not formed, it is becaufe the fea is able to carry off immediately all the depofite which it receives.

379. Mr Kirwan has denied on another principle the power of the fea to carry to a diftance the materials delivered into it : " Notwithftanding," fays he, " many particles of earth are by rivers conducted to the fea, yet *none are conveyed to any diftance*, but are either depofited at their mouths, or rejected by currents or by tides; and the reafon is, becaufe the tide of flood is always more impetuous and forcible than the tide of ebb, the advancing waves being preffed forward by the countlefs number behind them, whereas the retreating are preffed backward by a far fmaller number, as muft be evident to an attentive fpectator ; and hence it is that all floating things caft into the fea, are at laft thrown on fhore, and not conveyed into the mid regions of the fea, as they fhould be if the reciprocal undulations of the tides were equally powerful *."

380. But

---

* Kirwan's Geol. Effays, p. 439.

380. But if the *attentive fpectator*, inftead of trufting to a vague impreffion, or liftening to fome crude theory of undulations, reflects on one of the moft fimple facts refpecting the ebbing and flowing of the tides, he will be very little difpofed to acquiefce in the above conclufion. He has only to confider, that the flowing of the tide requires juft fix hours, and the ebbing of it likewife fix hours ; fo that the fame body of water flows in upon the fhore, and retreats from it, in the fame time. The quantity of matter moved, therefore, and the velocity with which it is moved, are in both cafes the fame ; and it remains for Mr Kirwan to fhew in what the difference of their force can poffibly confift.

The force with which the waves ufually break upon our fhores, does not arife from the velocity of the tide being greater in one direction than in another. In the main ocean, the waves have no progreffive motion, and the columns of water alternately rife and fall, without any other than a reciprocating motion: a kind of equilibrium takes place among the undulations, and each wave being equally acted upon by thofe on oppofite fides, remains fixed in its place. Near the fhore this cannot happen ; the water on the land fide from its fhallownefs being incapable of of rifing to the height neceffary to balance the great undulations which are without. The water runs, therefore, as it were, from a higher to a lower level, fpreading itfelf towards the land fide. This produces the breakers on our fhores, and the furf of the tropical feas. A rock or a fand-bank coming within a certain diftance of the furface, is fufficient, in any part of the ocean, to obftruct the natural fucceffion of undulations ; and, by deftroying the mutual reaction of the waves, to give them a progreffive inftead of a reciprocating motion.

381. It is, however, but from a fmall diftance, that the waves are impelled againft the fhore with a progreffive motion. The border of breakers that furrounds any coaft is narrow, compared with the diftance to which the *detritus* from the land is confeffedly carried ; the water, while it advances at the furface, flows back at the bottom ; and thefe contrary motions are fo nearly equal, that it is but a very momentary accumulation of the water that is ever produced on any fhore.

If it were otherwife, and if it were true that the fea throws out every thing, and carries away nothing, we fhould have a conftant accumulation of earth and fand along all fhores whatfoever, at leaft wherever a ftream ran into the fea.

E e   This,

This, as is abundantly evident, is quite contrary to the fact.

So, alfo, the bars formed at the mouths of rivers, after having attained a certain magnitude, increafe no farther, not becaufe they ceafe to receive augmentations from the land, but becaufe their diminution from the fea, increafing with their magnitude, becomes at length fo great, as completely to balance thofe augmentations. When properly examined, therefore, the phenomena, which have been propofed as moft inconfiftent with the indefinite tranfportation of ftony bodies, afford very fatisfactory proofs of that operation.

382. It is true, that bodies which float in the water, when carried along on the tops of the waves towards a fhelving beach, having acquired a certain velocity, are thrown farther in upon the land than the diftance they would have floated to, if they had been fimply fuftained by the water. The depth of water, therefore, at the place where they take the ground, is not likely to be fuch as to float them again, and to carry them out towards the fea. They are, therefore, left behind; and this produces an appearance of a force impelling floating bodies towards the land, much greater and more general than really takes place.

Thefe

These observations may serve to show, how unsound the principles are from which Mr Kirwan's conclusions are deduced : they are perhaps more than is necessary for that purpose : it might have been sufficient to observe, that the increase of land on the sea-shore is limited, though the augmentation from the land is certainly indefinite, a proof that the diminution from the sea is constant and equal to the increase.

383. "Mariners," says Mr Kirwan, "were accustomed, for some centuries back, to discover their situation, by the kind of earth or sand brought up by their founding plummets ; a method which would prove fallacious, if the surface of the bottom did not continue invariably the same *."

The fact here stated, that mariners, when navigation was more imperfect than it is now, had very frequent recourse to this method, and that they still use it occasionally, is very true. But from this, the only inference that can be fairly deduced is, that the changes at the bottom of the sea are very slow, and the variation but little ; not merely from one year to another, but even from one century to another. The rules by which the mariner judged of his position from the quality of the earth which the lead brought up, and which were deduced no

E e 2   doubt

---

* Geol. Essays, p. 440.

doubt from obfervations made at no very great diftance of time, might be fufficient for his purpofe, though a flow change had been all the while going forward. Such obfervations could at beft have little accuracy, and could not be affected by fmall variations. It is the flownefs of the change, that makes the experience of one age applicable, in this, as in innumerable other inftances, to the obfervations of the next. If a long interval is taken, we will look in vain for the fame uniformity of refults. A pilot, who would at prefent judge of his pofition in the German Ocean, by comparing his foundings with thofe taken by PYTHEAS, (fuppofing them known) in his navigation of that fea, more than 2000 years ago, could hardly be expected to determine his latitude and longitude with great exactnefs ; and I know not if the moft zealous advocate for the immutability of the earth's furface, would be willing to truft his fafety in a fhip that was guided by fuch antiquated rules.

NOTE

NOTE XX. § 118.

Inequalities in the Planetary Motions.

384. The affertion that, in the planetary motions, we difcover no mark, either of the commencement or termination of the prefent order, refers to the late difcoveries of LA GRANGE and LA PLACE, which have contributed fo much to the perfection of phyfical aftronomy. From the principle of univerfal gravitation, thefe mathematicians have demonftrated, that all the variations in our fyftem are periodical ; that they are confined within certain limits ; and confift of alternate diminution and increafe. The orbits of the planets change not only their pofition, but even their magnitude and their form : the longer axis of each has a flow angular motion ; and, though its length remains fixed, the fhorter axis increafes and diminifhes, fo that the form of the orbit approaches to that of a circle, and recedes from it by turns. In the fame manner, the obliquity of the ecliptic, and the inclination of the planetary orbits, are fubject to change ; but the changes are fmall, and, being firft in one direction, and then in the oppofite,

E e 3   they

they can never accumulate fo as to produce a permanent or a progreffive alteration. Thus, in the celeftial motions, no room is left for the introduction of diforder ; no irregularity or difturbance, arifing from the mutual action of the planets, is permitted to increafe beyond certain limits, but each of them, in time, affords a correction for itfelf. The general order is conftant, in the midft of the variation of the parts ; and, in the language of La Place, there is a certain mean condition, about which our fyftem perpetually *ofcillates*, performing fmall vibrations on each fide of it, and never receding from it far *. The fyftem is thus endowed with a ftability, which can refift the lapfe of unlimited duration ; it can only perifh by an external caufe, and by the introduction of laws, of which at prefent no veftige is to be traced.

385. The fame *calculus* to which we are indebted for thefe fublime conclufions, informs us of two circumftances, which mark the law here treated of as an effect of wife defign, to the entire exclufion both of neceffity and chance. One of thefe circumftances confifts in the planetary motions being all in the fame direction, or all *in confequentia*, as it is called by the aftronomers.

---

* Expofition du Syftême du Monde, par La Place, Livre iv. chap. 6. p. 199. 2d edit.

mers. This is effential to the compenfation and ftability above mentioned * : had one planet circulated round the fun in a direction from eaft to weft, and another in a direction from weft to eaft, the difturbances they would have produced on one another's motion would not necef- farily have been periodical ; their irregularities might have continually increafed, and they might have deviated in the courfe of ages from their original condition, beyond any limits that can be affigned.

The other circumftance, on which the ftability of our fyftem depends, is the fmall eccentricity of the planetary orbits, or their near approach to circles. Were their orbits very eccentric, an opening would be given to progreffive change, that might fo far increafe, as to prove the de- ftruction of the whole. But neither the move- ment of all the planets in the fame direction, nor the fmall eccentricity of their orbits, can be afcribed to accident, fince that either of thefe fhould happen by chance, in as many inftances as there are planets, both primary and fecondary, is almoft infinitely improbable. Again, that any neceffity in the nature of things fhould have either determined the *direction* of the planetary motions, or proportioned the *quantity* of them

E e 4

to

---

* La Place, *ibid.*

to the intensity of the central force, cannot be admitted, as these are things unavoidably conceived to be quite independent of one another. It remains, therefore, that we consider the laws, which make the disturbances in our system correct themselves, and by that means give firmness and permanence to it, as a proof of the confummate wisdom with which the whole is constructed.

386. The geological system of Dr Hutton, resembles, in many respects, that which appears to preside over the heavenly motions. In both, we perceive continual vicissitude and change, but confined within certain limits, and never departing far from a certain mean condition, which is such, that, in the lapse of time, the deviations from it on the one side, must become just equal to the deviations from it on the other. In both, a provision is made for duration of unlimited extent, and the lapse of time has no effect to wear out or destroy a machine, constructed with so much wisdom. Where the movements are all so perfect, their beginning and end must be alike invisible.

NOTE

NOTE XXI. § 122.

Changes in the apparent Level of the Sea.

387. In fpeaking of the natural epochas marked out by the phenomena of the mineral kingdom, we have fuppofed a greater fimplicity, and
feparation of effects from one another, than probably takes place in nature. We have, for inftance, abftracted, in fpeaking of the wafte and
degradation of the land, from that elevation
which may have been carried on at the fame
time. This appeared neceffary to be done, in
order to fimplify as much as poffible the view
that was to be given of the whole; but there
can be no doubt, that, while the land has
been gradually worn down by the operations
on its furface, it has been raifed up by the expanfive forces acting from below. There is
even reafon to think, that the elevation has not
been uniform, but has been fubject to a kind
of ofcillation, infomuch, that the continents have
both afcended and defcended, or have had their
level alternately raifed and depreffed, independently of all action at the furface, and this

within

within a period comparatively of no great extent.

It will be easily understood, that the facts we are going to state, each taken singly, prove nothing more than a change of the line in which the surface of the sea intersects the surface of the land, leaving it uncertain to which of the two the change ought really to be ascribed. Taken in combination, however, these facts may determine what each of them separately cannot ascertain. I shall first, therefore, mention some of the principal observations relative to the change above mentioned, and shall then compare them, in order to discover whether it is most probable that this change has been produced by the motion of the land or of the sea.

388. If we begin with examining the coasts of our own island, we shall find clear evidence every where, that the sea once reached higher up upon the land than it does at present. The marks of an ancient sea-beach are to be seen beyond the present limits of the tide, and beds of sea-shells, not mineralized, are found in the loose earth or soil, sometimes as high as thirty feet above the present level of the sea. Some of these on the shores of the Frith of Forth are very well known, and have been often mentioned. Indeed, on the shores of that frith, many monuments appear, which would seem to carry the difference

difference between the prefent and the ancient level of the fea, to more than forty feet. The ground on which the Botanic Garden of Edinburgh is fituated, after a thin covering of foil is removed, confifts entirely of fea-fand, very regularly ftratified, with layers of a black carbonaceous matter, in thin lamellæ, interpofed between them. Shells I believe are but rarely found in it, but it has every other appearance of a fea-beach. The height of this ground above the prefent level of the fea is certainly not lefs than 40 feet.

389. On almoft every part of the coaft where the rocks do not rife quite abrupt and precipitous from the fea, fimilar marks of the lowering of the fea, or the rifing of the land, may be obferved. On the fhores oppofite to ours, the fame appearances are remarked. The author of the Lettre Critique to M. de Buffon, tells us, that he had found the bottom of a bafon at Dunkirk, which he had reafon to think was dug about 950 years ago, ten feet and a half above the prefent low-water mark, though it muft have been originally under it. The bottom of this bafon is in the native chalk. From this, the fame author concludes, that the fea at Dunkirk lowers its level at the rate of an inch nearly in feven years. The obfervation was made in 1762,

1762, (Lettre à M. le Comte de Buffon, &c. p. 55.) *.

390. The shores of the Low Countries, and of Holland, have been often instanced in proof of the same kind of changes, and it has been supposed, that, independently of those artificial barriers which at present exclude the waters of the ocean from overflowing a great part of this tract, nature herself has brought it nearer to the surface than it had formerly been. It is indeed certain, that those countries, to a very great extent inland, have either been under the sea at some period, by no means remote if compared with the great revolutions of the globe, or that they are entirely alluvial, and of the same sort with the Deltas formed at the mouths of rivers. The relative changes, however, of the sea and land on this tract, have been differently represented, and I am unwilling, on

---

* In the county of Suffolk, near Wood Bridge, at the distance of seven or eight miles from the sea, are the Crag-pits, in which prodigious quantities of sea-shells are discovered, many of them perfect and quite solid, (Pennant's Arctic Zoology, Introd. p. 6.). Lincolnshire affords various proofs of the same kind; but some other circumstances in the appearance of that coast, just about to be taken notice of, indicate changes of a more complicated nature.

on that account, to found any argument on them.

391. If we proceed farther to the north, to the ſhores of the Baltic for inſtance, we have undoubted evidence of a change of level in the ſame direction as on our own ſhores. The level of this ſea has been repreſented as lowering at ſo great a rate as 40 inches in a century. Celſius obſerved, that ſeveral rocks which are now above water, were not long ago ſunken rocks, and dangerous to navigators; and he particularly took notice of one, which, in the year 1680, was on the ſurface of the water, and in the year 1731 was $20\frac{1}{2}$ Swediſh inches above it. From an inſcription near Aſpô, in the lake Melar, which communicates with the Baltic, engraved, as is ſuppoſed, about five centuries ago, the level of the ſea appears to have ſunk in that time no leſs than 13 Swediſh feet *. All theſe facts, with many more which it is unneceſſary to enumerate, make the gradual depreſſion, not only of the Baltic, but of the whole northern ocean, a matter of certainty.

392. Suppoſing theſe changes of level between the ſea and land to be ſufficiently aſcertained, the ſuppoſition which at firſt occurs is, that the motion

---

* Friſii Opera, tom. iii. p. 274.

tion has been in the fea rather than in the land, and that the former has actually defcended to a lower level. The imagination naturally feels lefs difficulty in conceiving, that an unftable fluid like the fea, which changes its level twice every day, has undergone a permanent depref-fion in its furface, than that the land, the *terra firma* itfelf, has admitted of an equal elevation. In all this, however, we are guided much more by fancy than reafon ; for, in order to deprefs or elevate the abfolute level of the fea, by a gi-ven quantity, in any one place, we muft deprefs or elevate it by the fame quantity over the whole furface of the earth ; whereas no fuch neceffity exifts with refpect to the elevation or depreffion of the land. To make the fea fubfide 30 feet all round the coaft of Great Britain, it is neceffary to difplace a body of water 30 feet deep over the whole furface of the ocean. The quantity of matter to be moved in that way is incomparably greater than if the land itfelf were to be elevated ; for though it is nearly three times lefs in fpecific gravity, it is as much great-er in bulk, as the furface of the ocean is greater than that of this ifland.

393. Befides, the fea cannot change its level, without a proportional change in the folid bottom on which it refts. Though there be reafon to fup-

pose that such changes in the bottom do actually take place, yet they are probably much flower and more imperceptible than thofe which we are here confidering. It is evident, therefore, that the fimpleft hypothefis for explaining thofe changes of level, is, that they proceed from the motion, upwards or downwards, of the land itfelf, and not from that of the fea. As no elevation or depreffion of the fea can take place, but over the whole, its level cannot be affected by local caufes, and is probably as little fubject to variation as any thing to be met with on the furface of the globe.

394. Other obfervations, however, made on different fhores from the preceding, give greater certainty to this conclufion, and make it clear, that the motion or change which we are now treating of is not to be afcribed to the fea itfelf.

The obfervations juft mentioned prove, that the level of the North Sea is lower now than it was heretofore ; but it appears, that in the Mediterranean, the oppofite takes place. Very accurate obfervations made by MANFREDI, render it certain, that the fuperficies of the Hadriatic was higher about the middle of the laft century, than toward the beginning of the Chriftian æra.

Some repairs that were carrying on in the cathedral church of Ravenna, in the year 1731, afforded

afforded him an opportunity of obferving, that the ancient, and probably original, pavement, was four feet and a half below the prefent, and nearly a foot under the level of the fea at high water *. Now, when the church was built, this cannot have been the pofition of the pavement, relatively to the level of the fea, for it would have fubjected the floor to be under water twice in twenty-four hours, and muft have done fo the more unavoidably, becaufe at that time (the beginning of the 5th century) the walls of Ravenna were wafhed by the fea. The fact that this pavement is under the high-water mark, by the quantity juft mentioned, was afcertained by actual levelling. This refult was confirmed by fimilar facts, obferved by ZENDRINI at Venice.

395. Manfredi himfelf attributes all this to the elevation of the furface of the fea, and has entered into a long calculation to afcertain at what rate that furface may be fuppofed to rife, on account of the earth and fand brought down by the rivers, and fpread out over the bottom of the fea. But as the fact of the rife of the level
of

---

* Commentarii Academiæ Bononienfis, tom. ii. pars 1ma, p. 237, &c. and pars 2da, p. 1. &c.

of the fea is not general, and as the contrary is
obferved in the north feas, as already proved,
this hypothefis will not explain the apparent rife
in the level of the Hadriatic.

396. Though a local fubfidence, or fettling of
the ground, could hardly account for this change,
the pavement being perfect in its level, and the
walls of the cathedral without any fhake, yet a
fubfidence that has extended to a great tract, as
to the whole of Italy, if the mafs moved has
continued parallel to itfelf, and changed its place
flowly, will agree very well with the appearances.
The facts here ftated are alfo the more deferving of attention, that about Ravenna, the land,
at the fame time that it has funk in its level,
has extended its furface, and has encroached on
the fea. Since the time of AUGUSTUS, the line of
the coaft has been carried farther out by about
three miles *. This laft is the undoubted effect
of the degradation of the land by the rivers;
and here we have very clear evidence of the
forces, both under and above the furface, producing their refpective effects at the fame time,
fo that while the furface is raifed by earth
brought down by the rivers, every given point in

F f   the

* Manfredi, *ibid.*

the ground is depreſſed and let down to a lower level *.

397. On the ſouthern coaſt of Italy ſimilar facts have been obſerved. BREISLAC, in his *Topographia Fiſica della Campania di Roma* †, from certain appearances in the gulfs of Bajia and Naples, concludes, that at the beginning of the Chriſtian æra, the level of the ſea was lower on that part of the coaſt than it is now. The facts which he mentions are the following: 1*mo*, The remains of an ancient road are now to be ſeen in the Gulf of Bajia at a conſiderable diſtance from the land. 2*do*, Some ancient buildings belonging to Porto Julio are at preſent covered by the ſea. 3*tio*, Ten columns of granite at the foot of Monte Nuovo, which appear to have belonged to the Temple of the Nymphs, are alſo nearly covered by the ſea. 4*to*, The pavement of the Temple of Serapis is now ſomewhat lower than the high-water mark, though it cannot be ſuppoſed that this edifice when built was expoſed to the inconvenience of having its floor frequently under water. 5*to*, The ruins of a palace, built

---

* On the coaſt of Dalmatia alſo, the riſing of the level of the ſea has been remarked, particularly at the ruins of Diocletian's palace of Spalatro.

† Cap. vi. p. 300.

built by Tiberius in the island of Caprea, are now entirely covered by the sea.

Thus, it appears that the level of the sea is sinking in the more northern latitudes, and rising in the Mediterranean, and it is evident that this cannot happen by the motion of the sea itself. The parts of the ocean all communicating with one another, cannot rise in one place and fall in another ; but, in order to maintain a level surface, must rise equally or fall equally over the whole of its extent. If, therefore, we place any confidence in the preceding observations, and they are certainly liable to no objection, either from their own nature or the character of the observers, we must consider it as demonstrated, that the relative change of level has proceeded from the elevation or depression of the land itself. This agrees well with the preceding theory, which holds, that our continents are subject to be acted upon by the expansive forces of the mineral regions ; that by these forces they have been actually raised up, and are sustained by them in their present situation.

398. According to some other facts stated by the same ingenious author, it appears, that on the coast of Italy the progress of the sea in ascending, or of the land in descending, has not

F f 2   been

been uniform during the period above mentioned, but that different ofcillations have taken
place ; fo that, from about the beginning of the
Chriftian æra, till fome time in the middle ages,
the fea rofe to be fixteen feet higher than at prefent, from which height it has defcended till it,
became lower than it is now, and from that ftate
of depreffion it is now rifing again. Breiflac in-
fers this from two facts, which he combines very ingenioufly with the preceding, viz. the remains of fome ancient buildings, at the foot of
Monte Nuovo, five or fix feet above the prefent
level of the fea, in which are found the fhells of
fome of thofe little marine animals that eat into
ftone : And again, the marble columns of the
temple of Serapis, which are alfo perforated by
pholades, to the height of fixteen feet above
the ground. All thefe changes Breiflac afcribes
to the motion of the fea itfelf ; a fuppofition
which, as we have feen, cannot poffibly be admitted, fince nothing can permanently affect the
level of the fea in one place, which does not affect it in all places whatfoever.

399. Appearances, which indicate fuch alternations as have juft been mentioned in the level of
the fea, are to be met with on fome other coafts.
In England, on the coaft of Lincolnfhire, the remains of a foreft have been obferved, which are
now

now entirely covered by the sea *. The submarine stratum which contains the remains of
this forest, can be traced into the country to a
great distance, and is found throughout all the
fens of Lincolnshire. The stratum itself is a-
bout four feet thick; it is covered in some places by a bed of clay sixteen feet thick, and under it for twenty feet more is a bed of soft mud,
like the scourings of a ditch, mixed with shells
and silt.

Here then we have a stratum which must
have been once uppermost on the surface of the
dry land, though one part of it is now immersed
under the sea, and another covered with earth,
to the depth of sixteen feet. A change of level
in the sea itself will not explain these appearances: they can only be explained by supposing
the whole tract of land to have subsided, which
is the hypothesis adopted by the author of the
description in the Transactions, M. CORRIA DE
SERRA; the subsidence, however, is not here
understood to arise from the mere yielding of
some of the strata immediately underneath, but
is conceived to be a part of that geological system of alternate depression and elevation of the
surface, which probably extends to the whole
mineral kingdom. To reconcile all the differ-

F f 3   ent

---

* Phil. Transf. 1799. p. 145.

ent facts, I should be tempted to think, that the forest which once covered Lincolnshire, was immersed under the sea by the subsidence of the land to a great depth, and at a period considerably remote ; that when so immersed, it was covered over with the bed of clay which now lies on it, by deposition from the sea, and the washing down of earth from the land ; that it has emerged from this great depth till a part of it has became dry land ; but that it is now sinking again, if the tradition of the country deserves any credit, that the part of it in the sea is deeper under water at present than it was a few years ago. This might also serve to reconcile, in some measure, the phenomena of this submarine forest with the appearances which indicate an extension of the land on the coast of Lincolnshire. Indeed the extension of the land is no direct proof, either of its own elevation, or of the depression of the sea, as we may conclude from the instance of Ravenna already mentioned.

400. We have concluded from the facts stated above, that the level of the sea rises in the Mediterranean, and sinks in the more northern latitudes ; and thence some have suspected, that the level of the sea had in general a tendency to rise towards the equator, and to sink towards

wards the poles. This is the notion of Frisi, as has been already remarked, and he suggests, that this rise of the sea may be owing to a slight acceleration in the earth's diurnal motion. But there are facts which shew, that between the tropics the relative level of the sea and land has sunk, and is lower at present than it was at some former period, probably not extremely remote. The opinion of Frisi, therefore, is unsupported by observation, and, as has been already shewn, cannot be justified from theory.

Between the tropics, islands are formed from the mere accumulation of coral; and it is the peculiarity of those regions, to produce rocks that have not passed through the usual process of mineral consolidation *. The islots, however, which are thus formed, must have their bases laid on a solid rock, though perhaps at a great depth; and it is not probable, that after they are once raised above the surface of the sea, they can still rise farther, except by some elevation of the rock which serves as their founda-

F f 4   tion.

---

* Dr Foster, in his Voyage round the World, (vol. ii. p. 146.) gives an instance in the South Sea Islands, where the surface of the island, though entirely a coral rock, was raised forty feet above the level of the sea.

tion *. Now, at Palmerſton iſland, which comprehends nine or ten low iſlots, that may be reckoned the heads of a great reef of coral rock, Captain Cook informs us of his having ſeen, " far beyond the reach of the ſea, even in the moſt violent ſtorms, elevated coral rocks, which, on examination, appeared to have been perforated in the ſame manner that the rocks are that now compoſe the outer edge of the reef. This evidently ſhews," he adds, " that the ſea had formerly reached ſo far; and ſome of theſe perforated rocks were almoſt in the centre of the iſland †."

The ſame excellent navigator, giving an account of the peninſula at Cape Denbigh, remarks : " It appeared to me, that this peninſula muſt have been an iſland in remote times; for there were marks of the ſea having flowed over the iſthmus."

401. We are here touching on one of thoſe ſubjects, where we feel much the want of accurate and ancient obſervations, and where it is not from the infancy, but the maturity of ſcience that any thing approaching to certainty can be looked for. The utmoſt that we can expect at preſent, is

---

* A very curious account of the formation of ſuch iſlands is given by A Dalrymple Eſq; in the Philoſophical Tranſactions, vol. lvii. p. 394.

† Cook's Third Voyage. vol. i. p. 221.

is an anticipation, which future ages muſt certainly modify, and correct. The beſt thing, in the mean time, that can be done for the advancement of this branch of geological knowledge, is to aſcertain with exactneſs the relative level of the ſea, and of ſuch points upon the land as can be diſtinctly marked, and pointed out to ſucceeding ages. This is not ſo eaſy as it may at firſt appear. Where every object changes, it is difficult to find a meaſure of change, or a fixed point from which the computation may begin. The aſtronomers already feel this inconvenience, and when they would refer their obſervations to an immoveable plane, that ſhall preſerve its poſition the ſame in all ages, they meet with difficulties, which cannot be removed but by a profound mathematical inveſtigation.

In geology, we cannot hope to be delivered from this embarraſſment in the ſame manner; and we have no reſource but to multiply obſervations of the difference of level; to make them as exact as poſſible, and to ſelect points of compariſon that have a chance of being long diſtinguiſhed. The improvements in barometrical meaſurements, which give ſuch facility to the determination of heights, along with ſo conſiderable a degree of accuracy, will furniſh an accumulation of facts that muſt one day be of great value to the geologiſt.

NOTE

Note XXII. § 123.

Foſſil Bones.

402. The remains of organiſed bodies, at preſent included in the ſolid parts of the globe, may
be divided into three claſſes. The firſt conſiſts
of the ſhells, corals, and even bodies of fiſh, and
amphibious animals, which are now converted
into ſtone, and make integrant parts of the ſolid
rock. All theſe are parts of animals that exiſted *before the formation of the preſent land,* or
even of the rocks whereof it conſiſts. Theſe remains have been already treated of, and the evidence which they furniſh muſt ever be regarded
as of the utmoſt importance in the theory of the
earth. The ſecond claſs conſiſts of remains,
which, by the help of ſtalactitical concretions, are
converted into ſtone. Theſe are the *exuviæ* of
animals, which exiſted on the very ſame continents on which we now dwell, and are no doubt
the moſt ancient among their inhabitants, of
which any monument is preſerved. In compariſon of the firſt claſs, they muſt, nevertheleſs, be
conſidered as of very modern origin.

403. The third claſs conſiſts of the bones of
animals found in the looſe earth or ſoil; theſe
have not acquired a ſtony character, and their nature

ture appears to be but little changed, except by the progress of decomposition and of mouldering into earth. No decided line can be drawn between the antiquity of this and the preceding clafs, as there may be between the preceding and the firft. In fome inftances, the objects of this third clafs may be coeval with thofe of the fecond; in general, they muft be accounted of later origin, as they are certainly not preferved in a manner fo well fitted for long continuance.

404. The animal remains of the fecond clafs, are generally found in the neighbourhood of limeftone ftrata, and are either enveloped or penetrated by calcareous, or fometimes ferruginous matter. Of this fort are the bones found in the rock of Gibraltar, and on the coaft of Dalmatia. The latter are peculiarly marked for their number, and the extent of the country over which they are fcattered, leaving it doubtful whether they are the work of fucceffive ages, or of fome fudden cataftrophe that has affembled in one place, and overwhelmed with immediate deftruction, a vaft multitude of the inhabitants of the globe. Thefe remains are found in greateft abundance in the iflands of Cherfo and Ofero; and always in what the Abbé Fortis calls an *ocreo-ftalactitic earth*. The bones are often in the ftate of mere fplinters, the broken and confufed relics of various animals, concreted with fragments of marble

and

and lime, in clefts and chafms of the ftrata *.
Sometimes human bones are faid to be found in
thefe confufed maffes.

405. A very remarkable collection of bones in
this ftate is found in the caves of Bayreuth in Fran-
conia. Many of thefe belong, as is inferred with
great certainty from the ftructure of their teeth,
to a carnivorous animal of vaft fize, and having
very little affinity to any of thofe that are now
known. The bones are found in different ftates,
fome being without any ftalactitical concretion,
and having the calcareous earth ftill united to
the phofphoric acid, fo that they belong to the
third, rather than the fecond, of the preceding di-
vifions. In others, the phofphoric acid has wholly
difappeared, and given place to the carbonic.

The number of thefe bones, accumulated in
the fame place, is matter of aftonifhment, when
it is confidered, that the animals to which they
belonged were carnivorous, fo that more than
two can never have lived in the fame cavern at
the fame time. The caves of Bayreuth feem to
have been the den and the tomb of a whole dy-
nafty of unknown monfters, that iffued from this
central fpot to devour the feebler inhabitants of
the woods, during a long fucceffion of ages, before

---

* Travels into Dalmatia, p. 449.

fore man had fubdued the earth, and freed it from all domination but his own.

406. The foffil bones of the fecond and third clafs, but chiefly of the third, have now afforded matter of conjecture and difcuffion for more than a century. The facts with refpect to them are very numerous and interefting, but can be confidered here only very generally.

The remains of this kind, confift of the bones only of large animals, fo that they have generally been compared with thofe of the elephant, the rhinoceros, the hippopotamus, or other animals of great fize. The bones of fmaller animals have alfo been found, but much more rarely than the other. It is ufually remarked, that the bones thus difcovered in the earth are larger than thofe of the fimilar living animals.

Another general fact concerning thefe remains, is, that they are found in all countries whatfoever, but always in the loofe or travelled earth, and never in the genuine ftrata. Since the year 1696, when the attention of the curious was called to this fubject, by the fkeleton of an elephant dug up in Thuringia, and defcribed by Tentzelius *, there is hardly a country in Europe which has not afforded inftances of the

* Phil. Tranf. vol. xix. p. 757.

the fame kind. Foffil bones, particularly grinders and tufks of elephants, have been found in other places of Germany, in Poland, France, Italy, Britain, Ireland, and even Iceland *. Two countries, however, afford them in greater abundance by far than any other part of the known world; namely, the plains of Siberia in the old continent, and the flat grounds on the banks of the Ohio in the new †.

407. When the bones in Siberia were firft difcovered, they were fuppofed to belong to an animal that lived under ground, to which they gave the name of the *mammouth*; and the credit beftowed on this abfurd fiction, is a proof of the ftrong defire which all men feel of reconciling extraordinary appearances with the regular courfe of nature. Much fkill, however, in natural hiftory was not required to difcover that many of the bones in queftion refembled thofe of the elephant, particularly the grinders and the tufks of that animal. Others refembled the bones of the rhinoceros; and a head of that kind, having the hide

---

* A grinder of an elephant found in Iceland, is defcribed by *Bartholinus*, Actor. Hafniens. vol. i. p. 83.

† The foffil bones on the Ohio are defcribed in two papers by Mr P. Collinfon, Phil. Tranf. vol. lvii. p. 464. and 468.

hide preferved upon it, was found in Siberia, and is ftill in the imperial cabinet at Peterfburgh.

Pallas has defcribed the foffil bones which he found in the mufeum at Peterfburgh, on his being appointed to the fuperintendence of it, and enumerates, not only bones that belong, in his opinion, to the elephant and rhinoceros, but others that belong to a kind of buffalo, very different from any now known, and of a fize vaftly greater *. He has alfo defcribed, in another very curious memoir, the bones of the fame kind that he met with in his travels through the north-eaft parts of Afia.

The foffil bones found on the banks of the Ohio, refemble in many things thofe of Siberia; like them they are contained in the foil or alluvial earth, and never in the folid ftrata; like them too they are no otherwife changed from their natural ftate, than by being fometimes flightly calcined at the furface; they are alfo of great fize, and in great numbers, being probably the remains of feveral different fpecies.

408. Two inquiries concerning thefe bones have excited the curiofity of naturalifts; firft, to difcover among the living tribes at prefent inhabiting

biting

---

* Novi Comment. Petrop. tom. xiii. (1768) p. 436. and tom. xvii. p. 576, &c.

biting the earth, thofe to which the foſſil remains may with the greateſt probability be referred ; and, ſecondly, to find out the cauſe
why theſe remains exiſt in ſuch quantities, in
countries where the animals to which they belong, whatever they be, are at preſent unknown.
The ſolution of the firſt of theſe queſtions, is
much more within our reach than the ſecond,
and at any rate muſt be firſt ſought for.

On the authority of ſo eminent a naturaliſt as
Pallas, the bones from Siberia may ſafely be referred to the elephant, the rhinoceros, and buffalo, as mentioned above, though perhaps to varieties of them with which we are not now acquainted. With reſpect to the bones of North
America, the queſtion is more doubtful, for they
have this particular circumſtance attending them,
viz. that along with the thigh-bones, tuſks, &c.
which might be ſuppoſed to belong to the elephant, grinders are always found of a ſtructure and
form entirely different from the grinders of that a-
nimal *. Some naturaliſts, particularly M. D'Au-
BENTON, referred theſe grinders to the hippopotamus; but Dr W. HUNTER appears to have proved,
in a very ſatisfactory manner, that they cannot
have

* See Mr Collinſon's papers above referred to, Phil.
Tranſ. vol. lvii.

have belonged to either of the animals juſt mentioned, but to a *carnivorous* animal of enormous
ſize, the race of which, fortunately for the preſent
inhabitants of the earth, ſeems now to be entirely extinct *. The foundation of Dr Hunter's
opinion is, that in theſe grinders the enamel is
merely an external covering; whereas, in the
elephant, and other animals deſtined to live on
vegetable food, the enamel is intermixed with
the ſubſtance of the tooth †.

409. Though this argument appears to be of
conſiderable weight, yet CAMPER, who was greatly ſkilled in comparative anatomy, and who had
ſtudied this ſubject with particular attention, was
of opinion, that theſe grinders belong to a ſpecies
of elephant. This opinion he ſtates in a letter to Pallas, who had found grinders and o-
ther bones of this ſame animal, on the weſtern

G g   declivity

---

* Phil. Tranſ. vol. lviii. p. 3, &c.

† A foſſil grinder in the collection of JOHN MACGOW-
AN, Eſq; of Edinburgh, anſwers nearly to Mr Collinſon's
deſcription, and is very well repreſented by the figure
which accompanies it. This grinder weighs four pounds
one-fourth avoirdupois; the circumference of the *corona*
is eighteen inches; the coat of enamel is one fourth of
an inch thick; there are five double teeth; in Mr Collinſon's ſpecimen there are only four.

declivity of the Oural mountains *. Camper
denies that the animal is carnivorous, becauſe
the *inciſores*, or canine teeth, are wanting ; and
he argues farther, from the weight of the head,
which may be inferred from the weight of the
grinders, that the neck muſt have been ſhort,
and the animal muſt have been furniſhed with a
proboſcis. He afterwards abandoned the latter
hypotheſis, and gave it as his opinion, that the
incognitum was neither carnivorous, nor a ſpecies
of the elephant †.

410. Neverthelefs, CUVIER, in a *mémoire* read
before the National Inſtitute of Paris, maintains,
that the foſſil bones of the new continent, as well as
moſt of thoſe of the old, belong to certain ſpecies of
the elephant; of which, at leaſt, two do not now
exiſt, and are only known from remains preſerved
in the ground. He diſtinguiſhes them thus ‡:

*Elephas mammonteus,—maxillâ obtuſiore, lamel-
lis molarium tenuibus, rectis.*

*Elephas Americanus,—molaribus multicuſpidi-
bus, lamellis poſt detritionem quadri-lobatis.*

The latter ſpecies, which is meant to include
the *animal incognitum*, is ſaid to have lived, not
only

---

* Acta Acad. Petrop. tom. i. (1777) pars poſterior,
p. 213, &c.

† *Ibid.* tom. ii. (1784) p. 262.

‡ Mémoires de l'Inſtitut National, Sciences Phyſiques,
tom. ii. p. 19., &c.

only in America, but in many parts of the old
continent.   Yet fome late inquiries into the
ftructure of the teeth of graminivorous animals,
and particularly of the elephant, make it very
improbable that the *incognitum* has belonged to
this genus *.   The grinders of the elephant have
been found to confift of three fubftances, enamel, bone, and what is called the *crufta petrofa*,
applied in layers, or folds contiguous to one another ; and no veftige of this ftructure appears in
the grinders of the unknown animal of the Ohio †.

G g 2   At

---

* See Mr Home's obfervations on the teeth of graminivorous animals, Phil. Tranf. 1799.   Alfo, An Effay on
the ftructure of the teeth, by Dr Blake.

† In a paper inferted in the fourth volume of the A-
merican Philofophical Tranfactions, an account is given
of two different grinders that are found at the Salt-Licks
near the Ohio.   One of them refembles the grinder of
the elephant, and may have belonged to the elephas
Americanus of Cuvier ; the other agrees pretty nearly
with the grinder of Dr Hunter's *animal incognitum*.   The
author of the paper thinks that the *animal incognitum* was
not wholly carnivorous, as the *incifores*, or canine teeth,
are never found.   At the Great Bone-Lick, bones of
fmaller animals, particularly of the buffalo kind, have
been difcovered.   The faline impregnation of the earth
at thefe Licks muft no doubt have contributed to the prefervation of the bones.   Tranf. American Phil. Soc,
vol. iv. (1799) p. 510, &c.

At the fame time, Dr Hunter's affertion, that this animal was carnivorous, is rendered doubtful, not only by the want of *canine* teeth, but alfo from the refemblance between its grinders and thofe of the wild boar, which Mr HOME has obferved to be confiderable *. The grinder of the boar is fimilar to that of the elephant, in the extent of the mafticating furface, but not at all in the internal ftructure; and the fame is true of the tooth of the *animal incognitum*, fo that a confiderable probability is eftablifhed, that it and the boar are of the fame genus, and both deftined to live occafionally either on animal, or vegetable food.

411. Another *animal incognitum* found in South America has been defcribed by Cuvier, and appears to be of a different genus from the *incognitum* of the North. Thus, if we include the two *incognita* of America, the *elephas mammonteus*, the unknown buffalo of Pallas, and the great animal of Bayreuth, we have at leaft five diftinct genera, or fpecies of the animal kingdom, which exifted on our continents formerly, but do not exift on them now. The number is probably much greater: Pallas mentions foffil horns of a gazelle, of an unknown fpecies; and horns of *deer* are often found, that cannot be referred to any fpecies now exifting. Thofe extinct

---

* Obfervations on the grinding teeth of the wild boar and *animal incognitum*. Phil. Tranf. 1801, p. 319.

tinct races have been remarkable for their size : some of the ancient elephants appear to have been three times as large as any of the present *.

412. The inhabitants of the globe, then, like all the other parts of it, are subject to change : It is not only the individual that perishes, but whole *species*, and even perhaps *genera*, are extinguished. It is not unnatural to consider some part of this change as the operation of man. The extension of his power would necessarily subvert the balance that had before been established between the inhabitants of the earth, and the means of their subsistence. Some of the larger and fiercer animals might indeed dispute with him, for a long time, the empire of the globe ; and it may have required the arm of a Hercules to subdue the monsters which lurked in the caves of Bayreuth, or roamed on the banks of the Ohio. But these, with others of the same character, were at length exterminated : the more innocent species fled to a distance from man ; and being forced to retire into the most inaccessible parts, where their food was scanty, and their migration checked, they may have degenerated from the size and strength of their ancestors, and some species may have been entirely extinguished.

But besides this, a change in the animal kingdom seems to be a part of the order of nature,

G g 3   and

---

* Camper, Nov. Acta Petrop. tom. ii. (1784) p. 257.

and is vifible in inftances to which human power cannot have extended. If we look to the moft ancient inhabitants of the globe, of which the remains are preferved in the ftrata themfelves, we find in the fhells and corals of a former world hardly any that refemble exactly thofe which exift in the prefent. The fpecies, except in a few inftances, are the fame, but fubject to great varieties. The vegetable impreffions on flate, and other argillaceous ftones, can feldom be exactly recognifed ; and even the infects included in amber, are different from thofe of the countries in which the amber is found.

413. Suppofing, then, the changes which have taken place in the qualities and habits of the animal creation, to be as great as thofe in their ftructure and external form, we can have no reafon to wonder if it fhould appear, that fome have formerly dwelt in countries from which the fimilar races are now entirely banifhed. The power of living in a different climate, of enduring greater degrees of cold or of heat, or of fubfifting on different kinds of food, may very well have accompanied the other changes. Though one fpecies of elephant may now be confined to the fouthern parts of Afia, another may have been able to endure the feverer climates of the north ; and the fame may be true of the buffalo or the rhinoceros. In all this no phyfical

fical impoffibility is involved ; though whether
it is a probable folution of the difficulty concerning the origin of thefe animal remains, can only
be judged of from other circumftances.

414. If we confider attentively the facts that refpect the Siberian foffil bones, there will appear
infurmountable objections to every theory that
fuppofes them to be exotic, and to have been
brought into their prefent fituation from a diftant country.

The extent of the tract through which thefe
bones are fcattered, is a circumftance truly wonderful.   Pallas affures us *, that there is not a
river of confiderable fize in all the north of Afia,
from the Tanais, which runs into the Black Sea,
to the Anadyr, which falls into the Gulf of
Kamtchatka, in the fides or bottom of which
bones of elephants and other large animals have
not been found.   This is efpecially the cafe
where the rivers run in plains through gravel,
fand, clay, &c. ; among the mountains, the bones
are rarely difcovered.   The extent of the tract
juft mentioned exceeds four thoufand miles ; and
how the bones could be diftributed over all that
extent, by any means but by the animals having

G g 4   lived

---

* De Reliquiis Animalium exoticorum, per Afiam
Borealem repertis.—Nov. Comment. Petrop. tom. xvii.
(1772) p. 576.

lived there, it feems impoffible to conceive. No torrent nor inundation could have produced this effect, nor could the bones brought in that way have been laid together fo as to form complete fkeletons.

415. One fact recorded by the fame author, feems calculated to remove all uncertainty. It is that of the carcafe of a rhinoceros, almoft entire, and covered with the hide, found in the earth in the banks of the river Wilui, which falls into the Lena below Jacutfk *. Some of the mufcles and tendons were actually adhering to the head when Pallas received it. The head, after being dried in an oven, is ftill preferved in the mufeum at Peterfburgh. The prefervation of the fkin and mufcles of this natural mummy, as Pallas calls it, was no doubt brought about by its being buried in earth that was in a ftate of perpetual congelation; for the place is in the parallel of 64°, where the ground is never thawed but to a very fmall depth below the furface.

But by what means can we account for the carcafe of a rhinoceros being buried in the earth, on the confines of the polar circle? Shall we afcribe it to fome immenfe torrent, which, fweeping acrofs the defarts of Tartary, and the mountains of Altai, tranfported the productions of India

---

* Pallas. *ubi fupra*, p. 586. Alfo, Voyages de Pallas, tom. iv. p. 131.

dia to the plains of Siberia, and interred in the mud of the Lena the animals that had fed on the banks of the Barampooter or the Ganges? Were all other objections to fo extraordinary a fuppofi- tion removed, the prefervation of the hide and mufcles of a dead animal, and the adhefion of the parts, while it was dragged for 2000 miles over fome of the higheft and moft rugged mountains in the world, is too abfurd to be for a moment ad- mitted. Or fhall we fuppofe that this carcafe has been floated in by an inundation of the fea, from fome tropical country now fwallowed up, and of which the numerous iflands of the Indian Archipelago are the remains? The heat of a tropical climate, and the putrefcence naturally arifing from it, would foon, independently of all other accidents, have ftripped the bones of their covering. Indeed this *inftantia fingularis*, as in every fenfe it may properly be called, feems cal- culated for the exprefs purpofe of excluding eve- ry hypothefis but one from being employed to explain the origin of foffil bones. It not only ex- cludes the two which have juft been mentioned, but it excludes alfo that of Buffon, viz. that thefe bones are the remains of animals which lived in Siberia, when the arctic regions enjoyed a fine climate, and a temperature like that which fouthern Afia now poffeffes. From the preferva- tion of the flefh and hide of this rhinoceros, it is plain, that when the body was buried in the

earth,

earth, the climate was much the fame that it is now, and the cold fufficient to refift the progrefs of putrefaction.

Pallas takes notice of the inconfiftency of the ftate of this fkeleton, with the hypothefis of Buffon; but he does not obferve that the inconfiftency is equally great between it and his own hypothefis, the importation of the foffil bones by an inundation of the fea, and that flefh or mufcle muft have been entirely confumed long before it could be carried by the waves to the parallel of 64°, from any climate which the rhinoceros at prefent inhabits.

416. The prefence of petrified marine objects in places where fome of the foffil bones are found, is no proof that the latter have come from the fea, though it is produced as fuch both by Pallas himfelf, and afterwards by Kirwan. Thefe marine bodies are the fhells and corals that have been parts of calcareous rocks, from which being detached by the ordinary progrefs of difintegration, they are now contained in the beds of fand or gravel where the animal remains are buried. They have nothing in common with thefe remains; they are real ftones, and belong to another, and a far more remote epocha. Such objects being found in the fame place where the bones lie, argues only that the ftrata in the higher grounds, from which the gravel has come, are calcareous; and nothing can fhew in a ftronger light

light the neceffity of diftinguifhing the different condition of foffil bodies, united by the mere circumftance of contiguity, before we draw any inference as to their having a common origin. If the marine remains were in the fame condition with the bones ; if they were in no refpect mineralized ; then the conclufion, that both had been imported by the fea, would have great probability; but without that, their prefent union muft be held as cafual, and can give no infight into the origin of either.

417. On the whole, therefore, no conclufion remains, but that thefe bones have belonged to fpecies of elephants, rhinoceros, &c. which inhabited the very countries where their remains are now buried, and which could endure the feverity of the Siberian climate. The rhinoceros of the Wilui certainly lived on the confines of the Polar circle, and was expofed to the fame cold while alive, by which, when dead, its body has been fo long, and fo curioufly preferved.

Thefe animals may alfo have lived occafionally farther to the fouth, among the valleys between the great ranges of mountains that bound Siberia on that fide. Foffil bones are but rarely found in thefe valleys, probably becaufe they have been wafhed down from thence into the plains. We muft obferve, too, that thofe animals may have migrated with the feafons, and by that means avoided the rigorous

winter

winter of the high latitudes. The dominion of man, by rendering such migration to the larger animals difficult or impossible, must have greatly changed the economy of all those tribes, and narrowed the circle of their enjoyments and existence. The heaps in which the fossil bones appear to be accumulated in particular places, especially in North America, have a great appearance of being connected with the migrations of animals, and the accidents that might bring multitudes of them into the same spot.

What holds of Siberia and of North America, is applicable, *a fortiori*, to all the other places where animal remains are found in the same condition. Thus we are carried back to a time when many larger species of animals, now entirely extinct, inhabited the earth, and when varieties of those that are at present confined to particular situations, were, either by the liberty of migration, or by their natural constitution, accommodated to all the diversities of climate. This period, though beyond the limits of ordinary chronology, is posterior to the great revolutions on the earth's surface, and the latest among geological epochas.

NOTE

NOTE XXIII. § 128.

Geology of KIRWAN *and* DE LUC.

418. The two champions of the Neptunian
fyftem, who have diftinguifhed themfelves moft
by their hoftility to Dr Hutton, are DE LUC
and KIRWAN. They have carried on their attack nearly on the fame plan, and have employed againft their antagonift the weapons both
of theology and fcience. With a fpirit as in-
jurious to the dignity of religion, as to the free-
dom of philofophical inquiry, they have difre-
garded a maxim enforced by the authority of Bacon, and by all our experience of the paft ; " *Tan-
to magis hæc vanitas inhibenda venit et coërcenda,
quia, ex divinorum et humanorum male-fana admix-
tione, non folum educitur philofophia phantaftica,
fed etiam religio hæretica. Itaque falutare admo-
dum eft, fi mente fobriá, fidei tantum dentur quæ
fidei funt* *."

Proceeding

---

* The whole paffage is deferving of attention, and
it feems as if the prophetic fpirit of Bacon had addreffed
it to the cofmologifts of the prefent day. " *Peffima enim
res eft errorum* APOTHEOSIS, *et pro pefte intellectús habenda
eft, fi vanis accedat veneratio. Huic autem vanitati non-
nulli ex modernis fummá levitate ita indulferunt, ut, in pri-
mo capitolo* GENESEOS, *et aliis Scripturis Sacris, philofo-
phiam naturalem fundari conati funt :* Inter VIVA *quæren-
tes* MORTUA." Nov. Organum, lib. i. aphor. 65.

Proceeding, accordingly, in direct oppofition to rules that have never yet been violated with impunity, and miftaking the true object of a theory of the earth, they carry back their inquiries to a period prior to the prefent feries of caufes and effects, where, having neither experience nor analogy to direct them, they pretend to be guided by a fuperior light. They would have us to confider their geological fpeculations as a commentary on the text of MOSES ; they endeavour to explain the action of creative power, and, with indifcreet curiofity, would tear off the veil which the hand of the prophet has fo wifely refpected. But the veil cannot be torn off, and all that is behind it muft be to man as that which never has exifted.

419. M. de Luc has neverthelefs treated very diffufely of the hiftory of the folar fyftem, previous to the eftablifhment of the prefent laws of nature, and has dwelt on it with great complacency, and fingular minutenefs of detail. His tenth letter to LA METHERIE has the following title :

" On the Hiftory of the Earth, from the time when that planet was penetrated by *light*, till the appearance of the fun ; a portion of time which includes the origin of heat, and of the figure of the earth ; of its primeval ftrata, of the ancient fea, of our continents, as the bottom of
that

that fea, of the great chains of mountains, and
of vegetation *.''

I muſt confeſs that I am unacquainted with every thing of this letter but the title; and could not
eaſily be prevailed on to follow any man who pro-
feſſedly goes out of nature in ſearch of knowledge;
who pretends to give the hiſtory of our planetary
ſyſtem when there was no ſun, and to enumerate
the events which took place between the exiſtence of that luminary, and the exiſtence of
light. The abſurdity of ſuch an undertaking
admits of no apology; and the ſmile which it
might excite, if addreſſed merely to the fancy,
gives place to indignation when it aſſumes the
air of philoſophic inveſtigation.

420. It ſets, however, in a ſtrong light, the in-
conſiſtencies that may be obſerved in the intellectual character of the ſame individual, to conſider
that the author of this ſtrange and inconſiſtent
reverie,

---

* Journal de Phyſique, tom. 37. (1790) partie 2de,
p. 332. As I may not have done juſtice to this extraordinary title, it may be right to preſent it in the original. " Sur l'Hiſtoire de la TERRE, depuis que cette pla-
nette fut penetrée de LUMIERE, juſqu'à l'apparition du
SOLEIL; eſpace de tems qui renferme les ORIGINES de
la *chaleur*, et de la *figure* de notre globe; de ſes *couches
primordiales*, de *l'ancienne mer*, de nos *continens*, comme
fond de cette mer, de leurs grandes chaînes de *montagnes*, et de la *vegetation*."

reverie is, neverthelefs, an excellent obferver, and well fkilled in experimental inquiries. It will hardly be believed that he who writes the hifto-ry of the earth before the formation of the fun, is verfed in the principles of inductive reafoning; and that he has added much to the ftock of geo-logical knowledge, having obferved accurately, and defcribed with great perfpicuity and can-dour. His *Lettres Phyfiques* are full of valuable and juft obfervations, though accompanied with reafonings that do not feem always entitled to the fame praife; and in another work he has fuc-ceeded where many men of genius had failed, and has made confiderable improvements in a branch of the mathematics, without borrowing almoft any affiftance from the principles of that fcience *.

421. Some of the fame obfervations apply to Mr Kirwan. His Geological Effays have alfo for their object to explain the firft origin of things; and to fay that he has not fucceeded, in an at-tempt where no man ever can fucceed, im-plies no reproach on the execution of his work, whatever it may do on the defign. We have indeed no criterion by which the execution of it can be eftimated : what would in any other place be a blemifh, may be here deferving of praife; and if the work is full of confufion and perplexity

---

* Effai fur les Modifications de l Atmofphere.

perplexity, thefe are qualities inherent in the
fubject which it is intended to defcribe. It were,
no doubt, to be wifhed, that after emerging into
the regions of day, Mr Kirwan had been as fuccefsful in copying the beauty and fimplicity of
nature, as in reprefenting the diforder and in-
confiltency of the chaotic mafs. But his cofmology is without unity in its principles, or confiftency in its parts: the caufes introduced, are,
for the moft part, fuch as will account for one
fet of appearances juft as well as for another;
or, if any of them is likely to prove inadequate
to the effect afcribed to it, a new and arbitrary
hypothefis is always ready to come to its affiftance. The information given is feldom exact:
a multitude of facts brought together, without
the order and difcuffion effential to precife knowledge; and an infinity of quotations, amaffed
without criticifm or comparifon, afford proofs of
extenfive reading, but of the moft hafty and fuperficial inquiry. Thus we have feen paffages
from ULLOA and FRISI, produced in fupport of
opinions, which, when fairly ftated, they had
the moft direct tendency to overthrow.

422. In one refpect, the geological writings of
Kirwan are far inferior to De Luc's: They are
evidently the productions of a man who has not
feen nature with his own eyes; who has ftudied

H h mineralogy

mineralogy in cabinets, or in books only ; but who has feldom beheld foffils in their native place. With the balance in his hand, and the external characters of WERNER in his view, he has examined minerals with diligence, and has difcovered many of thofe marks which ferve to afcertain their places, in a fyftem of artificial arrangement. But to *reafon* and to *arrange* are very different occupations of the mind ; and a man may deferve praife as a mineralogift, who is but ill qualified for the refearches of geology.

423. The fame hurry and impatience are vifible in the manner in which his argument againft Dr Hutton is ufually conducted. He has feldom been careful to make himfelf mafter of the opinions of his adverfaries ; and what he gives as fuch, and directs his reafonings againft, have often no refemblance to them whatfoever. Without any intention to deceive others, but deceived himfelf, he ufually begins with mifreprefenting Dr Hutton's notions, and then proceeds to the refutation of them. In this imaginary conteft, it will readily be fuppofed, that he is in general fuccefsful : when a man has the framing both of his own argument, and that of his antagonift, he muft be a very unfkilful logician if he does not come off with the advantage.

424. It

424. It is but juſtice, however, to the Neptuniſts, to acknowledge, that they are not all liable
to the cenſure of beginning their reſearches from
a period antecedent to the exiſtence of the laws
of nature.   This abſurdity does not, ſo far as I
know, infect the ſyſtem of Werner.   That mineralogiſt has not propoſed to explain the firſt o-
rigin of things, though he has ſuppoſed, at ſome
former period, a condition of the globe very
unlike the preſent, viz. the entire ſubmerſion of
the ſolid under the fluid part.

NOTE XXIV. § 129.

Syſtem of BUFFON.

425. The affinity of Dr Hutton's theory to
that of Buffon, is nothing more than what ariſes
from their making uſe of the ſame agents, viz.
fire and water, in producing the preſent condition of the earth's ſurface.   In almoſt all other
reſpects the two theories are extremely different.   The order in which tho e agents are employed in them, is directly oppoſite, as has already been remarked ; Buffon introducing the
action of fire firſt, and of water only in the ſecond place, to waſte and deſtroy mineral bodies,

H h 2   and

and afterwards to difpofe them anew, and arrange them into ftrata. He makes no provifion for the confolidation of thefe ftrata, nor any
for their angular elevation ; he has no means of
explaining the unftratified rocks ; nor any, but
one extremely imperfect, for explaining the inequalities of the earth's furface.

Again, Buffon miftook, in fqme degree, the
true object of a theory of the earth ; and though
he did not go back, like the geologifts juft named,
to a time when the laws of nature were not
fully eftablifhed, he begins from a condition of
things too unlike the prefent to be the bafis of
any rational fpeculation. He does not, indeed,
undertake to examine the ftate of our planetary
fyftem before the fun exifted ; for from fuch ex-
travagance, even when moft difpofed to indulge
his fancy, he would furely have revolted. But
he treats of the world, when the earth and the
planets had juft ceafed to be a part of the fun, and
were newly detached from the body of that luminary *.

This hypothefis concerning the origin of the
planets, contrived chiefly to account for the circumftance

---

* According to Buffon, the granite is the true folar
matter, unchanged but by its congelation.

cumstance of their motion being all in the same
direction, and in other respects not only unsupported, but even inconsistent with the principle
of gravitation, has nothing in common with a
theory, confined as Dr Hutton's is, within the.
field which must for ever bound our inquiries,
and not venturing to speculate about the earth,
when in a condition totally different from the
present.

426. In what relates to the future, the two
systems are not more like than in what relates to
the past. Buffon represents the cooling of our
planet, and its loss of heat, as a process continually advancing, and which has no limit, but
the final extinction of life and motion over all
the surface, and through all the interior, of the
earth. The death of nature herself is the distant but gloomy object that terminates our
view, and reminds us of the wild fictions of the
Scandinavian mythology, according to which, *an-
nihilation* is at last to extend its empire even to the
gods. This dismal and unphilosophic vision was
unworthy of the genius of Buffon, and wonderfully ill suited to the elegance and extent of his
understanding. It forms a complete contrast
to the theory of Dr Hutton, where nothing is
to be seen beyond the continuation of the present order ; where no latent seed of evil threat-
ens final destruction to the whole; and where the

movements are fo perfect, that they can never terminate of themfelves. This is furely a view of the world more fuited to the dignity of NA-TURE, and the wifdom of its AUTHOR, than has yet been offered by any other fyftem of cofmology.

427. I have often quoted Buffon in the courfe thefe *Illuftrations*, and moft commonly for the purpofe of combating his opinions; but I am very fenfible, neverthelefs, of the obligations under which he has laid all the fciences connected with the natural hiftory of the earth.

The extent and variety of his knowledge, the juftnefs of his reafonings, the greatnefs of his views, his correct tafte, and manly eloquence, qualified him, better, perhaps, than any other individual, to compofe the Hiftory of Nature. The errors into which he has fallen, are almoft all the unavoidable confequences of the circumftances in which he was placed; and if their amount is eftimated by the proportion that they bear to the general excellence of the work, they will be reckoned but of fmall account. Buffon began to write when many parts of natural hiftory had made but little progrefs; when the quantity of authentic information was fmall, and when fcientific and correct defcription was hardly to be found. Many of the greateft and moft important facts in geology were quite unknown, and

and fcarcely any part of the mineral kingdom had
been accurately furveyed ; and, with fuch materials as this ftate of things afforded, it is not
wonderful if fome parts of the edifice he erected
have not proved fo folid and durable as the reft.
Had he appeared fomewhat later ; had he been
farther removed from the time when reafonings
a priori ufurped the place of induction ; and had
he been as willing to correct the errors into
which he had been betrayed by imperfect information, as he was ingenious in defending
them, his work would probably have reached as
great perfection, as it is given for any thing
without the fphere of the accurate fciences to
attain.   If he had examined the natural hiftory
of the earth more with his own eyes, and been as
careful to delineate it with fidelity as force; if he
had liftened with greater care to the philofophers around him ; had he attended to the de-
monftrations of NEWTON more, and defpifed the
arrangements of LINNÆUS lefs ; he would have
produced a work, as fingular foi its truth as for
its beauty, and would have gone near to merit
the eulogy pronounced by the enthufiafm of his
countrymen, MAJESTATI NATURÆ PAR INGE-
NIUM.

H h 4   NOTE

Note xxv. § 130.

Figure of the Earth.

428. That the earth is a fpheroidal body, compreffed at the poles, or elevated at the equator, is a fact eftablifhed by many accurate experiments ; and though thefe experiments do not exactly coincide, as to the degree of oblatenefs which they give to that fpheroid, they agree fufficiently to put it beyond all difpute, that the earth, though folid, has nearly the fame figure which it would affume if fluid, in confequence of its rotation on its axis.

Now, it is not at all obvious, to what phyfical caufe this phenomenon is to be afcribed. The earth, as it exifts at prefent, has none of the conditions that render the affumption of the figure of equilibrium in any way neceffary to it. Conftituted as it is, its parts cohere with forces incomparably too great to obey the laws of ftatical preffure, or to affume any one figure rather than another, on account of the centrifugal tendency which refults from its revolution on its axis. There is no neceffity that its fuperficies fhould be every where level, or perpendicular to the direction of gravity, nor that every two columns,

lumns, ftanding on the fame bafe, any where
within it, and reaching from thence to any two
points of the furface, fhould be of fuch weights
as precifely to balance one another. Neither of
thefe, indeed, is at all conformable to fact.
They are, however, the very fuppofitions on
which the determination of the fpheroid of e-
quilibrium is founded ; and as they certainly do
in no degree belong to the earth, it feems ftrange
that the refult deduced from them fhould be in
any way applicable to it. This coincidence
remains, therefore, to be explained ; and it muft
greatly enhance the merit of any geological fyftem, if it can connect this great and enigmatical phenomenon with the other facts in the natural hiftory of the earth.

429. To eftablifh fuch a connection, has, accordingly, been a favourite object with geologifts,
whether they have embraced the Neptunian or
Vulcanic theory : both have thought that they
were entitled to fuppofe the primeval fluidity
of the globe, the one by water, and the other by
fire ; and in whatfoever way that fluidity was
produced, the refult of it could be no other than
the fpheroidal figure of the whole mafs, agreeably to the laws of hydroftatics. If in this fluid
ftate the earth was homogeneous, the fpheroid
would be accurately elliptical, and the compreffion at the poles would be $\frac{1}{230}$ of the radius of
the

the equator ; if the fluid was denſer toward the centre, the flattening would be leſs : and in either caſe, the body, as it acquired ſolidity, may be ſuppoſed to have retained its ſpheroidal figure with little variation. But though the fluidity of the earth will account for the phenomenon of its oblate figure, it may reaſonably be queſtion-ed, whether this fluidity can be admitted, in conſiſtency with other appearances. According to what is eſtabliſhed above, none of the appear-ances in the mineral kingdom indicate more than a partial fluidity in any former condition of the earth. The preſent ſtrata, made up as they are of the ruins of former ſtrata, though ſoftened by heat, have not been rendered fluid by it, and have even poſſeſſed their ſoftneſs in parts, and in ſucceſſion, not altogether, nor at the ſame time.

The unſtratified, and more cryſtallized ſub-ſtances, were caſt in the boſom of others, which were ſolid at the time when they were fluid. In all this, therefore, there is no indication of a fluidity prevailing through the whole maſs, or even over the whole ſurface of the earth, and therefore nothing that can explain the ſpheroid-al figure which it has acquired. The ſuppoſi-tion, then, of the entire body of the earth, or even of its external cruſt, having been fluid, though it might account for the compreſſion at

the

the poles, does not connect that fact with the o-
ther facts in the natural history of the globe, and
fails, therefore, in the point moft eſſential to a
theory. It is liable, alſo, to other objections ;
whether it be conceived to have proceeded from
fire or from water ; whether it has happened on
the principles of Buffon or of Werner.

430. Firſt, let us ſuppoſe that the fluidity of
the earth, or of the external cruſt of it, at leaſt
to a certain depth, proceeded from a ſolution
of the whole in the waters of the ocean ; and,
waving all the objections that have been ſtated
to this hypotheſis, on account of the abſolute in-
ſolubility of many mineral ſubſtances in water, let us ſuppoſe them all ſoluble in a certain
degree, and let us compute the quantity of the
menſtruum, which, on the ſuppoſitions moſt favourable to the ſyſtem, muſt have been required
to this great geologico-chemical operation.

The ſiliceous earth, though not ſoluble in water *per ſe*, yet, after being diſſolved in that fluid
by means of an alkali, was found by Dr Black,
in his analyſis of the Geyſer water, to remain
ſuſpended in a quantity of water, between 500
and 1000 times its own weight. This is one of
the facts moſt favourable to the Neptunian theory ; and that every advantage may be given to
that theory, we ſhall take the leaſt of the numbers juſt mentioned, and ſuppoſe that ſiliceous
earth

earth may be diffolved or fufpended in 500 times its weight of water.

Taking this for the extreme degree of infolubility of mineral fubftances, (though there are many of which the infolubility is abfolute, or, to fpeak in the language of calculation, infinitely great), we may fuppofe the infolubility of all the reft, or the quantities of water in which they are diffolved, to be ranged in a defcending fcale from 500 to 0, the extreme degree of deliquefcence. Then, taking the arithmetical mean between thefe extremes, it will give us 250, as the proportion of water in which mineral fubftances may at an average be diffolved. But this average is much lefs than the truth ; for the quantity of filiceous earth is great in comparifon of any of the reft, and the mineral fubftances that are extremely foluble in water are but in a fmall quantity; therefore, when we fuppofe mineral bodies, at a medium, to be foluble in 250 times their own weight of water, we make a fuppofition extremely favourable to the Neptunian fyftem.

431. This is the proportion between the *weight* of the folvent, and of the fubftances held in folution : to have the proportion of their *bulks*, we may fuppofe the fpecific gravity of mineral bodies in general to be to that of water as 5 to 2, and then we have the ratio of bulks, that of

250

250 × 5 to 2 × 1, or of 625 to 1. It follows, then, that minerals in general cannot be suppofed foluble in lefs than 625 times their bulk of water.

432. Again, it muft be allowed to the Neptunifts, that the fluidity of the whole earth is not neceffary to account for its affuming the fpheroidal figure. It is fufficient if the whole of that cruft or fhell of matter was fluid, which is contained between the actual furface of the terreftrial fpheroid, and the furface of the fphere infcribed within it; that is, of the fphere which has for its diameter the polar axis of the earth. The whole of the minerals which compofe this fhell, muft at leaft have been diffolved in water, and have formed the chaotic mafs of Mr Kirwan. The volume of the water required for this was not lefs than 625 times the bulk of the fpheroidal fhell that has juft been mentioned.

But, affuming the difference between the polar axis and the equatorial diameter to be $\frac{1}{300}$ of the latter, which is the fuppofition moft agreeable to the phenomena, it is eafy to fhew that the magnitude of the above fpheroidal fhell, or the difference between the folid content of the earth, and the fphere infcribed in it, is greater than $\frac{1}{151}$, and lefs than $\frac{1}{150}$ of the whole earth; fo

that

that the earth is lefs than 151 times the fpheroidal fhell.

The volume of the water, therefore, neceffary
to hold in folution the materials of this fhell, is
to the volume of the whole earth as 625 to 151,
or in a greater ratio than that of four to one: and
fuch, therefore, at the very leaft, is the quantity
of water which Mr Kirwan fuppofes, after it ceafed to act in its chemical capacity, to have retired into caverns in the interior of the earth.
Thus the Neptunifts, in their account of the
fpheroidal figure of the earth, are reduced to a
cruel dilemma, and are forced to choofe between a phyfical and a mathematical impoffibility.

If we would inquire whether the opinion of
the igneous origin of minerals, as commonly received by the Vulcanifts, is capable of affording
a better folution of this difficulty, the theory of
M. de Buffon is the firft that prefents itfelf.

433. That philofopher confiders the exiftence
of the fpheroidal figure as a proof that the whole
of the earth muft have been originally fluid; and
as the fluidity of the whole can only be afcribed
to fufion, he has fuppofed that the earth was
originally a mafs of melted matter ftruck off
from the fun by the collifion of a comet; and
that this mafs, when made to revolve on its
axis,

axis, put on a fpheroidal figure, which it has retained, though now cooled down to congelation.

This fyftem need not be confidered in detail; the foundation of it is laid in fuch defiance of the principles of geometry and mechanics, that the architect, notwithftanding all the fertility of his invention, and all the refources of his genius, was never able to give any folidity to the ftructure.

But it will be faid, that we may take a part of the fyftem, without venturing on the whole, and may fuppofe that the earth, or at leaft the external cruft of it, has been fluid by fire, though we do not inquire into the caufe of this fire, or into the manner in which it was produced.

It is indeed true, that, when this is done, we have not the fame fort of abfurdity to encounter that we met with in the Neptunian fyftem, and that the Vulcanic theory does not, like it, come into direct collifion with an axiom of geometry. There are, neverthelefs, great objections to it; for though all the phenomena of the mineral kingdom atteft a fluidity of igneous origin, yet it is a fluidity that was never more than partial; and though it has been over all the earth, has been over it in fucceffion only. Befides, we are not entitled

to

to affume the exiftence, and again the difappearance of fuch a great quantity of heat, without af-
figning fome caufe for the change.

434. Since, then, neither the hypothefis of the
Neptunifts or the Vulcanifts, affords any good
explanation of the figure of the earth, or fuch
a one as can connect it with the other appearances in its natural hiftory, it remains to inquire, whether the fyftem that fuppofes a partial
and fucceffive fluidity, like Dr Hutton's, has
any refource for explaining this great phenomenon.

Of this fubject Dr Hutton has not treated ;
and when I was firft made acquainted with
his fyftem, it appeared to me a very ferious objection to it, that it did not profefs to give an
explanation of fo important a fact as the oblate
figure of the earth : On confidering the matter
more clofely, however, I found that there were
principles contained in it from which a very fatisfactory folution (and, I think, the only fatisfactory folution) of that difficulty might be deduced. This folution I fhall endeavour to explain,
in as far, at leaft, as is neceffary for the purpofe
of general illuftration.

It is laid down in Dr Hutton's theory, that
the furface of the earth is perpetually changed
by the *detritus* of the land ; and that from the
materials

materials thus afforded, new horizontal ſtrata are perpetually formed at the bottom of the ſea. If this be true, and if the alternations of decay and renovation have been often repeated, it is certain, that the figure of the earth, whatever it may have originally been, muſt be brought at length to coincide with the ſpheroid of equilibrium.

435. Here it is neceſſary to remark, that the expreſſions, *figure of the earth*, and *ſurface of the earth*, are each of them occaſionally taken in two different ſenſes.

The ſurface of the earth, in its moſt obvious ſenſe, is that which bounds the whole earth, and includes all its inequalities ; it is a ſurface extremely irregular, riſing to the tops of the mountains, deſcending to the bottoms of the valleys, and having the continuity of its curvature often interrupted, or ſuddenly changed. This may be called the *aɛtual* ſurface, and the figure bounded by it, the *aɛtual* figure, of the earth.

The ſurface of the earth, in another ſenſe, is one that is every where horizontal, and is the ſame which water aſſumes when at reſt.

This ſuperficies is determined by the circumſtance of its being conſtantly perpendicular to the direɛtion of gravity ; it is the ſurface marked out by levelling, and may be ſuppoſed to be continued from the ſea, through the interior of the land, till it meet the sea again. The figure bounded by this horizontal surface, may properly be called the *statical* figure of the earth.

When it is said that the figure of the earth is an oblate spheroid, it is the statical, not the actual figure which is meant; and the degrees of the meridian which astronomers measure, are also referred to the superficies of the former.

436. Suppose now a body like the earth, but with its actual figure infinitely more irregular, having a sea circumfused around it, the water will descend into the lowest situations, and will so arrange itself, that its surface shall be perpendicular every where to the plumb-line, or to the direction of gravity, in which state only it can remain at rest. The figure of the superficies which the sea must thus take will be of a continuous curvature, and will return into itself; though it may, if the actual figure is very irregular, be far either from a sphere or a spheroid. If, however, we suppose the solid parts of this mass subject to be dissolved or worn away, and carried down to the ocean, there will be a tendency to give to the whole body the same figure that it would have assumed, if it had been entirely fluid, and subject to the

laws

laws of hydroſtatics. This tendency is the reſult of two principles.

437. Let us ſuppoſe the body juſt deſcribed to
have no rotation, ſo that the particles of it are
actuated only by the forces of coheſion and of
attraction.

It is then clear, that every particle taken away
by attrition from the parts above the level of
the ſea, and depoſited under the ſurface of it,
makes the general figure more compact, bringing the remoter parts nearer to the centre of
gravity of the whole ; ſo that, in time, if the
body is homogeneous, all the points of the ſurface will become equally diſtant from that centre. Thus the *actual* figure changes continually,
and approaches nearer to the *ſtatical*.

While this change is going forward in the
actual figure, there is another produced on the
ſtatical, that tends very much to accelerate the
final coincidence of the two.

The effect of the inequalities of the land, that
riſe above the horizontal ſurface, is, by their attraction, to render the parts of that ſurface immediately under them, more convex, *cæteris pari-*
bus, than the reſt. Again, where there are parts
of extraordinary depth in the ſea, that is, where
the ſolid and denſer parts are far removed from
the ſurface of the ocean, the curvature of the ſu-

perficies

perficies of the fea is thereby diminifhed, and that fuperficies is rendered lefs convex than it would be if the fea were fhallower. Thefe propofitions are both capable of ftrict mathematical demon-ftration. Hence the taking away of any particle of matter from the top of a mountain tends to di-minifh the curvature of the horizontal furface un-der the mountain, where it is greateft; and the depofition of the fame particle at the bottom of the fea, tends to increafe the curvature of this fuperficies where it is leaft. The general ten-dency, therefore, being to increafe the curva-ture where it is leaft, and to diminifh it where it is greateft, muft be to bring about an uniform curvature throughout, that is, a fpherical figure. Thus, by the wafte and fubfequent ftratification of the land, the direction of gravity is continu-ally altered; it is more and more concentrated, and the figure brought nearer to that which a fluid would affume.

438. If now we fuppofe the body to revolve on its axis, all other things remaining as before, the furface bounding the fea will become different from what it was in the former cafe, and will be more fwelled out toward the middle or equatorial regions. The land above the level of the fea will ftill, as before, be worn down and depofited in the bottom of the fea, fo as to form ftrata nearly parallel to its furface: the tendency, therefore,

is

is to render the real figure of the planet nearer to the statical. At the same time the *statical* figure is changed, as explained above; so that the two figures mutually approach, and the limit, or ultimate figure to which they tend, is one over which the ocean might be diffused every where to the same depth, for then the causes of change would entirely cease. But this figure is no other than the spheroid of equilibrium, which, therefore, is the effect which the waste and reconsolidation of the land would necessarily produce, if the process were continued indefinitely, without interruption. In this, as in many other instances, when a body is subject to the action of causes by which its form is *gradually* changed, the figure best adapted to resist those changes, is the figure which the changes themselves ultimately produce.

Also, whatever be the irregularities of density, the tendency to a change of figure will not cease till the body is moulded into that particular spheroid which admits of being covered with water every where to the same depth *. Thus

it

---

* In the same manner as a transition is thus made from an irregular figure to a spheroid of equilibrium, so, if the actual figure were at first more simple than the spheroid, it would still be changed into this last by degrees.

Let

it appears, that a folid of an irregular figure, and
of irregular denfity, provided it be in part covered

Let us conceive, for inftance, that the earth is at reft,
and is a perfect fphere of folid matter, furrounded by an
ocean every where of equal depth, for example, of one
mile. Then, if a rotatory motion be communicated to
it, fo that it fhall revolve on its axis in twenty-four hours,
in confequence of the centrifugal force, the water circum-
fufed about the fphere will immediately rife up under the
equator, and will become part of a fpheroidal furface, (not
elliptical, but nearly fo), the equatorial diameter of which
is greater than the polar axis, in the ratio of 588 to 577.
By this means the water will be accumulated at the equator to the depth of nearly 2.5 miles, and form a zone furrounding the earth, and extending about 37° on each
fide of the equator. The remainder of the furface will
be left dry, forming two vaft circumpolar continents,
that reach 53° on every fide of the poles, and that are
elevated in the middle more than four miles above the
level of the fea.

Such would be the ftate of our globe, on the hypothefis above laid down; and, if there were no wafte or deftruction of the land, this order of things would be permanent, and neither the folid nor fluid part of the mafs
could ever acquire any other figure than that which has
been defcribed. But, if the fame laws be fuppofed
to regulate the action of the atmofphere in thofe circumftances, that do actually regulate it according to the prefent conftitution of the globe, the vapours raifed up from
the furface of the fea, would be carried by the winds
over

vered with water; and be at the same time subject to waste above the surface of the sea, and
reconsolidation under it, has a tendency to acquire, in time, the same figure that it would have
acquired had it been entirely fluid.

I i 4   439. In

---

over the land, where they would be condensed and precipitated in rain. Thus, all the agents of destruction would
be let loose on the two great circumpolar continents;
rivers would be formed; the land would become deeply
intersected by ravines; those ravines would gradually
open into wide valleys; the masses of greatest resistance
would be shaped into hills and mountains: and from
a superficies originally smooth and uniform, the same
inequalities would be produced which at present diver-
sify the surface of the earth.

While the parts of the sphere without the spheroid
are thus continually diminished, the loose earth and sand
washed down from them, will be deposited at the bottom of the sea, and will form strata parallel to the surface of the superincumbent water. The actual and statical figure are thus brought nearer one another; and,
at the same time the statical is changed, on the principle
already explained (the change in the direction of gravity), and is made continually to approximate to a state,
which when it has attained, no farther change can take
place, viz. an oblate elliptic spheroid, of which the surface is perpendicular to the direction of gravity, having
the equatorial diameter to the polar axis in the ratio of
230 to 229.

439. In the preceding reafonings, we have fuppofed the procefs of decay and fubfequent ftratification to be carried on without interruption, till the whole of the land is covered by the fea. This fuppofition is ufeful for explaining the nature of the forces which have determined the figure of the earth; but there is no reafon to think that it has ever been realized in its full extent, the elevation of ftrata from the bottom of the fea interrupting the progrefs, and producing new land in one place as the old decays in another. The very fame land alfo, which is wafted at its furface, may perhaps be lifted up by the forces that are placed under it; or it may be let down, undergoing alterations of its level, from caufes that we do not perceive, but of which the action is undoubted (§ 387). But notwithftanding thefe interruptions, the general tendency to produce in the earth a fpheroidal figure may remain, and more may be done by every revolution, to bring about the attainment of that figure than to caufe a deviation from it. This figure, therefore, though never likely to be perfectly acquired, will be the *limiting* or *afymptotic* figure, if it may be fo called, to which the earth will continually approach.

440. If the preceding conclufions are juft, and if the figure of equilibrium is only an afymptotic figure, to which that of the earth may approximate,

proximate, but cannot perfectly attain, we are not to be furprifed if confiderable deviations from it are actually obferved. This has accordingly happened, infomuch, that the refults deduced from the moft accurate meafurement of degrees of the meridian, differ from one another, in the oblatenefs they give to the earth, by nearly one-half of the quantity to be determined. When we compare the degrees meafured in France, and in fome other countries of Europe, with thofe meafured in Peru, we obtain for the compreffion at the poles, lefs than $\frac{1}{300}$ of the radius of the earth. But when we compare the degrees meafured in France with one another, and with thofe lately meafured in England, we find that they are beft reprefented by a fpheroid that has its compreffion $\frac{1}{150}$ of its femi-axis *. There is reafon to think, therefore, that the meridians are not elliptical ; and other obfervations feem to fhow, that they are not even fimilar to one another ; or that the earth is not, ftrictly fpeaking, a folid of revolution ; fo, alfo, the comparifon of the degree meafured at the Cape of Good Hope, with thofe meafured on the opposite

---

* Expofition du Syftême du Monde, par La Place, p. 61. 2d edit.

oppofite fide of the equator, creates a fufpicion, that the northern and fouthern hemifpheres are not perfectly alike, and that the earth is not e- qually compreffed at the Arctic and the Antarctic poles. Thefe irregularities, though they do not affect the general fact of the earth's compreffion at the poles, fhew that the true ftatical figure is but imperfectly attained ; and though this may be accounted for, without having recourfe to the principles involved in our theory, it is in a man- ner very unfatisfactory, and, by help of fuppofi- tions, not at all confiftent with the original flui- dity afcribed to the whole mafs, or to the exte- rior cruft of the earth.

441. As the principles here laid down explain how a folid body may attain very nearly the figure which a fluid would acquire in order to preferve its parts in equilibrio ; and fince the oblate figure belongs to other of the planets as well as the earth, and the globular to all the great bodies of the univerfe, this fuggefts an ana- logy that goes deep into the economy of na- ture, and extends far beyond the limits within which the mineralogift is wont to confine his fpeculations.

442. That no very irregular figure is found among the planetary bodies, may therefore be confidered as a proof of the univerfality of that fyftem of wafte and reconfolidation that we have

been

been endeavouring to trace in the natural hiſtory of the earth. A farther proof of the ſame ariſes from conſidering, that for every given maſs of matter, having a given period of rotation, there are two different ſpheroids that anſwer the conditions of eſtabliſhing an equilibrium among its parts, the one near to the ſphere, and the other very diſtant from it, and ſo oblate as to have a lenticular form. Thus the earth, ſuppoſing it homogeneous, might either be in equilibrio, by means of the figure which it actually has, or of one in which the polar was to the equatorial diameter as 1 to 768. The ſame is true of the other planets ; and yet we no where find that this highly compreſſed ſpheroid is actually employed by nature. The reaſon, no doubt, is, that in ſo oblate a ſpheroid, the equilibrium between the gravitating and the centrifugal force is of the kind that does not re-eſtabliſh itſelf when diſturbed ; ſo that the parts let looſe, and not kept in their place by firm coheſion, would fly off altogether. In ſuch a body, the waſte at the ſurface would lead to an entire change of form, and therefore the conſtitution here ſuppoſed could not be permanent.

443. In the ſyſtem of Saturn, we have a great deviation from the general order, which, neverthelefs, has led to a very unexpected verification of ſome of the concluſions deduced above. A

principle

principle extremely like that which is the basis
of all the foregoing reasonings, led one of the
greatest philosophers of the present age to discover the revolution of Saturn's ring on its axis,
and even to determine the velocity of that revolution, such as it has been since found by observation. LA PLACE, laying it down as a maxim, that
nothing in nature can exist, where there are causes of change, not balanced or compensated by
other causes *, concluded, that the parts of the
ring must be held from falling down to the body
of the planet by some other force than their mere
cohesion to one another. Were it otherwise, every
particle detached from the ring, by any means,
must descend in a straight line, almost perpendicular to the surface of Saturn; and the final
destruction of the ring must be inevitable. The
only force that could balance this effect of gravitation, seemed to be a centrifugal force, ari-
sing from the rotation of the ring on an axis
passing through its centre, and perpendicular to
its plane. La Place proceeded to inquire what
celerity of rotation was adequate to this effect,
and found that one of ten hours and a quarter
would be required, which is almost precisely
the time afterwards determined by Dr HER-
SCHEL from actual observation. If, with this
rotation,

---

* La Place, *ubi supra*, p. 242.

rotation, the ring is a folid annulus generated by the rotation of a very flat ellipfis about a given point in its greater axis, coinciding with the centre of Saturn, it may be fo conftituted, that the attraction of Saturn, combined with the centrifugal force, may produce a force perpendicular to its furface, and may enable detached parts to remain at reft, animals, for inftance, to walk on its furface, and fluids to be *in equilibrio*. The fyftem of Saturn is thus fortified againft the lapfe of time, as effectually as that of the earth itfelf ; and the means by which this is accomplifhed, feem to prove, that the weapons which time employs, are in both cafes the fame, viz. the flow wearing and decompofition of the folid parts. This flow wearing may have produced the figure by which its action is moft effectually refifted.

444. Thus Dr Hutton's theory of the earth comes at laft to connect itfelf with the refearches of phyfical aftronomy. The conclufion to be drawn from this coincidence is to the credit of both fciences. When two travellers, who fet out from points fo diftant as the mineralogift and the aftronomer, and who follow routes fo different, meet at the end of their journey, and agree in their report of the countries through which they have paffed, it affords no flight prefumption, that they have kept the right way, and

and that they relate what they have actually
feen.

Note xxvi. § 133.

Prejudices relating to the Theory of the Earth.

445. Among the prejudices which a new theory of the earth has to overcome, is an opinion,
held, or affected to be held, by many, that geological fcience is not yet ripe for fuch elevated
and difficult fpeculations. They would, therefore, get rid of thefe fpeculations, *by moving the
previous queftion*, and declaring that at prefent
we ought to have no theory at all. We are not
yet, they allege, fufficiently acquainted with the
phenomena of geology ; the fubject is fo various
and extenfive, that our knowledge of it muft for
a long time, perhaps for ever, remain extremely
imperfect. And hence it is, that the theories
hitherto propofed have fucceeded one another
with fo great rapidity, hardly any of them
having been able to laft longer than the difcovery
of a new fact, or a fact unknown when it was invented. It has proved infufficient to connect this
fact with the phenomena already known, and has
therefore been juftly abandoned. In this manner, they fay, have paffed away the theories of
Woodward, Burnet, Whifton, and even of Buffon ;

fon; and fo will pafs, in their turn, thofe of
Hutton and Werner.

446. This unfavourable view of geology, ought
not, however, to be received without examination ; in fcience, prefumption is lefs hurtful than
defpair, and inactivity is more dangerous than
error.

One reafon of the rapid fucceffion of geological theories, is the miftake that has been made
as to their object, and the folly of attempting
to explain by them the firft origin of things.
This miftake has led to fanciful fpeculations that
had nothing but their novelty to recommend
them, and which, when that charm had ceafed, were rejected as mere fuppofitions, incapable of proof. But if it is once fettled, that
a theory of the earth ought to have no other
aim but to difcover the laws that regulate the
changes on the furface, or in the interior of
the globe, the fubject is brought within the
fphere either of obfervation or analogy ; and
there is no reafon to fuppofe, that man, who
has numbered the ftars, and meafured their
forces, fhall ultimately prove unequal to this inveftigation.

447. Again, theories that have a rational object, though they be falfe or imperfect in their
principles, are for the moft part approximations
to the truth, fuited to the information at the

time

time when they were propofed. They are fteps, therefore, in the advancement of knowledge, and are terms of a feries that muft end when the real laws of nature are difcovered. It is, on this account, rafh to conclude, that in the revolutions of fcience, what has happened muft continue to happen, and becaufe fyftems have changed rapidly in time paft, that they muft neceffarily do fo in time to come.

He who would have reafoned fo, and who had feen the ancient phyfical fyftems, at firft all rivals to one another, and then fwallowed up by the Ariftotelian; the Ariftotelian phyfics giving way to thofe of Des Cartes; and the phyfics of Des Cartes to thofe of Newton; would have predicted that thefe laft were alfo, in their turn, to give place to the philofophy of fome later period. This is, however, a conclufion that hardly any one will now be bold enough to maintain, after a hundred years of the moft fcrupulous examination have done nothing but add to the evidence of the NEWTONIAN SYSTEM. It feems certain, therefore, that the rife and fall of theories in times paft, does not argue, that the fame will happen in the time that is to come.

448. The multifarious and extremely diverfified object of geological refearches, does, no doubt, render the firft fteps difficult, and may very well

well account for the inftability hitherto obferved in fuch theories ; but the very fame thing
gives reafon for expecting a very high degree
of certainty to be ultimately attained in thefe
inquiries.

Where the phenomena are few and fimple,
there may be feveral different theories that will
explain them in a manner equally fatisfactory ;
and in fuch cafes, the true and the falfe hypothefes are not eafily diftinguifhed from one another.
When, on the other hand, the phenomena are
greatly varied, the probability is, that among
them, fome of thofe *inftantiæ crucis* will be
found, that exclude every hypothefis but one,
and reduce the explanation given to the higheft
degree of certainty. It was thus, when the
phenomena of the heavens were but imperfectly known, and were confined to a few general and fimple facts, that the Philolaic could
claim no preference to the Ptolemaic fyftem :
The former feemed a poffible hypothefis ; but
as it performed nothing that the other did
not perform, and was inconfiftent with fome
of our moft natural prejudices, it had but few
adherents. The invention of the telefcope, and
the ufe of more accurate inftruments, by multiplying and diverfifying the facts, eftablifhed its
credit ; and when not only the general laws,
but alfo the inequalities, and difturbances of

K k   the

the planetary motions were underſtood, all phyſical hypotheſes vaniſhed, like phantoms, before the philoſophy of NEWTON. Hence the number, the variety, and even the complica- tion of facts, contribute ultimately to ſeparate truth from falſehood; and the ſame cauſes which, in any caſe, render the firſt attempts toward a theory difficult, make the final ſucceſs of ſuch attempts juſt ſo much the more probable.

This maxim, however, though a general en- couragement to the proſecution of geological inquiries, does not amount to a proof that we are yet arrived at the period when thoſe inqui- ries may ſafely aſſume the form of a theory. But that we are arrived at ſuch a period, appears clear from other circumſtances.

449. It cannot be denied, that a great multi- tude of facts, reſpecting the mineral kingdom, are now known with conſiderable preciſion; and that the many diligent and ſkilful obſervers, who have ariſen in the courſe of the laſt thirty years, have produced a great change in the ſtate of geo- logical knowledge. It is unneceſſary to enu- merate them all; FERBER, BERGMAN, DE LUC, SAUSSURE, DOLOMIEU, are thoſe on whom Dr Hutton chiefly relied; and it is on their obſer- vations and his own that his ſyſtem is founded. If it be ſaid, that only a ſmall part of the earth's ſurface has yet been ſurveyed, and deſcribed

with

with fuch accuracy as is found in the writers just named, it may be anfwered, that the earth is conftructed with fuch a degree of uniformity, that a tract of no very large extent may afford inftances of all the leading facts that we can ever obferve in the mineral kingdom. The variety of geological appearances which a traveller meets with, is not at all in proportion to the extent of country he traverfes ; and if he take in a portion of land fufficient to include primitive and fecondary ftrata, together with mountains, rivers, and plains, and unftratified bodies in veins and in maffes, though it be not a very large part of the earth's furface, he may find examples of all the moft important facts in the hiftory of foffils. Though the labours of mineralogifts have embraced but a fmall part of the globe, they may therefore have comprehended a very large proportion of the phenomena which it exhibits ; and hence a prefumption arifes, that the outlines, at leaft, of geology have now been traced with tolerable truth, and are not fufceptible of great variation.

450. When the phenomena of any clafs are in general ambiguous, and admit of being explained by different or even oppofite theories ; if few of thofe exclufive facts are known, which admit but of one or a few folutions, then we have no right to expect much from our endeavours to generalize, except the knowledge

K k 2 of

of the points where our information is most deficient, and to which our observations ought chiefly to be directed. But that many of the exclusive and unambiguous instances are known, in the natural history of the globe, I think is evident from the reasoning in the foregoing pages, where so many examples have occurred of appearances that give the most direct negative to the Neptunian system, and exclude it from the number of possible hypotheses, by which the phenomena of geology can be explained. The abundance of such instances is an infallible sign, that the mass of knowledge is in that state of fermentation, from which the true theory may be expected to emerge.

451. Another indication of the same kind, is the near approach that even the most opposite theories make, in some respects, to one another. There are so many points of contact between them, that they appear to approximate to an ultimate state, in which, however unwillingly, they must at last coincide. That ultimate form, too, which all these theories have a tendency to put on, if I am not deceived, is no other than that of the Huttonian theory.

452. The first example I shall take from the system of Saussure. It is to be regretted, that this excellent geologist has no where given us a complete account of his theory. Some of the

leading

leading principles of it are, however, unfolded in the courfe of his obfervations, and enable us to form a notion of its general outline. It was evidently far removed from the fyftem of fubterraneous heat, and feems, efpecially in the latter part of the author's life, to have been very much accommodated to the prevailing fyftem of WERNER. Neverthelefs, with fo little affinity between their general views, Sauffure and Hutton agree in that moft important article which regards the elevation of the ftrata. Sauffure plainly perceived the impoffibility of the ftrata being formed in the vertical fituations which fo many of them now occupy; and he takes great pains to demonftrate this impoffibility, from fome facts that have been referred to above. He alfo believed that this elevation had been given to ftrata that were originally level, by a force directed upwards, or by the *refoulement* of the beds, not by their falling in, as is the opinion of De Luc and fome other of the Neptunifts.

Now, whoever admits this principle, and reafons on it confiftently, without being afraid to follow it through all its confequences, muft unavoidably come very clofe to the Huttonian theory. He muft fee, that a power which, acting from below, produced this great effect, can never have belonged to water, unlefs rarefied

into

into fteam by the application of heat. But if it be once admitted that heat refides in the mineral regions, the great objection to Dr Hutton's fyftem is removed ; and the theorift, who was furnifhed with fo active and fo powerful an agent, would be very unfkilful in the management of his own refources, if he did not employ it in the work of confolidating as well as in that of raifing up the ftrata. A little attention will fhew, that it is qualified for both purpofes ; though infuperable objections muft, no doubt, offer themfelves, where the effects of compreffion are not underftood. We may fafely conclude, then, that the accurate and ingenious Oreologift of Geneva ought to have been a *Plutonift,* in order to give confiftency to the principles which he had adopted, and to make them coalefce as parts of one and the fame fyftem. If he embraced an oppofite opinion, it probably was from feeling the force of thofe objections that arife from our difcovering nothing in the bowels of the earth like the remains left by combuftion, or inflammation, at its furface. The fecret by which thefe feeming contradictions are to be reconciled, was unknown to this mineralogift, and he has accordingly decided ftrongly againft the action of fire, even in the cafe of thofe unftratified fubftances that have the greateft affinity to volcanic lava.

453. The

453. The theoretical conclusions of another accurate and skilful observer, Dolomieu, furnish a still more remarkable example of a tendency to union between systems professedly hostile to one another.

This ingenious mineralogist, observing the interposition of the basalt between stratified rocks, so that it had not only regular beds of sandstone for its base, but was also covered with beds of the same kind, saw plainly that these appearances were inconsistent with the supposition of common volcanic explosions at the surface. He therefore conceived, that the volcanic eruption had happened at the bottom of the sea, (the level of which, in former ages, had been much higher than at present), and that the materials afterwards deposited on the lava, had been in length of time consolidated into beds of stone. It is evident, that this notion of submarine volcanoes, comes very near, in many respects, to Dr Hutton's explanation of the same appearances. If the only thing to be accounted for were the phenomenon in question, it cannot be denied that Dolomieu's hypothesis would be perfectly sufficient ; but Dr Hutton, to whom this phenomenon was familiar, and who, like Dolomieu, conceived the basalt to have been in fusion, was convinced that the retreat of the sea was not a fact well attested by geological appearances, and

K k 4

if

if admitted, was inadequate to account for the facts usually explained by it. He conceived, therefore, that such lava as the preceding had flowed not only at the bottom of the sea, but in the bowels of the earth, and having been forced up through the fissures of rocks already formed, had heaved up some of these rocks, and interposed itself between them. This agrees with the other facts in the natural history both of the basaltes and the strata.

It is plain, that, in this, there is a great approach of the two theories to one another : both maintain the igneous origin of basaltes, and its affinity to lava ; both acknowledge that this lava cannot have flowed at the surface, and that the strata which cover it have been formed at the bottom of the sea. They only differ as to the mode in which the submarine or subterraneous volcano produced its effect, and that difference arises merely from the one geologist having generalized more than the other. Dolomieu sought to connect the basalt with the lavas that proceed from volcanic explosions at the surface ; Dr Hutton sought not only to connect these two appearances with one another, but also with the other phenomena of mineralogy, particularly with the veins of basaltes, and the elevation of the strata.

454. In

454. In another point, the coincidence of Dolomieu's opinions and Dr Hutton's is ſtill more ſtriking. The former has remarked, that many of the extinguiſhed volcanoes are in granite countries, and that, neverthelefs, the lavas that they have erupted contain no granitic ſtones. There muſt be, therefore, ſays he, ſomething under the granite, and this laſt is not, at leaſt in all caſes, to be confidered as the baſis of the mineral kingdom, or as the body on which all others reſt. In this ſyſtem, therefore, granite is not always a primordial rock, any more than in Dr Hutton's.

But Dolomieu makes a ſtill nearer advance to the Huttonian theory ; for he fuppoſes, that under the ſolid and hard cruſt of the globe, there is a ſphere of melted ſtone, from which this baſaltic lava was thrown up. The ſyſtem of fubterraneous heat is here adopted in its utmoſt extent, and in that form which is confidered as the moſt liable to objection, viz. the exiſtence of it at the preſent moment, in ſuch a degree as to melt rocks, and keep them in a ſtate of fuſion. In this concluſion, the two theories agree perfectly; and if they do ſo, it is only becaufe the nature of things has forced them into union, notwithſtanding the diſſimilitude of their fundamental principles.

This

This ought to be confidered as a ftrong proof, that the phenomena known to mineralogifts are fufficient to juftify the attempts to form a theory of the earth, and are fuch as lead to the fame conclufions, where there was not only no previous concert, but even a very marked oppofition. I have already obferved, that there is a greater tendency to agree among geological theories, than among the authors of thofe theories.

455. Another circumftance worthy of confideration is, that in the fearch which the Neptunifts have made, for facts moft favourable to the aqueous formation of minerals, we find hardly any of a kind that was unknown to the author of the fyftem here explained. The appearances on which WERNER grounds his opinion with refpect to bafaltes, and by which he would exclude the action of fire from any fhare in the formation of it, are all comprehended in the alternation of that rock with beds, or ftrata obvioufly of aqueous origin. Now thefe appearances were well known to Dr Hutton, and are eafily explained by his theory, provided the effects of compreffion are admitted. From this, and the other circumftances juft obferved, I am difpofed to think, that the great facts on which every geological fyftem muft depend, are now known, and that it is not too bold an anticipation to fay, that a theory of the earth, which

explains

explains all the phenomena with which we are
at prefent acquainted, will be found to explain
all thofe that remain to be difcovered.

456. The time indeed was, and we are not yet
far removed from it, when one of the moft important principles involved in Dr Hutton's theory was not only unknown, but could not be difcovered. This was before the caufticity produced in limeftone by expofure to fire was underftood, and when it was not known that it arofe
from the expulfion of a certain aerial fluid, which
before was a component part of the ftone. It
could not then be perceived, that this aerial part
might be retained by preffure, even in fpite of
the action of fire, and that in a region where
great compreffion exifted, the abfence of caufticity was no proof that great heat had not been
applied. The difcoveries of Dr BLACK, therefore,
mark an era, before which men were not qualified
to judge of the nature of the powers that had
acted in the confolidation of mineral fubftances.
Thofe difcoveries were, indeed, deftined to produce a memorable change in chemiftry, and in
all the branches of knowledge allied to it ; and
have been the foundation of that brilliant progrefs, by which a collection of practical rules,
and of infulated facts, has in a few years rifen
to the rank of a very perfect fcience. But even
before they had explained the nature of carbonic

nic gas, and its affinity to calcareous earth, I am not sure but that Dr Hutton's theory was, at least, partly formed, though it must certainly have remained, even in his own opinion, exposed to great difficulties. His active and penetrating genius soon perceived, in the experiments of his friend, the solution of those difficulties, and formed that happy combination of principles, which has enabled him to explain the most enigmatical appearances in the natural history of the earth.

As we are not yet far removed from the time when our chemical knowledge was too imperfect to admit of a satisfactory explanation of the phenomena of mineralogy, so it is not unlikely that we are approaching to other discoveries that are to throw new light on this science. It would, however, be to argue strangely to say, that we must wait till those discoveries are made before we begin any theoretical reasonings. If this rule were followed, we should not know where the imperfections of our science lay, nor when the remedies were found out, should we be in a condition to avail ourselves of them. Such conduct would not be caution, but timidity, and an excess of prudence fatal to all philosophical inquiry.

457. The truth, indeed, is, that in physical inquiries, the work of theory and observation must

go

go hand in hand, and ought to be carried on at the fame time, more efpecially if the matter is very complicated, for there the clue of theory is neceffary to direct the obferver. Though a man may begin to obferve without any hypothefis, he cannot continue long without feeing fome general conclufion arife ; and to this nafcent theory it is his bufinefs to attend, becaufe, by feeking either to verify or to difprove it, he is led to new experiments, or new obfervations. He is led alfo to the very experiments and obfervations that are of the greateft importance, namely, to thofe *inftantiæ crucis*, which are the *criteria* that naturally prefent themfelves for the trial of every hypothefis. He is conducted to the places where the tranfitions of nature are moft perceptible, and where the abfence of former, or the prefence of new circumftances, excludes the action of imaginary caufes. By this correction of his firft opinion, a new approximation is made to the truth ; and by the repetition of the fame procefs, certainty is finally obtained. Thus theory and obfervation mutually affift one another; and the fpirit of fyftem, againft which there are fo many and fuch juft complaints, appears, neverthelefs, as the animating principle of inductive inveftigation. The bufinefs of found philofophy is not to extinguifh this fpirit, but to reftrain and direct its efforts.

458. It

458. It is therefore hurtful to the progreſs of phyſical ſcience to repreſent obſervation and theory as ſtanding oppoſed to one another. Berg-man has ſaid, " Obſervationes veras quàm in-genioſiſſimas fictiones ſequi præſtat ; naturæ my-ſteria potius indagare quàm divinare."

If it is meant by this merely to ſay, that it is better to have facts without theory, than theory without facts, and that it is wiſer to inquire into the ſecrets of nature, than to gueſs at them, the truth of the maxim will hardly be controverted. But if we are to underſtand by it, as ſome may perhaps have done, that all theory is mere fiction, and that the only alternative a philoſopher has, is to devote himſelf to the ſtudy of facts unconnect-ed by theory, or of theory unſupported by facts, the maxim is as far from the truth, as I am con-vinced it is from the real ſenſe of Bergman. Such an oppoſition between the buſineſs of the theoriſt and the obſerver, can only occur when the ſpeculations of the former are vague and in-diſtinct, and cannot be ſo *embodied* as to become viſible to the latter. But the philoſopher who has aſcended to his theory by a regular genera-lization of facts, and who deſcends from it again by drawing ſuch palpable concluſions as may be compared with experience, furniſhes the infalli-ble means of diſtinguiſhing between *perfect ſci-ence* and *ingenious fiction.* Of a geological theory that

that has ftood this double teft of the analytic and fynthetic methods, Dr Hutton has furnifhed us with an excellent inftance, in his explanation of granite. The appearances which he obferved in that ftone led him to conclude, that it had been melted, and injected while fluid, among the ftratified rocks already formed. He then confidered, that if this is true, veins of granite muft often run from the larger maffes of that ftone, and penetrate the ftrata in various directions; and this muft be vifible at thofe places where thefe different kinds of rock come into contact with one another. This led him to fearch in Arran and Glen-tilt for the phenomena in queftion; the refult, as we have feen, afforded to his theory the fulleft confirmation, and to himfelf the high fatisfaction which muft ever accompany the fuccefs of candid and judicious inquiry.

459. It cannot, however, be denied, that the impartiality of an obferver may often be affected by fyftem; but this is a misfortune againft which the want of theory is not always a complete fecurity. The partialities in favour of opinions are not more dangerous than the prejudices againft them; for fuch is the fpirit of fyftem, and fo naturally do all men's notions tend to reduce themfelves into fome regular form, that the very belief that there can be no theory, becomes a theory itfelf, and may have no inconfiderable

fway

ſway over the mind of an obſerver. Beſides, one man may have as much delight in pulling down, as another has in building up, and may chooſe to diſplay his dexterity in the one occupation as well as in the other. The want of theory, then, does not ſecure the candour of an obſerver, and it may very much diminiſh his ſkill. The diſcipline that ſeems beſt calculated to promote both, is a thorough knowledge of the methods of inductive inveſtigation; an acquaintance with the hiſtory of phyſical diſcovery; and the careful ſtudy of thoſe ſciences in which the rules of philoſophizing have been moſt ſucceſsfully applied.

FINIS.

CATALOG OF DOVER BOOKS

Classics of Science

THE DIDEROT PICTORIAL ENCYCLOPEDIA OF TRADES AND INDUSTRY, MANUFACTURING AND THE TECHNICAL ARTS IN PLATES SELECTED FROM "L'ENCYCLOPEDIE OU DICTIONNAIRE RAISONNE DES SCIENCES, DES ARTS, ET DES METIERS" OF DENIS DIDEROT, edited with text by C. Gillispie. The first modern selection of plates from the high point of 18th century French engraving, Diderot's famous Encyclopedia. Over 2000 illustrations on 485 full page plates, most of them original size, illustrating the trades and industries of one of the most fascinating periods of modern history, 18th century France. These magnificent engravings provide an invaluable glimpse into the past for the student of early technology, a lively and accurate social document to students of cultures, an outstanding find to the lover of fine engravings. The plates teem with life, with men, women, and children performing all of the thousands of operations necessary to the trades before and during the early stages of the industrial revolution. Plates are in sequence, and show general operations, closeups of difficult operations, and details of complex machinery. Such important and interesting trades and industries are illustrated as sowing, harvesting, beekeeping, cheesemaking, operating windmills, milling flour, charcoal burning, tobacco processing, indigo, fishing, arts of war, salt extraction, mining, smelting iron, casting iron, steel, extracting mercury, zinc, sulphur, copper, etc., slating, tinning, silverplating, gilding, making gunpowder, cannons, bells, shoeing horses, tanning, papermaking, printing, dying, and more than 40 other categories. 920pp. 9 x 12. Heavy library cloth.   T421 Two volume set **$18.50**

THE PRINCIPLES OF SCIENCE, A TREATISE ON LOGIC AND THE SCIENTIFIC METHOD, W. Stanley Jevons. Treating such topics as Inductive and Deductive Logic, the Theory of Number, Probability, and the Limits of Scientific Method, this milestone in the development of symbolic logic remains a stimulating contribution to the investigation of inferential validity in the natural and social sciences. It significantly advances Boole's logic, and describes a machine which is a foundation of modern electronic calculators. In his introduction, Ernest Nagel of Columbia University says, "(Jevons) . . . continues to be of interest as an attempt to articulate the logic of scientific inquiry." Index. liii + 786pp. 5⅜ x 8.
S446 Paperbound **$2.98**

*DIALOGUES CONCERNING TWO NEW SCIENCES, Galileo Galilei. A classic of experimental science which has had a profound and enduring influence on the entire history of mechanics and engineering. Galileo based this, his finest work, on 30 years of experimentation. It offers a fascinating and vivid exposition of dynamics, elasticity, sound, ballistics, strength of materials, and the scientific method. Translated by H. Crew and A. de Salvio. 126 diagrams. Index. xxi + 288pp. 5⅜ x 8.   S99 Paperbound **$1.75**

DE MAGNETE, William Gilbert. This classic work on magnetism founded a new science. Gilbert was the first to use the word "electricity," to recognize mass as distinct from weight, to discover the effect of heat on magnetic bodies; invented an electroscope, differentiated between static electricity and magnetism, conceived of the earth as a magnet. Written by the first great experimental scientist, this lively work is valuable not only as an historical landmark, but as the delightfully easy-to-follow record of a perpetually searching, ingenious mind. Translated by P. F. Mottelay. 25 page biographical memoir. 90 fix. lix + 368pp. 5⅜ x 8.   S470 Paperbound **$2.00**

*OPTICKS, Sir Isaac Newton. An enormous storehouse of insights and discoveries on light, reflection, color, refraction, theories of wave and corpuscular propagation of light, optical apparatus, and mathematical devices which have recently been reevaluated in terms of modern physics and placed in the top-most ranks of Newton's work! Foreword by Albert Einstein. Preface by I. B. Cohen of Harvard U. 7 pages of portraits, facsimile pages, letters, etc. cxvi + 412pp. 5⅜ x 8.   S205 Paperbound **$2.25**

A SURVEY OF PHYSICAL THEORY, M. Planck. Lucid essays on modern physics for the general reader by the Nobel Laureate and creator of the quantum revolution. Planck explains how the new concepts came into being; explores the clash between theories of mechanics, electrodynamics, and thermodynamics; and traces the evolution of the concept of light through Newton, Huygens, Maxwell, and his own quantum theory, providing unparalleled insights into his development of this momentous modern concept. Bibliography. Index. vii + 121pp. 5⅜ x 8.
S650 Paperbound **$1.15**

A SOURCE BOOK IN MATHEMATICS, D. E. Smith. English translations of the original papers that announced the great discoveries in mathematics from the Renaissance to the end of the 19th century: succinct selections from 125 different treatises and articles, most of them unavailable elsewhere in English—Newton, Leibniz, Pascal, Riemann, Bernoulli, etc. 24 articles trace developments in the field of number, 18 cover algebra, 36 are on geometry, and 13 on calculus. Biographical-historical introductions to each article. Two volume set. Index in each. Total of 115 illustrations. Total of xxviii + 742pp. 5⅜ x 8.   S552 Vol I Paperbound **$1.85**
S553 Vol II Paperbound **$1.85**
The set, boxed **$3.50**

CATALOGUE OF DOVER BOOKS

*THE THIRTEEN BOOKS OF EUCLID'S ELEMENTS, edited by T. L. Heath. This is the complete EUCLID — the definitive edition of one of the greatest classics of the western world. Complete English translation of the Heiberg text with spurious Book XIV. Detailed 150-page introduction discusses aspects of Greek and medieval mathematics: Euclid, texts, commentators, etc. Paralleling the text is an elaborate critical exposition analyzing each definition, proposition, postulate, etc., and covering textual matters, mathematical analyses, refutations, extensions, etc. Unabridged reproduction of the Cambridge 2nd edition. 3 volumes. Total of 995 figures, 1426pp. 5⅜ x 8.   S88, 89, 90 — 3 vol. set, Paperbound **$6.00**

*THE GEOMETRY OF RENE DESCARTES. The great work which founded analytic geometry. The renowned Smith-Latham translation faced with the original French text containing all of Descartes' own diagrams! Contains: Problems the Construction of Which Requires Only Straight Lines and Circles; On the Nature of Curved Lines; On the Construction of Solid or Supersolid Problems. Notes. Diagrams. 258pp.   S68 Paperbound **$1.50**

*A PHILOSOPHICAL ESSAY ON PROBABILITIES, P. Laplace. Without recourse to any mathematics above grammar school, Laplace develops a philosophically, mathematically and historically classical exposition of the nature of probability: its functions and limitations, operations in practical affairs, calculations in games of chance, insurance, government, astronomy, and countless other fields. New introduction by E. T. Bell. viii + 196pp.   S166 Paperbound **$1.35**

DE RE METALLICA, Georgius Agricola. Written over 400 years ago, for 200 years the most authoritative first-hand account of the production of metals, translated in 1912 by former President Herbert Hoover and his wife, and today still one of the most beautiful and fascinating volumes ever produced in the history of science! 12 books, exhaustively annotated, give a wonderfully lucid and vivid picture of the history of mining, selection of sites, types of deposits, excavating pits, sinking shafts, ventilating, pumps, crushing machinery, assaying, smelting, refining metals, making salt, alum, nitre, glass, and many other topics. This definitive edition contains all 289 of the 16th century woodcuts which made the original an artistic masterpiece. It makes a superb gift for geologists, engineers, libraries, artists, historians, and everyone interested in science and early illustrative art. Biographical, historical introductions. Bibliography, survey of ancient authors. Indices. 289 illustrations. 672pp. 6¾ x 10¾. Deluxe library edition.   S6 Clothbound **$10.00**

GEOGRAPHICAL ESSAYS, W. M. Davis. Modern geography and geomorphology rest on the fundamental work of this scientist. His new concepts of earth-processes revolutionized science and his broad interpretation of the scope of geography created a deeper understanding of the interrelation of the landscape and the forces that mold it. This first inexpensive unabridged edition covers theory of geography, methods of advanced geographic teaching, descriptions of geographic areas, analyses of land-shaping processes, and much besides. Not only a factual and historical classic, it is still widely read for its reflections of modern scientific thought. Introduction. 130 figures. Index. vi + 777pp. 5⅜ x 8.
                    S383 Paperbound **$2.95**

CHARLES BABBAGE AND HIS CALCULATING ENGINES, edited by P. Morrison and E. Morrison. Friend of Darwin, Humboldt, and Laplace, Babbage was a leading pioneer in large-scale mathematical machines and a prophetic herald of modern operational research—true father of Harvard's relay computer Mark I. His Difference Engine and Analytical Engine were the first successful machines in the field. This volume contains a valuable introduction on his life and work; major excerpts from his fascinating autobiography, revealing his eccentric and unusual personality; and extensive selections from "Babbage's Calculating Engines," a compilation of hard-to-find journal articles, both by Babbage and by such eminent contributors as the Countess of Lovelace, L. F. Menabrea, and Dionysius Lardner. 11 illustrations. Appendix of miscellaneous papers. Index. Bibliography. xxxviii + 400pp. 5⅜ x 8.   T12 Paperbound **$2.00**

*THE WORKS OF ARCHIMEDES WITH THE METHOD OF ARCHIMEDES, edited by T. L. Heath. All the known works of the greatest mathematician of antiquity including the recently discovered METHOD OF ARCHIMEDES. This last is the only work we have which shows exactly how early mathematicians discovered their proofs before setting them down in their final perfection. A 186 page study by the eminent scholar Heath discusses Archimedes and the history of Greek mathematics. Bibliography. 563pp. 5⅜ x 8.   S9 Paperbound **$2.00**

History of Science and Mathematics

THE STUDY OF THE HISTORY OF MATHEMATICS, THE STUDY OF THE HISTORY OF SCIENCE, G. Sarton. Two books bound as one. Each volume contains a long introduction to the methods and philosophy of each of these historical fields, covering the skills and sympathies of the historian, concepts of history of science, psychology of idea-creation, and the purpose of history of science. Prof. Sarton also provides more than 80 pages of classified bibliography. Complete and unabridged. Indexed. 10 illustrations. 188pp. 5⅜ x 8. **T240 Paperbound $1.25**

A HISTORY OF PHYSICS, Florian Cajori, Ph.D. First written in 1899, thoroughly revised in 1929, this. is still best entry into antecedents of modern theories. Precise non-mathematical discussion of ideas, theories, techniques, apparatus of each period from Greeks to 1920's, analyzing within each period basic topics of matter, mechanics, light, electricity and magnetism, sound, atomic theory, etc. Stress on modern developments, from early 19th century to present. Written with critical eye on historical development, significance. Provides most of needed historical background for student of physics. Reprint of second (1929) edition. Index. Bibliography in footnotes. 16 figures. xv + 424pp. 5⅜ x 8. **T970 Paperbound $2.00**

A HISTORY OF ASTRONOMY FROM THALES TO KEPLER, J. L. E. Dreyer. Formerly titled A HISTORY OF PLANETARY SYSTEMS FROM THALES TO KEPLER. This is the only work in English which provides a detailed history of man's cosmological views from prehistoric times up through the Renaissance. It covers Egypt, Babylonia, early Greece, Alexandria, the Middle Ages, Copernicus, Tycho Brahe, Kepler, and many others. Epicycles and other complex theories of positional astronomy are explained in terms nearly everyone will find clear and easy to understand. "Standard reference on Greek astronomy and the Copernican revolution," SKY AND TELESCOPE. Bibliography. 21 diagrams. Index. xvii + 430pp. 5⅜ x 8. **S79 Paperbound $1.98**

A SHORT HISTORY OF ASTRONOMY, A. Berry. A popular standard work for over 50 years, this thorough and accurate volume covers the science from primitive times to the end of the 19th century. After the Greeks and Middle Ages, individual chapters analyze Copernicus, Brahe, Galileo, Kepler, and Newton, and the mixed reception of their startling discoveries. Post-Newtonian achievements are then discussed in unusual detail: Halley, Bradley, Lagrange, Laplace, Herschel, Bessel, etc. 2 indexes. 104 illustrations, 9 portraits. xxxi + 440pp. 5⅜ x 8. **T210 Paperbound $2.00**

PIONEERS OF SCIENCE, Sir Oliver Lodge. An authoritative, yet elementary history of science by a leading scientist and expositor. Concentrating on individuals—Copernicus, Brahe, Kepler, Galileo, Descartes, Newton, Laplace, Herschel, Lord Kelvin, and other scientists—the author presents their discoveries in historical order, adding biographical material on each man and full, specific explanations of their achievements. The full, clear discussions of the accomplishments of post-Newtonian astronomers are features seldom found in other books on the subject. Index. 120 illustrations. xv + 404pp. 5⅜ x 8. **T716 Paperbound $1.65**

THE BIRTH AND DEVELOPMENT OF THE GEOLOGICAL SCIENCES, F. D. Adams. The most complete and thorough history of the earth sciences in print. Geological thought from earliest recorded times to the end of the 19th century—covers over 300 early thinkers and systems: fossils and hypothetical explanations of them, vulcanists vs. neptunists, figured stones and paleontology, generation of stones, and similar topics. 91 illustrations, including medieval, renaissance woodcuts, etc. 632 footnotes and bibliographic notes. Index. 511pp. 5⅜ x 8. **T5 Paperbound $2.00**

THE STORY OF ALCHEMY AND EARLY CHEMISTRY, J. M. Stillman. "Add the blood of a red-haired man"—a recipe typical of the many quoted in this authoritative and readable history of the strange beliefs and practices of the alchemists. Concise studies of every leading figure in alchemy and early chemistry through Lavoisier, in this curious epic of superstition and true science, constructed from scores of rare and difficult Greek, Latin, German, and French texts. Foreword by S. W. Young. 246-item bibliography. Index. xiii + 566pp. 5⅜ x 8. **S628 Paperbound $2.45**

HISTORY OF MATHEMATICS, D. E. Smith. Most comprehensive non-technical history of math in English. Discusses the lives and works of over a thousand major and minor figures, from Euclid to Descartes, Gauss, and Riemann. Vol. I: A chronological examination, from primitive concepts through Egypt, Babylonia, Greece, the Orient, Rome, the Middle Ages, the Renaissance, and up to 1900. Vol. 2: The development of ideas in specific fields and problems, up through elementary calculus. Two volumes, total of 510 illustrations, 1355pp. 5⅜ x 8. Set boxed in attractive container. **T429,430 Paperbound the set $5.00**

CATALOGUE OF DOVER BOOKS

A CONCISE HISTORY OF MATHEMATICS, D. Struik. A lucid, easily followed history of mathematical ideas and techniques from the Ancient Near East up to modern times. Requires no mathematics but will serve as an excellent introduction to mathematical concepts and great mathematicians through the method of historical development. 60 illustrations including Egyptian papyri, Greek mss., portraits of 31 eminent mathematicians. Bibliography. xix + 299pp. 5⅜ x 8.
T255 Paperbound **$1.75**

A SHORT ACCOUNT OF THE HISTORY OF MATHEMATICS, W. W. Rouse Ball. Last previous edition (1908) hailed by mathematicians and laymen for lucid overview of math as living science, for understandable presentation of individual contributions of great mathematicians. Treats lives, discoveries of every important school and figure from Egypt, Phoenicia to late nineteenth century. Greek schools of Ionia, Cyzicus, Alexandria, Byzantium, Pythagoras; primitive arithmetic; Middle Ages and Renaissance, including European and Asiatic contributions; modern math of Descartes, Pascal, Wallis, Huygens, Newton, Euler, Lambert, Laplace, scores more. More emphasis on historical development, exposition of ideas than other books on subject. Non-technical, readable text can be followed with no more preparation than high-school algebra. Index. 544pp. 5⅜ x 8.
S630 Paperbound **$2.00**

ON MATHEMATICS AND MATHEMATICIANS, R. E. Moritz. A ten year labor of love by the discerning and discriminating Prof. Moritz, this collection has rarely been equalled in its ability to convey the full sense of mathematics and the personalities of great mathematicians. A collection of anecdotes, aphorisms, reminiscences, philosophies, definitions, speculations, biographical insights, etc., by great mathematicians and writers: Descartes, Mill, De Morgan, Locke, Berkeley, Kant, Coleridge, Whitehead, Sylvester, Klein, and many others. Also, glimpses into the lives of mathematical giants from Archimedes to Euler, Gauss, and Weierstrass. To mathematicians, a superb book for browsing; to writers and teachers, an unequalled source of quotation; to the layman, an exciting revelation of the fullness of mathematics. Extensive cross index. 410pp. 5⅜ x 8.
T489 Paperbound **$1.95**

SIR ISAAC NEWTON: A BIOGRAPHY, Louis Trenchard More. Standard, definitive biography of Newton, covering every phase of his life and career in its presentation of the renowned scientific genius as a living man. Objective, critical analysis of his character as well as a careful survey of his manifold accomplishments in many areas of science, and in theology, history, politics, finance. Text includes letters by Newton and acquaintances, many other papers, some translated from Latin to English by the author. Scientists, teachers of science will especially be interested in this book, which will appeal to all readers concerned with history of ideas, development of science. Republication of original (1934) edition. 1 full-page plate. Index. xii + 675pp. 5⅜ x 8½.
S79 Paperbound **$2.50**

GUIDE TO THE LITERATURE OF MATHEMATICS AND PHYSICS, N. G. Parke III. Over 5000 entries included under approximately 120 major subject headings, of selected most important books, monographs, periodicals, articles in English, plus important works in German, French, Italian, Spanish, Russian (many recently available works). Covers every branch of physics, math, related engineering. Includes author, title, edition, publisher, place, date, number of volumes, number of pages. A 40-page introduction on the basic problems of research and study provides useful information on the organization and use of libraries, the psychology of learning, etc. This reference work will save you hours of time. 2nd revised edition. Indices of authors, subjects. 464pp. 5⅜ x 8.
S447 Paperbound **$2.49**

The more difficult books are indicated by an asterisk (*)

Dover publishes books on art, music, philosophy, literature, languages, history, social sciences, psychology, handcrafts, orientalia, puzzles and entertainments, chess, pets and gardens, books explaining science, intermediate and higher mathematics mathematical physics, engineering, biological sciences, earth sciences, classics of science, etc. Write to:

> Dept. catrr.
> Dover Publications, Inc.
> 180 Varick Street, N. Y. 14, N. Y.

1378
5-03